2

RESPIRATION

PIERRE DEJOURS

Faculté de Médecine de Paris

TRANSLATED BY
LEON E. FARHI, M.D.

School of Medicine,
State University of New York
at Buffalo

WITH A FOREWORD BY
HERMANN RAHN, Ph.D

NORTHEASTERN JUNIOR COLLEGE
LIBRARY   29624

New York   OXFORD UNIVERSITY PRESS   1966

Copyright © 1966 by Oxford University Press, Inc.
Library of Congress Catalogue Card Number: 66-12546

This book is a translation of Chapter One, *Respiration,* by Pierre Dejours,
from volume 3 of *Physiologie,* edited by Charles Kayser and first published
by Editions Médicales Flammarion, Paris © 1963.

Printed in the United States of America

Foreword

It is indeed a pleasure to write a foreword for this book which introduces the area of mammalian and human respiration to the medical student. Pierre Dejours is well known among his American colleagues since the days when he came to Rochester, New York, to work under Wallace O. Fenn. He has closely followed the scientific advances in this country as well as in Europe and has presented here a broad and well balanced introduction to a field which has made enormous strides over the last decades.

This is not intended to be a definitive treatise. It is, however, addressed to the beginning student. This refreshing approach provides a brief but excellent historical perspective upon which our modern knowledge is based. It seemed important that our American students should also be exposed to this lucid treatment of the field of respiration.

The author has shown great skill in introducing the physics and chemistry of respiration in a simple manner without deluging the medical student with an avalanche of equations. While these cumbersome algebraic expressions can today no longer be completely avoided in an up-to-date review, if over-emphasized they would impair the enthusiasm of even the most serious student.

Respiration is more than physiology of the pulmonary system; it must encompass the whole transport system from the external environment to the cell. Thus the importance of the role of the circulatory system and of the diffusion processes are also stressed. The author's views on the regulation of ventilation are simply presented, reflecting his own researches in this area. It is to his credit that this area is not over-emphasized. Instead of stressing the application of respiration physiology to the clinical area, he has chosen normal man exposed to various stresses to illustrate the integrated processes which are involved. Thus an excellent discussion of hypoxia in general and man at altitude and under high pressures concludes this book.

The illustrations are mostly original, well chosen, and simply presented. The literature references are generally in the English language; and it will be a refreshing experience for the American medical student to note that publications in other languages have also made important contributions to this field.

State University of New York at Buffalo   HERMANN RAHN
November 1965   Lawrence D. Bell Professor of Physiology

Preface

Respiration is translated from Volume III of a French textbook entitled *Physiologie*, edited by Dr. Charles Kayser, Professor of Physiology at the Faculty of Medicine in Strasbourg, and published in 1963 by the Editions Médicales Flammarion of Paris.

At that time there was not available any introductory text to respiration for students of biology and the medical sciences. This section of the textbook, appropriate for beginning students in physiology, is also intended to be used by graduate students new to this particular field. The approach has been to consider the body as a system of gas exchanges and to give a general outline of the different aspects of respiratory physiology.

As I wrote a short chapter entitled "Exercice Musculaire" for Volume II of *Physiologie, Respiration* does not deal as much as is desirable with the subject of respiratory gas exchange in muscular exercise. It has seemed necessary, therefore, to insert here one original figure from the chapter "Exercice Musculaire," Figure 45 b, without which several pages of the present book would be obscure.

The talent of Dr. Leon Farhi is two-faceted: Dr. Farhi is as fluent in French as he is in English, and he is an outstanding respiration physiologist. Usually an author whose work has been translated is satisfied to say that the translator has expressed his original thoughts well in another language. But Dr. Farhi has done more; in many instances he has found words which better convey my ideas than those I used in my own language. I want to express my gratitude to Dr. Farhi for having given so much of his time to a long and tedious work.

At this point I would like to acknowledge the persevering and fruitful efforts of Professor Charles Kayser in editing *Physiologie*. Finally, I want to express my debt to Professor Wallace O. Fenn of the University of Rochester and Professor Hermann Rahn of the State University of New York at Buffalo for their continuous encouragement and support in this endeavor.

Paris, France
December 1965

PIERRE DEJOURS
Professor at the Faculty of Medicine

Contents

Respiration

I

Basic Concepts in Respiratory Physiology and Their Historical Development

Modern respiratory physiology is based on six basic concepts:

FIRST CONCEPT:

Pulmonary ventilation is required to maintain life.

This fact was doubtless known in ancient times, when death sentences were carried out by choking the convicts. Are the thoracic movements themselves necessary, or is it the ventilation they produce? Vesalius, in 1543, noted that opening the thorax and producing pulmonary collapse do not cause death if rhythmic pulmonary movements are maintained by means of a pump. At that time, this observation led to the conclusion that pulmonary movements were necessary to maintain life.

Hooke (1667) repeated Vesalius's experiment and showed that if, after opening the thorax, the lungs are punctured and air is then forced through the trachea and escapes through the puncture holes on the lung surface, life is maintained, although there are no thoracic movements. Therefore, thorax and lung movements are necessary to life only because they ensure a certain air flow through the lungs.

The concept according to which the thoracic movements are caused by periodic exertion of muscular forces on a deformable container is derived from the eighteenth-century physiologists, particularly Haller (1747) and Hamberger (1749).

SECOND CONCEPT:

(a) The body consumes oxygen and produces carbon dioxide. It is the site of a phenomenon similar to the combustion of inanimate matter. It is this combustion which generates animal heat.

3

(b) *Animal heat comes from oxidation of organic substances.*
(c) *Nitrogen is not, properly speaking, a respiratory gas.*

(a) The composition of expired gas differs from that of inspired air. Expired gas contains less oxygen and more carbon dioxide than ambient inspired air. Therefore, during respiration, the changes in expired gas composition are similar to those taking place during the combustion of inanimate matter. If the inspired gas does not contain oxygen, death occurs. The body is therefore the site of a phenomenon similar to the combustion of inanimate matter. This combustion of body matter within the body is the source of animal heat.

Aristotle (fourth century B.C.) thought that the main purpose of respiration was to cool the blood. This is not, of course, the main role of respiration, although the thermal tachypnea that is observed in some animals corresponds exactly to Aristotle's conception. Five centuries later, Galen stated that the body takes up from air a principle which serves to form the "vital spirit" and eliminates "fuliginous wastes" with the expired gas.

As to the origin of animal heat, Descartes attributed it to fermentation, and Hales (1733) to friction of blood along the walls of the vessels.

The English chemists from Oxford (Boyle, 1660; Lower, 1669; Mayow, 1674) came close to discovering respiratory gas exchange and the origin of animal heat. They noticed that air is required to maintain life, exactly as it is required for combustion of inanimate matter. According to Mayow, "nitro-aereal spirit" (now called oxygen), which is part of ambient air, is fixed by blood.

However, the work of the English chemists did not attract much attention, and during the following century all the phenomena dealing with respiration, combustion, and oxidation were explained by "phlogiston," an obscure principle devised by Stahl.

Lavoisier, by his own experiments as well as by deductions from those of his predecessors and of his contemporaries, put an end to the phlogiston theory in 1777. In 1789, Lavoisier, in collaboration with Seguin, summarized his views as follows:

"Boyle, Hales, Black and Priestley are the first to have noticed that respiration has a marked effect on atmospheric air, that it decreases the volume of air and changes its nature and that in a short time interval, the fluid which is required for this function loses the property of maintaining the life of animals.

"Without really understanding what was taking place in this kind of experiment, the chemists who upheld Stahl's doctrine tried to explain its results. They succeeded in doing so with their characteristic ease, that is, by means of their usual principle, phlogiston, a real Proteus serving any purpose and changing form and color.

"On the basis of available knowledge, and limiting ourselves to simple ideas that can easily be grasped by anyone, we can state, in general, that respiration is but a slow combustion of carbon and of hydrogen, similar in all points to that taking place in a lamp or a burning candle, and that, from this point of view, animals which breathe are really combustible bodies which burn and are consumed.

"In respiration, as in combustion, it is the atmospheric air which supplies oxygen and heat, but in respiration, it is the substance itself of the animal, the blood, that supplies the combustible material. If animals did not regain repeatedly by food what they lose by respiration, the oil of the lamp would soon be exhausted, and the animal would perish, as a lamp goes out when it lacks sustenance" (Lavoisier and Seguin, 1789).

Thus, it was chemists who discovered the origin of animal heat and the significance of the respiratory phenomenon. The chemists encountered tremendous difficulties in characterizing gases by their physical and chemical qualities, of which they had only imperfect knowledge, and tried to define gases by their biological properties. Thus gases are often named because of their biological properties: nitrogen is a "*mofette*,* incapable of maintaining the respiration of animals and the kindling and combustion of bodies" (Lavoisier); oxygen is pure vital air, "eminently respirable," "the respirable portion of air"; the "irritant" property of carbon dioxide has served to characterize this gas.

(b) Lavoisier thought that in the respiratory process, oxygen reacted chemically with carbon and hydrogen.

"One must know first of all that a humor, which separates from blood, oozes continuously in the bronchi, and filters across the lung membranes, and is made up mainly of hydrogen and carbon.

"It is this humor which, finely divided as it comes out of the endings of the exhaling vessels of the lungs, burns in part, decomposing the vital air with which it comes in contact and forms, during this combustion, water and carbon dioxide" (Lavoisier and Seguin, 1790).

In the nineteenth century, mainly as a result of the work of German chemists and physiologists (Liebig, 1842; Pettenkofer and Voit, 1863), it was recognized that oxidation affects complex organic substances: carbohydrates, lipids, and proteins.

(c) The only effect of atmospheric nitrogen is to limit the fractional concentration and the partial pressure of oxygen. Other gases, such as helium or hydrogen, can be substituted for nitrogen.

In 1777, Lavoisier wrote:

* *Mofette* is an obsolete term for an irrespirable gas, found mainly in volcanic areas and mines.

"Respiration acts only on the portion of pure air, that is, air eminently respirable, contained in atmospheric air. The excess, that is, the mephitic part, is a purely passive medium, which enters the lung and goes out nearly as it entered, that is, without change and without alteration." (Eminently respirable air is oxygen and the mephitic part is nitrogen.)

In their last publication (1790) Seguin and Lavoisier said:

"This led to the assumption that it would be possible to substitute for the nitrogen, which enters in the composition of atmospheric air, an equal volume of any other gas, provided this be neither acid nor alkaline and be devoid of harmful properties. The experiment confirmed this hypothesis absolutely.

"We tried putting guinea pigs under glass jars filled with a mixture of vital air and pure hydrogen, in approximately the same volume proportions as are found between vital air and nitrogen in atmospheric air. They were able to stay a long time without any apparent distress . . ."

However, prolonged breathing of pure oxygen is usually fatal. Although nitrogen is not a respiratory gas, properly speaking, it is nevertheless necessary, for reasons given on page 221.

THIRD CONCEPT:

Oxidation takes place in the cells. Circulation of blood effects the transport of oxygen and carbon dioxide between lungs and tissues, blood being endowed with the property of binding or liberating rapidly large quantities of these gases.†

This concept answers questions as to where the oxygen that is taken up in the lungs is consumed and where the carbon dioxide eliminated by the lungs is produced; or in other words what is the site of the oxidations.

Although he expressed some reservations about this, Lavoisier thought that the oxidations took place in the lungs.

"Respiration, which takes place in the lungs and possibly also in other parts of the system, is a slow combustion of part of the hydrogen and of the carbon contained in blood, and generates heat which is absolutely necessary to the maintenance of animal heat" (Lavoisier and Seguin, 1790).

Hassenfratz, in 1791, quotes Lagrange's opinion:

"If all the heat that is distributed to the body economy was generated in the lungs, the temperature of the lungs would be so high as to raise continual fears about their destruction.

† The blood circulation mechanism was recognized by Harvey in the seventeenth century. However, the role of circulation was clarified only later. Circulation is just as indispensable to life as pulmonary ventilation, since circulatory arrest causes death in a very short time by abolishing gas exchange. For this reason, the study of circulation could well be included in the study of respiratory function. This is usually not done, possibly because blood circulation fulfills other roles, in addition to gas transport.

"He ‡ thought therefore that it was most probable that all the heat produced in the animal economy was not evolved in the lungs alone, but in all parts where blood circulates."

Later, M. Berthelot noted that even if the combustion did indeed take place in the lungs, the temperature increase would be small. Nevertheless, the doubts raised by Lagrange and Hassenfratz about the site of oxidation proved to be absolutely justified.

However, if the oxidations do not take place in the lungs, it is necessary that the blood be able to transport large quantities of oxygen and carbon dioxide. In 1669, Boyle showed that a large amount of gas could be extracted from blood exposed to vacuum. This method was taken up later by Collard de Martigny (1830), and by H. G. Magnus (1837), the latter showing that blood contains large amounts of oxygen and carbon dioxide. Liebig (1851) and L. Meyer (1857) showed that oxygen was found in blood in a chemical combination, and F. Holmgren (1863) proved that this chemical combination of oxygen takes place with hemoglobin. Finally, the relationship between the amount of hemoglobin and the partial pressure of oxygen was studied by Ludwig (1870). As far as carbon dioxide is concerned, Zuntz (1867) discovered that a large amount of this gas was bound chemically as an alkaline compound.

Venous blood contains less oxygen and more carbon dioxide than arterial blood (Magnus, 1837 and 1845), and therefore gas exchange takes place in the tissues. Pflüger stated categorically in 1872 that practically all the oxidations (and therefore production of all the body energy) take place in the cells of the tissues.

FOURTH CONCEPT:
The rate of gas exchange and of energy expenditure is variable.

Gas exchange is increased by digestion, muscular exercise, and the effort to combat cold or heat (Lavoisier and Seguin, 1789).

"The result of what we have said is that the amount of vital air that different subjects consume is very variable, and that it is not absolutely the same in any circumstance of life, or at any instant of the day.

"Is he (man) inactive and at rest? Circulation is sluggish, as is respiration. He consumes less (vital) air, he exhales through his lung less carbon and hydrogen, and consequently needs less food. Is he forced to take part in strenuous work? Respiration becomes faster, he consumes more air, loses more hydrogen and carbon, and consequently he needs nourishment more often and in larger quantities."

‡ Lagrange.

In the same publication, Lavoisier and Seguin show that oxygen "consumption is increased by cold" as well as during digestive periods.

FIFTH CONCEPT:

The rate of gas exchange is determined by body requirements.

It is known that the rate of combustion of a lump of coal, for instance, increases when the partial pressure of oxygen is higher. In the living body, this does not hold: a change in partial pressure in the ambient air, at least over a wide range of variation, does not change the metabolic rate. More specifically, inspiration of pure oxygen does not increase cellular metabolism. On the contrary, a very marked increase in inspired oxygen pressure leads to a decrease in oxidation (Paul Bert). A decrease in oxygen pressure (altitude) does not decrease the gas exchange rate as long as hypoxia is not very marked.

"Whether animals breathe pure vital air, or this same air mixed with a varied proportion of nitrogen, the quantity of vital air they consume is always the same, with only minor differences" (Lavoisier and Seguin, 1789).

SIXTH CONCEPT:

Functional behavior of the ventilatory and circulatory systems is regulated according to the gas exchange requirements of the body.

The problem, stated in the second half of the nineteenth century, is still unsolved today.

The preceding concepts show that ventilatory and circulatory behavior change when metabolic rate varies. Indeed, any change in energy expenditure involves a variation of oxygen consumption and of production of carbon dioxide, and therefore a readjustment of the exchanges:

— between lungs and tissues on one hand, a function fulfilled by blood circulation;

— between the environment and the alveolar spaces on the other hand, a function assigned to pulmonary ventilation. The rate at which ventilatory and circulatory systems operate is closely related to the metabolic rate.

In addition, when the properties of inspired air change, it is possible to observe a certain number of ventilatory, circulatory, and blood reactions that bring about better conditions for the metabolic oxidative processes in the tissues.

These facts show the existence of mechanisms which regulate the circulatory and ventilatory behavior as a function of energetic metabolic rate and of the characteristics of inspired gas, and in such a way that the conditions to which cells are exposed vary relatively little. To appreciate this result fully, it is only necessary to imagine the important changes that would take place in operating conditions of the cells in the absence of these regulatory mechanisms. This concept is one of the aspects of the principle of constancy of the *milieu intérieur*, a principle developed by Claude Bernard.

As stated above, it is not customary to study the regulation of circulation within the framework of a study of the respiratory function. As to regulation of pulmonary respiration, the first problem which is raised concerns the origin of the ventilatory phenomenon itself, and Le Gallois (1812) is the first to have made pertinent observations in this area (see quotation on p. 127). Breuer and Hering's discovery in 1868 of the role played by pulmonary proprioceptive sensitivity in controlling ventilatory movements leads to the notion of a ventilatory system made up of the respiratory centers, the thoracic ventilatory apparatus, and of the afferent proprioceptive pathways of pulmonary origin (Rosenthal, 1882).

It is this ventilatory system which is subject to regulation, and the first reports on the subject are those of Geppert and Zuntz (1888) and Haldane and Priestley (1905).

These different concepts can be summarized as follows:

The energy consumed by the body comes from tissue oxidation of the three organic types in the cells. These oxidations use oxygen and yield carbon dioxide. Oxygen comes from the ambient air, and carbon dioxide is released to the ambient air.

In multicellular organisms there are two steps in the transport of respiratory gas molecules between cells and environment: ventilation causes a to-and-fro movement of air between lungs and atmosphere, while the blood, circulating within the body, effects gas transport between lungs and other body tissues.

The rate of gas exchange is determined by the body requirements. Digestion, efforts to overcome heat or cold, and muscular activity increase energy expenditure and gas exchange rate.

The functional behavior of pulmonary respiration as well as the circulation are quantitatively related to gas exchange rate, and the body has at its disposal mechanisms which regulate these functions according to its needs.

2

Gas Laws, Units, Symbols, and Abbreviations Commonly Used in Respiratory Physiology

The object of respiratory physiology is to study oxygen and carbon dioxide in the living organism. However, it is not possible to understand some of the problems which arise in connection with these gases unless the essential gas laws are borne in mind. It is therefore imperative to review these laws first, in spite of the fact that it is understandably disappointing to start the study of respiratory physiology with a chapter on physics. It will also be necessary to describe a certain number of symbols, abbreviations, conventions, and units commonly used in respiratory physiology.

I. LAWS PERTAINING TO GASES IN A GAS PHASE

Gay-Lussac's Law or Charles's Law

This law indicates that when temperature increases and the pressure is maintained constant, gases expand according to the relationship

$$V_t = V_0(1 + \alpha t),$$

where V_t is the gas volume at temperature t,

V_0 is the gas volume at 0 °C,

α is the expansion coefficient of gases at constant pressure, and equals $\frac{1}{273}$.

t is the gas temperature in °C.

Boyle-Mariotte's Law

At constant temperature, the product $P \times V$, where P and V are the pressure and volume of a perfect gas, is constant. Doubling the pressure to which a gas is exposed decreases its volume by one half.

10

Equation of state

The combination of Gay-Lussac's Law and Boyle-Mariotte's Law gives the relationship

$$PV = nRT$$

where n is the number of gram-moles of gas, R is a constant having the same value for all perfect gases, and T is the absolute temperature, in °K (T = t + 273).

At 0 °C, when T = 273, and at a pressure of 760 mm Hg, a gram-mole (n = 1) of any perfect gas will have a volume of 22.41 l. Oxygen and nitrogen may be considered perfect gases. Carbon dioxide shows some deviation from ideal gases so that one gram-mole of CO_2 under the same conditions has a volume of 22.26 liters.

Dalton's Law of partial pressures

The partial pressure of a gas in a gas mixture of volume V is the pressure that this gas would exert if it occupied the same volume V in the absence of the other components of the mixture. Each of the gaseous components exerts a pressure that is proportional to the fraction of that species (the fraction of a gas corresponds to its percentage, e.g. 21/100 or 0.21). The sum of partial pressures equals the total pressure of the gas mixture.

The partial pressure of a given gas is equal to the product of the total pressure, P_B, times F, the fraction of the gas in the mixture:

$$P = P_B \cdot F.$$

For an example we can take an alveolar gas mixture from which water vapor has been removed and which contains O_2, CO_2, and N_2 at a barometric pressure, P_B, of 760 mm Hg. The first two lines of Table I show the fractions and the partial pressures in this dry mixture.

When the mixture is not dry, a fourth gas, water vapor, must be taken into account. It is generally stated that alveolar gas is saturated with water vapor, which exerts a pressure of 47 mm Hg at a body temperature of 37 °C.* Under these conditions, although the fractions of O_2, CO_2, and N_2 are usually measured in the dry gas, the presence of the water vapor must be taken into account when the true partial pressures of O_2, CO_2, and N_2, as they are exerted in the wet gas, are calculated.

---

* The work of Christie and Loomis (*J. Physiol.*, London, 1932, 77, 35–47) raises questions as to the exact conditions of alveolar gas. Even during resting conditions P_{H_2O} may be 2 mm Hg below saturation pressure at 37 °C, and the difference between the true P_{H_2O} and 47 mm Hg may reach several millimeters of mercury during hyperventilation.

In this case, the partial pressures are given by the formula:

$$P = (P_B - 47) \cdot F,$$

where F designates the fractions of O_2, CO_2, or N_2 in the dry mixture. The values in the third line of the table (the only data of physiological significance) are obtained by using this equation.

TABLE I

	O_2	CO_2	N_2	H_2O	TOTAL
Fraction, F (dry gas)	0.146	0.055	0.799	0	1.00
Partial pressure, P, mm Hg (dry gas)					
P = 760 × F	111	42	607	0	$760 = P_B$
Partial pressure mm Hg (wet gas)					
P = $(P_B - 47)$ × F	104	39	570	47	$760 = P_B$

II. PHYSICAL CONDITIONS OF GASES IN RESPIRATORY PHYSIOLOGY

BTPS conditions

As mentioned in the preceding section, it is usually accepted that lung temperature is the same as that of the rest of the body, and that water vapor pressure is the saturation pressure. The values usually given are 37 °C and 47 mm Hg, the latter figure indicating saturation pressure for water vapor at 37 °C. To be absolutely precise, true body temperature, or more exactly that of the thorax, should be used, but if body temperature is not very different from 37 °C, this value is usually accepted. The condition of gas in the lungs is stated as Body Temperature and Pressure, Saturated with water vapor, abbreviated as BTPS.

ATPS conditions

In most climates, ambient air is at a lower temperature than the gas in the lungs. It also contains less water vapor for two reasons: first of all, since the temperature is lower, the saturation pressure of water vapor is lower, and secondly, atmospheric air is usually not saturated with water vapor (in temperate climates relative humidity is usually said to be of the order of 50%, meaning that the water vapor pressure is about one half the saturation pressure). On the other hand, it is usually accepted that gas in a water spirometer is saturated with water vapor at spirometer temperature. Spirometer conditions are usually stated as Ambient Temperature and Pressure, Saturated, abbreviated as ATPS.

Conversion from ATPS volumes to BTPS volumes

As ambient air is inspired, it is heated and humidified, and as a result the volume increases, by thermal expansion (in accordance with Gay-Lussac's Law) and by addition of water molecules which evaporate in the airway. As a result, when a subject inspires one liter of ambient air, the change in thoracic volume, the only change of importance in terms of respiratory mechanics, is more than one liter. In temperate climates, the difference is of the order of 10%.

$$V_{BTPS} = V_{ATPS} \times \frac{273 + 37}{273 + t_A} \cdot \frac{P_B - P_{H_2O}}{P_B - 47},$$

where the first fraction indicates the expansion due to heat while the second shows the increase in volume due to addition of water vapor. In this equation,

273 is the melting point of ice in °K (degrees Kelvin)

37 is body temperature in °C (degrees centigrade)

t_A is the ambient temperature, e.g. inside the spirometer, measured in °C

P_B is the barometric pressure, in mm Hg

P_{H_2O} is the saturating water vapor pressure at t_A

47 is the saturating water vapor pressure at 37°, body temperature.

The product of the two fractions is the factor by which the volume, measured at ATPS, must be multiplied to obtain the lung volume change which occurs at BTPS. This factor can be read directly in Table II, or can be obtained using the nomogram presented by Albers (1959).

Table II shows the factors required to convert a volume expressed at ATPS (as it would be measured in a water spirometer) to the volume expressed at BTPS (corresponding lung volume change) at a barometric pressure of 760 mm Hg. Knowledge of the ambient temperature, t_A, is sufficient to determine the correction factor. As an example, at 20 °C, the factor is 1.102. This means that a liter of air, measured in a spirometer at 20 °C, where it is saturated with water vapor, corresponds to a change in thoracic volume of 1.102 l.

Saturating water vapor pressure at different temperatures is shown in the table. However, since this pressure depends only on temperature,

TABLE II

CONVERSION FACTORS FOR CHANGING VOLUMES "ATPS" (AMBIENT TEMPERATURE AND PRESSURE, SATURATED) TO "BTPS" (BODY TEMPERATURE, AMBIENT PRESSURE, SATURATED AT 37 °C).

WHEN AMBIENT TEMPERATURE IS	FACTOR IS	APPENDIX (Saturation water vapor pressure in mm Hg)
15 °C	1.128	12.8
16 °C	1.123	13.6
17 °C	1.118	14.5
18 °C	1.112	15.5
19 °C	1.107	16.5
20 °C	1.102	17.5
21 °C	1.096	18.7
22 °C	1.091	19.8
23 °C	1.085	21.1
24 °C	1.080	22.4
25 °C	1.075	23.8
26 °C	1.068	25.2
27 °C	1.063	26.7
28 °C	1.057	28.3
29 °C	1.051	30.0
30 °C	1.045	31.8
31 °C	1.039	33.7
32 °C	1.032	35.7
33 °C	1.026	37.7
34 °C	1.020	39.9
35 °C	1.014	42.2
36 °C	1.007	44.6
37 °C	1.000	47.0

knowledge of the latter suffices to find from the table the appropriate correction factor.

Although the barometric pressure, P_B, appears in the equation from which the correction factor is calculated, it is not shown in Table II. This is because at a given altitude, the small daily variations in P_B do not modify appreciably the correction factor. Thus, at 20 °C, assuming barometric pressures of 750, 760, and 770 mm Hg, the respective correction factors are 1.1024, 1.1018, and 1.1012, and the value of 1.102 can be used, even if the pressure is not exactly 760 mm Hg. On the other hand, at altitude, the correction factor is radically changed. At 4500 meters (15,000 feet, P_B = 429 mm Hg), at the same temperature of 20°, the factor is 1.140.

STPD conditions

Oxygen and carbon dioxide volumes must be expressed at normal or standard conditions, that is Standard Temperature and Pressure, Dry, abbreviated STPD. This is because when dealing in physiology with volumes of oxygen or carbon dioxide one is really interested in the number of O_2 and CO_2 molecules and not in the volume these molecules happen to occupy under the conditions in which they are measured. From the metabolic point of view, which deals with redox reactions, it is the number of molecules of O_2 used and of CO_2 produced that counts. It is therefore necessary to express O_2 and CO_2 volumes under well-defined conditions, which allow rapid calculation of the number of molecules they contain. This is easy with STPD conditions, since 1 gram-mole of any ideal gas always has a volume of 22.4 l STPD.

Conversion of ATPS volumes to STPD volumes

If the ATPS volumes of O_2 and CO_2 are known, it is possible to calculate the corresponding STPD volumes by using the formula:

$$V_{STPD} = V_{ATPS} \times \frac{273}{273 + t_A} \cdot \frac{P_B - P_{H_2O}}{760},$$

where the same symbols described on page 13 are used.

Table III is based on this equation, and indicates the correction factor

TABLE III

FACTORS FOR REDUCTION OF VOLUMES ATPS TO VOLUMES STPD

P_B mm Hg	TEMPERATURE, IN °C							
	18	19	20	21	22	23	24	25
695	0.839	0.835	0.830	0.826	0.822	0.818	0.813	0.809
700	0.845	0.841	0.837	0.832	0.828	0.824	0.819	0.815
705	0.851	0.847	0.843	0.838	0.834	0.830	0.825	0.821
710	0.857	0.853	0.849	0.845	0.840	0.836	0.832	0.827
715	0.863	0.859	0.855	0.851	0.846	0.842	0.838	0.833
720	0.870	0.865	0.861	0.857	0.852	0.848	0.844	0.839
725	0.876	0.872	0.867	0.863	0.859	0.854	0.850	0.845
730	0.882	0.878	0.873	0.869	0.865	0.860	0.856	0.851
735	0.888	0.884	0.879	0.875	0.871	0.866	0.862	0.857
740	0.894	0.890	0.886	0.881	0.877	0.872	0.868	0.863
745	0.900	0.896	0.892	0.887	0.883	0.878	0.874	0.869
750	0.907	0.902	0.898	0.893	0.889	0.884	0.880	0.875
755	0.913	0.908	0.904	0.900	0.895	0.891	0.886	0.881
760	0.919	0.915	0.910	0.906	0.901	0.897	0.892	0.887
765	0.925	0.921	0.916	0.912	0.907	0.903	0.898	0.893
770	0.931	0.927	0.922	0.918	0.913	0.909	0.904	0.899

by which volumes ATPS must be multiplied to obtain the STPD volume. This table requires knowledge of P$_B$ and of t$_A$, but circumvents the need for actual calculations.

Carpenter (1948) and Albers (1959) have presented more complete tables and a nomogram.

This table is used to reduce oxygen and carbon dioxide volumes to STPD conditions (0 °C, 760 mm Hg, dry). For instance, when the temperature is 21 °C and pressure is 740 mm Hg, the reduction factor is 0.881, which indicates that a volume of 250 ml ATPS corresponds to an STPD volume of 250 · 0.881 = 221 ml STPD.

III. LAWS PERTAINING TO GASES IN LIQUIDS

Partial pressure of a gas in a liquid

A liquid exchanges gas molecules with the gas phase with which it is in contact. Equilibrium between gas and liquid phases is said to exist when the number of gas molecules escaping from the liquid is equal to the number of molecules entering the liquid during a given interval of time. Just as a gas in a gas phase exerts a partial pressure, the same gas will exert a partial pressure if it is in a liquid phase. Under equilibrium conditions, the partial pressures of the gas in the gas and in the liquid phases are equal, and the liquid is said to be saturated with this gas. If the liquid is saturated, and the pressure of the gas phase is then suddenly decreased by a sufficient amount, gas will be evolved from the liquid (see page 226).

Henry's Law

The volume v of a given gas dissolved in a volume V of liquid is proportional to the partial pressure of that gas in the liquid, P, the relationship being

$$v = \alpha \frac{P}{760} \cdot V$$

where v is expressed at STPD, P is in mm Hg. The Greek letter α indicates the Bunsen solubility coefficient, and corresponds to the volume of gas, in ml STPD, dissolved in 1 ml of liquid when the partial pressure of this gas is 760 mm Hg.

The solubility coefficient decreases when the liquid temperature increases. As an example, solubility coefficients for oxygen in water at 30 °C and at 40 °C are respectively 0.0261 and 0.0231. The solubility coefficient α also changes with the state of the liquid. The solubility coefficients are different for water, red blood cells, plasma, and whole blood. These differences in solubility are due to other substances dissolved or in suspension — which decrease the volume of water in one ml of medium — and to adsorption of the gas molecules to blood colloids (this is then not, strictly speaking, dissolved gas, but it is nevertheless gas bound physically in the liquid).

TABLE IV

SOLUBILITY COEFFICIENTS IN WATER, PLASMA, RED CELLS, AND WHOLE BLOOD AT 38 °C   (from ROUGHTON, 1954).

	WATER	PLASMA	RED CELLS	WHOLE BLOOD
Oxygen...............	0.0232	0.0209	0.0260	0.0230
Carbon dioxide........	0.545			0.490
Nitrogen.............	0.0127			0.0137
Helium..............	0.0085			0.0087
Carbon monoxide......	0.01816			

In respiratory physiology, the amount of a gas contained in a liquid is usually expressed in volumes percent. For instance, the oxygen content of arterial blood is 20 vol %, which means that 100 ml of blood contain 20 ml of O_2 at STPD.

Laws governing gas diffusion

1) The rate of gas diffusion from one point of a gas mixture or a liquid to another is proportional to the difference between the pressures of that gas at the two points.

2) The rate of gas diffusion is inversely proportional to the square root of its molecular weight (Graham's Law).

3) In a liquid, rate of gas diffusion is proportional to the solubility of the gas in the liquid (the more soluble the gas, the faster its diffusion).

By combining laws 2) and 3), it is possible to compare diffusion rates of two gases in a liquid. For instance, in water at 38 °C, diffusion rates for CO_2 and O_2 will be in the following proportion:

$$\frac{\text{Rate of } CO_2 \text{ diffusion}}{\text{Rate of } O_2 \text{ diffusion}} = \frac{0.545}{0.023} \cdot \sqrt{\frac{32}{44}} = 20.2.$$

0.545 and 0.023 are the solubility coefficients of CO_2 and O_2 in water at 38 °C; 44 and 32 are the respective molecular weights. Thus, in water, CO_2 diffuses 20 times faster than O_2.

IV. LIST OF SYMBOLS AND ABBREVIATIONS

It is important to conform to this nomenclature, which is being more and more widely used:

I	stands for inspired gas
E	stands for expired gas
A	stands for alveolar gas
a	stands for arterial blood
c	stands for capillary blood
v	stands for venous blood
$\bar{v}$	stands for mixed venous blood
F	is the fractional concentration. For instance, the fractional concentration of O_2 in inspired gas is $F_{I_{O_2}}$.
P	is the partial pressure of a gas
$P_{A_{O_2}}$	is the partial pressure of oxygen in the alveolar gas
$P_{A_{CO_2}}$	is the partial pressure of carbon dioxide in the alveolar gas
$P_{a_{O_2}}$	is the partial pressure of oxygen in the arterial blood
$P_{a_{CO_2}}$	is the partial pressure of carbon dioxide in the arterial blood
P_B	is the barometric pressure
V_I	is the inspired volume
V_E	is the expired volume
V_D	is the volume of the dead space
V_T	is the tidal volume
V_A	is the alveolar tidal volume
f	is the respiratory frequency
$\dot{V}$	is a gas rate (ventilatory volume per unit of time)
$\dot{V}_E$	is the expiratory minute volume
$\dot{V}_A$	is the alveolar minute volume
$\dot{V}_{O_2}$	is the oxygen consumption or the oxygen uptake
$\dot{V}_{CO_2}$	is the carbon dioxide output or the carbon dioxide elimination
R	is the respiratory gas exchange ratio, $\dot{V}_{CO_2}/\dot{V}_{O_2}$
$\dot{Q}$	is blood flow rate, usually the cardiac output
C	is content of gas in a liquid, for instance
$C_{a_{CO_2}}$	is carbon dioxide content of arterial blood
D	is diffusing capacity of the lungs for a given gas, such as
D_{O_2}	is diffusing capacity of the lungs for oxygen
S	is saturation, for instance, oxygen saturation of mixed venous would be $S_{\bar{v}_{O_2}}$

$(P_{A_{O_2}} - Pa_{O_2})$ is the difference in partial pressures of oxygen between alveolar gas and arterial blood

$(Ca_{O_2} - C\bar{v}_{O_2})$ is the arterial-venous O_2 content difference

$(C\bar{v}_{CO_2} - Ca_{CO_2})$ is the venous-arterial CO_2 content difference

STPD   stands for 0 °C, 760 mm Hg, dry (standard conditions)

ATPS   stands for ambient temperature and pressure, saturated with water vapor

BTPS   temperature of 37 °C, ambient pressure, saturated with water vapor at 37 °C.

3
The Body as a Gas Exchange System—Basic Concepts

I. GENERAL DESCRIPTION OF THE GAS EXCHANGE SYSTEM

In the study of respiration, the body must be examined in terms of a gas exchange system. Oxido-reductions take place in the tissues. Blood supplies oxygen molecules to the tissues, and receives in return carbon dioxide molecules. The oxygen molecules come from the surrounding air, and must first be transported through the airways into the alveolar spaces, then cross the alveolar-capillary membrane, be ferried by the circulatory system from the lungs to the tissues, and pass through the walls of the peripheral capillaries in order to reach finally the cells where they are consumed. Carbon dioxide molecules, produced by the tissues, follow the same pathway in the opposite direction, finally disappearing into the atmosphere. Thus a continuous flux of O_2 and CO_2 molecules takes place in the different body compartments.

The continuous and opposed flows of O_2 and CO_2 can be summarized as follows.

II. MECHANISM OF OXYGEN AND CARBON DIOXIDE TRANSPORT AND DIFFUSION

Two radically different mechanisms are involved in the movement of O_2 and CO_2 molecules between the environment and the cells.

a) The migration of O_2 and CO_2 molecules across membranes and through interstitial and cellular fluids is due to *diffusion*, a passive physical phenomenon. The driving force which is responsible for the transfer is the difference in partial pressures of the gas along the diffusion path. The

20

distance covered by molecular diffusion is extremely short — barely a few micra.

b) The O_2 and CO_2 molecules are transported between peripheral capillaries and pulmonary capillaries on one hand and between the alveolar gas mass and the environment on the other, as part of a bulk flow of fluid (blood or air), the movement of which is governed by the cardiac and the ventilatory pumps respectively. This rapid transport mechanism is responsible for moving rapidly O_2 and CO_2 from one point of the gas exchange system to another, in some cases more than a foot away.

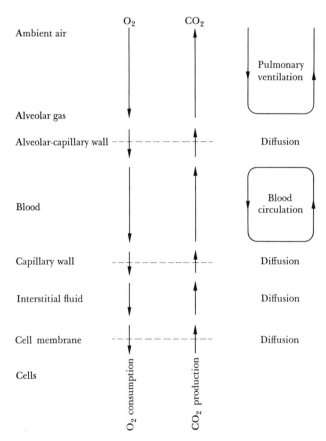

FIGURE 1.   Schematic drawing of the gas exchange system.

III. MAGNITUDE OF GAS EXCHANGE

The magnitude of the flows of oxygen and carbon dioxide, which can be expressed dimensionally as a flow rate (volume per unit time), is extremely variable. The O_2 and CO_2 flows are usually called O_2 uptake (or O_2 consumption) and CO_2 output (or CO_2 production) respectively. At rest, each represents approximately 200 ml/min, STPD, which is roughly 10 mM/min.

When the energy production of the body increases, the oxido-reductions are also increased, and higher figures for O_2 and CO_2 flows are encountered. The most common examples of such conditions are digestion, exposure to cold (and to a lesser degree, exposure to heat), and especially muscular exercise. Quantitatively, it is the latter that produces the greatest change in metabolism, thereby augmenting considerably the O_2 and CO_2 flows. On severe exertion, these flows can exceed 4500 ml/min STPD (approximately 200 mM/min).

IV. OXYGEN UPTAKE AND CARBON DIOXIDE OUTPUT ACTUALLY REPRESENT A FLOW DIFFERENCE

The arterial blood has a given oxygen content, Ca_{O_2}, higher than $C\bar{v}_{O_2}$, the O_2 content of mixed venous blood. This is tantamount to saying that there is a certain flow of oxygen (the product of the cardiac output $\dot{Q}$ times the arterial O_2 content) carried by the arterial blood from the lungs to the tissues, and another flow, of lesser magnitude, ferried by the venous blood from the tissues to the lungs. It is the difference between these two flows that represents $\dot{V}_{O_2}$, the net rate of O_2 uptake. This relationship, also known as Fick's equation, can be stated as:

$$\dot{V}_{O_2} = \dot{Q} \cdot Ca_{O_2} - \dot{Q} \cdot C\bar{v}_{O_2}.$$

The same type of relationship exists for carbon dioxide, the flow of CO_2 from tissues to lung exceeding the return flow by the amount eliminated by the respiration.

Nitrogen is present in all the tissues of the body. Although the N_2 molecules are continuously exchanged, the inflow equals the outflow, the net exchange being zero. This is in agreement with the accepted notion that molecular N_2 does not take part in any biochemical reaction in the human body, that is to say that it is neither consumed nor produced by the tissues.

V. PARTIAL PRESSURES OF RESPIRATORY GASES IN THE BODY

The respiratory gases exert a different partial pressure in the various parts of the body. For oxygen, the pressure decreases from atmosphere to cells, while the opposite is true for CO_2. Figure 2 shows how P_{O_2}, the partial pressure of oxygen, and P_{CO_2}, the partial pressure of carbon dioxide, vary

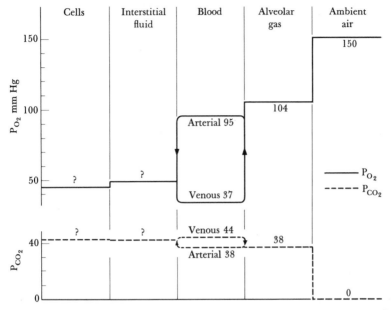

FIGURE 2. O_2 and CO_2 partial pressures, P_{O_2} and P_{CO_2}, in ambient air and in the different body compartments, at rest at sea level.

The mean partial pressures in the interstitial fluid must be between those found in arterial and in mixed venous blood, but P_{O_2} and P_{CO_2} in interstitial fluid and in the cells are not precisely known.

in resting man at sea level. The mechanisms which regulate the stepwise changes will be studied later. P_{N_2}, the nitrogen partial pressure, does not appear in the figure, simply because it is the same in all the compartments, except for a small difference between the alveoli and the rest of the organism. At sea level, P_{N_2} is approximately 570 mm Hg.

VI. VOLUMES OF GASES IN THE BODY —
BODY GAS STORES

The partial pressures of O_2 and CO_2 in each of the body compartments correspond to certain volumes of these gases, either dissolved or in chemical combination.

These volumes can act as gas stores. If, for instance, pulmonary ventilation is temporarily stopped, exchange of O_2 and CO_2 with the environment will cease, but the cells will continue to consume oxygen and produce carbon dioxide. The former is supplied by the gas volumes present in the various compartments, while the latter will accumulate in the body. These reserve volumes of O_2 and CO_2 can thus be considered as "gas stores," interposed between cells and environment. The amount of O_2 and CO_2 stored can vary, so that the O_2 and CO_2 exchange at the cellular level is not necessarily that measured at the same time between lung and environment.

VII. FORMS IN WHICH RESPIRATORY GASES ARE FOUND IN THE BODY

In addition to the relatively large volumes of O_2, CO_2, and N_2 that are present in the lung in gaseous form, a certain amount of these gases can be found in blood and tissues. The magnitude of this additional amount varies from one gas to the other as well as from one body compartment to the next.

Oxygen, nitrogen, and carbon dioxide are *dissolved* in all body fluids in an amount determined by solubility and partial pressure of the gas considered. These volumes are of little importance under normal conditions.

However, if nitrogen is stored only in its dissolved form, carbon dioxide and oxygen can be found also in reversible chemical combinations, in much larger quantities.

a) In tissues, the carbon dioxide is present as bicarbonate or bound to protein; in muscle, oxygen can be bound to myoglobin as oxymyoglobin (MbO_2).

b) In the plasma, there is a considerable amount of bicarbonate.

c) In the red blood cells, oxygen is bound to hemoglobin as oxyhemoglobin, HbO_2; carbon dioxide is present as carbaminohemoglobin and bicarbonate.

VIII. IMPORTANCE OF THE O_2, CO_2, AND N_2 STORES IN THE VARIOUS BODY COMPARTMENTS
(see Farhi and Rahn, 1955)

Table V shows the volumes of O_2, CO_2, and N_2 stored in the different compartments of a 70 kg (or 155 lb) man under normal resting conditions. These figures are based on the assumption that the blood volume — of which one-fourth has the composition of arterial blood, while the other three-fourths have the composition of mixed venous blood — represents 7.7% of the body weight. An additional assumption is that the partial pressures of gas in the tissues are those in the mixed venous blood. If this is acceptable for CO_2, which is very diffusible, it is certainly not for oxygen, but the error introduced is relatively small.

TABLE V

BODY GAS STORES

| | TISSUES ml STPD | BLOOD | | TOTAL blood + tissues ml STPD | ALVEOLAR GAS (2.5 l BTPS) $P_B = 760$ mm Hg, ml STPD |
		Venous, ml STPD	Arterial, ml STPD		
CO_2	3330	2120	650	6100	116
O_2	200	610	270	1080	300
N_2	fat free 490 fat 450	42	14	996	1560

Table V requires a few comments and qualifications.

a) The body CO_2 stores described in the table include only those that can be altered rapidly, within a few minutes or a few hours. The bone CO_2 stores (which exceed several times the amount given in the table) are not included because they represent a very stable combination, and therefore cannot be brought into play rapidly.

b) The CO_2 stores are much larger than the O_2 stores. This is due to the high solubility of CO_2 and to the fact that considerable amounts of CO_2 are present in reversible chemical combinations in blood and tissue. If the partial pressure of CO_2 in the venous blood and in the tissues of a 70 kg (155 lb) man increases by only 1 mm Hg, the body will store an additional 70 to 80 ml of CO_2.

c) The tissue O_2 stores are extremely small, and, in fact, only 50 ml of that volume (which corresponds to the physically dissolved O_2) are really mobile enough to be brought into play. The amount is this low because of limited oxygen solubility. If the partial pressure of O_2 in the tissues increases by 1 mm, the O_2 stores of a 70 kg (or 155 lb) man breathing air would increase by 1.4 ml.

The remaining 150 ml of the O_2 stores are to be found in muscle as oxygenated myoglobin, MbO_2. This changes only under exceptional conditions because of the high degree of affinity of myoglobin for oxygen (at a partial pressure of O_2 of 10 mm, myoglobin is still 75% saturated).

d) There are two reasons for the large amount of nitrogen found in the tissues. The first is that the partial pressure of N_2 to which the body is ex-

NORTHEASTERN JUNIOR COLLEGE
LIBRARY 29624
STERLING   COLORADO

posed is high (about 550 mm Hg at sea level) and the second is that the solubility of N_2 in fatty tissue is five times higher than in lean tissues.

The tissue N_2 stores shown in Table V assume that a 70 kg (or 155 lb) man has 10 kg of fatty tissue.

IX. GAS FLOW RATES AND STORES DURING THE STEADY STATE

During the steady state (or equilibrium conditions) the O_2 flow is equal in all parts of the system and the same is true for CO_2. More specifically, the O_2 uptake by the lung equals the O_2 consumption of the tissues while the amount of CO_2 produced is identical to that eliminated by the lung. Under these conditions, there is no net change in body O_2 and CO_2 stores although these undergo continuous exchange.

The respiratory quotient, abbreviated as R.Q., is defined as the ratio of CO_2 output to O_2 uptake. The R.Q. of the cells can be called metabolic, each tissue having its own R.Q. As an example, the figure for the brain is 1.0, while that for resting muscle is 0.7. When all cells of the body are considered, the overall R.Q. which will represent some mean value will be obtained. The R.Q. can be studied at several levels of the gas exchange system. During the steady state, this R.Q. is the same throughout the system, and, as an example, the respiratory gas exchange ratio, sometimes designated by the letter R (calculated from composition of inspired and expired gases), is equal to the metabolic gas exchange ratio.

In respiratory physiology, the existence of a steady state does not mean that gas exchange and the body functions that affect this exchange are absolutely constant, but simply indicates that the average values are maintained in a very narrow range. In other words, during the steady state, gas exchange rates measured during two relatively long periods are essentially the same; this is not necessarily true if the measurements pertain to only a short interval, because — even assuming a constant level of energy expenditure, and a constant cellular O_2 uptake and CO_2 output — circulation and ventilation undergo some cyclic changes, as yet inadequately defined. The O_2 and CO_2 exchange and stores will therefore also exhibit cyclic variations around a mean value, and it is in terms of constancy of this mean value that the steady state must be conceived.

X. VARIATIONS OF O_2 AND CO_2 PRESSURES AND STORES

A change in any one of the components of the gas exchange system will cause changes in O_2 and CO_2 partial pressures and therefore in the O_2 and CO_2

stores. Four different mechanisms can cause these changes in pressures and stores.

1) INCREASE IN TISSUE METABOLISM

This would be the case during muscular exercise, where the tissue partial pressure of CO_2 increases while the partial pressure of O_2 decreases. Partial pressures in venous blood vary in the same direction as in the tissues. The variations in partial pressures of arterial blood are modest except during very heavy exercise.

During moderate exercise ($\dot{V}_{O_2}$ = 1500 ml/min, STPD), the tissue and venous O_2 stores will decrease by approximately 40 ml STPD, and the CO_2 stores will increase by about 400 ml STPD.

2) CHANGES IN CARDIAC OUTPUT AT CONSTANT METABOLIC ACTIVITY AND VENTILATION

In this highly unphysiological but theoretically possible case, the partial pressures and content of O_2 and CO_2 in the mixed venous blood must change. If, for instance, cardiac output is doubled, $\bar{Cv}_{O_2}$ and $\bar{Pv}_{O_2}$ increase, $\bar{Cv}_{CO_2}$ and $\bar{Pv}_{CO_2}$ decrease, and the differences between arterial and venous contents ($Ca_{O_2} - \bar{Cv}_{O_2}$) and ($\bar{Cv}_{CO_2} - Ca_{CO_2}$) decrease by one half.

3) CHANGES IN VENTILATION AT CONSTANT METABOLISM AND CARDIAC OUTPUT

This case would occur during voluntary hyperventilation or hypoventilation. Alveolar gas composition changes, and during hypoventilation, for instance, $P_{A_{CO_2}}$ decreases while $P_{A_{O_2}}$ increases, causing changes in O_2 and CO_2 partial pressures in the whole body. As an example:

a) doubling the alveolar ventilation and maintaining the new ventilatory level for one hour increases body O_2 stores by 20 ml and decreases body CO_2 stores by 2000 ml,

b) on the other hand, a decrease of alveolar ventilation to one-half the normal value decreases body O_2 stores by 210 ml (most of which is contributed by the mixed venous blood) while body CO_2 stores increase by 4000 ml.

4) CHANGES IN INSPIRED GAS PROPERTIES

These may be either changes in pressure, such as occur with changes in altitude, or changes in O_2 or CO_2 fractions of the inspired gas. In these cases, the partial pressures would vary throughout the body. As an example, replacing the inspired air by 100% oxygen will increase the O_2 stores by 210 ml and the CO_2 stores by 70 ml (see p. 211).

XI. GAS FLOW RATES AND STORES DURING THE UNSTEADY STATE

The readjustments in O_2 and CO_2 flow rates and stores, which follow a functional change in one of the components of the gas transport system, require a long time. As an example, maintained hyperventilation at constant metabolic activity (voluntary hyperventilation) causes an increase in $P_{A_{O_2}}$ and in the total volume of oxygen in the alveolar gas, and, as a result, partial pressures of O_2 in blood and tissues, and the associated O_2 stores also increase. This increase in O_2 stores, occurring when the O_2 consumption by the cells remains unchanged, can occur only as a result of a temporary increase in the O_2 uptake from the environment. It is easy to understand that hypoventilation causes a transient decrease in O_2 uptake as a corollary to the decrease in O_2 stores.

The same events can be described for carbon dioxide, the difference being that, in this case, hypoventilation increases CO_2 pressures and stores throughout the body. This increase can occur only if part of the CO_2 produced by the cells is stored, resulting in a difference between the CO_2 actually produced and the CO_2 eliminated. The *apparent* production of CO_2 (obtained by gas exchange with the atmosphere) is inferior to the *metabolic* production.

Obviously these discrepancies between ventilatory and cellular gas exchange are only temporary and end when the gas stores have readjusted at a new level. However, this readjustment is much more rapid for O_2 (a matter of minutes) than for CO_2 (several hours, see Farhi and Rahn, 1960), and, as a result, the O_2 uptake returns to the previous equilibrium value much before the CO_2 output. This is partly due to the fact that the changes in CO_2 stores are several times higher than those taking place in O_2 stores.

The difference between the transient changes in O_2 and CO_2 exchange with the atmosphere is responsible for a change in respiratory gas exchange ratio during the period of readjustment of the stores. Thus, during hypoventilation, the drop in $P_{A_{O_2}}$ decreases to a minimal extent only the O_2 stores, while the CO_2 stores increase is several times higher, thanks to partial retention of the CO_2 produced. As a result, the respiratory gas exchange ratio is decreased. As long as the body gas stores are undergoing readjustments, the respiratory gas exchange ratio differs from the respiratory quotient. In respiratory physiology, one of the essential criteria of a steady state is the constancy of the respiratory gas exchange ratio.

XII. PLAN OF THE BOOK

Theoretically, the study of respiration should include all the components of the gas exchange system, from cellular respiratory phenomena to pulmonary gas exchange.

In practice we will not deal with either cellular respiration or circulation. The former is covered extensively in biochemistry texts, while the latter should be studied not only in terms of gas transport, but also in terms of the other important functions of circulation, such as the transport of chemicals and heat. However, blood as a physico-chemical gas transport system will be studied in this book (p. 30).

Insofar as pulmonary gas exchange is concerned, the study should include:

First, the mode of action of the thoracic pump, or ventilatory mechanics (p. 51); *secondly*, the respiratory gas exchange involving ventilation, alveolar ventilation and gas exchange, and the gas transfer between alveolar gas and blood, two closely related functions (p. 88).

The neural structures and mechanisms responsible for the periodic ventilatory act (composed of an inspiratory and an expiratory phase, each with a definite amplitude, time, and wave form) will be discussed under "Neural Control of Ventilation" (p. 127).

The ventilatory pump responds to changes that can affect the gas exchange system. More specifically, ventilation is tied up with the magnitude of gas exchange and with changes in barometric pressure and altitude. This aspect of regulation of ventilation is discussed on page 148.

4
Gas Transport in Blood

Gases may be found in blood in two different states: dissolved and chemically combined. Nitrogen is present only in the first form, while oxygen and carbon dioxide are present in both forms.

I. OXYGEN TRANSPORT IN BLOOD

Blood, sampled at any point in the body, always contains oxygen. Even samples that are the poorest in O_2 contain a few volumes percent. Only a minor fraction (about one hundredth) of the oxygen carried by arterial blood is present as dissolved gas, while the rest is chemically bound to hemoglobin.

A. Dissolved oxygen

In normoxia (defined as the situation which prevails during normal conditions, breathing air at sea level), the partial pressure of oxygen in arterial blood, Pa_{O_2}, is approximately 95 mm Hg. According to Henry's Law (p. 16), the amount of dissolved oxygen in this arterial blood is:

$$0.023 \cdot \frac{95}{760} = 0.0029, \text{ or } 0.29 \text{ volume per 100 volumes of blood } (0.29 \text{ vol}\%).$$

In a venous blood sample, where Pv_{O_2}, the partial pressure of O_2, is 40 mm Hg, the amount of dissolved oxygen is 0.12 vol%. In this example, the difference between the amounts of oxygen *dissolved* in arterial and venous blood is 0.17 vol%. This means that when 100 ml of blood perfuse an organ they will lose 0.17 ml of the dissolved oxygen present in the incoming blood. This is a very small amount in comparison to the 5.3 vol% that the blood has supplied to the tissues in this example.

30

On the other hand, when breathing 100% O_2, Pa_{O_2} may reach 640 mm Hg, and in this case the amount of oxygen dissolved is of definite importance, about 2 vol%, the bulk of which will be transferred to the tissues. (If the same arterio-venous oxygen difference considered before still prevails, the venous blood will now be less unsaturated. However, because of the C_{O_2}–P_{O_2} relationship, the Pv_{O_2} breathing oxygen will exceed that found when breathing air by only about 10 mm Hg, and the amount of dissolved oxygen remains very small.) During oxygen breathing the amount of dissolved oxygen carried by arterial blood (2 vol%) is still small in comparison to the total amount transported (22 vol%), but is almost entirely transferred to the tissues.

B. Chemically bound O_2.   The P_{O_2}–HbO_2 relationship

In normoxic conditions, the amount of O_2 transported in chemical combination is relatively high: the total oxygen content of arterial blood is 20 vol%, and since approximately 0.3 vol% are in physically dissolved form, 19.7 vol% are chemically bound.

The hemoglobin contained in the red blood cells reacts with oxygen to form oxyhemoglobin, according to the reaction $Hb + O_2 \rightleftharpoons HbO_2$, where Hb designates "reduced" or "non-oxygenated" hemoglobin.

The volume of O_2 bound is related to P_{O_2}, the partial pressure of oxygen. In order to investigate the link between P_{O_2} and HbO_2, a blood sample is divided in aliquots, and each is equilibrated with a different gas mixture (the O_2 fraction varying from one to the other), and the O_2 content of the various blood aliquots is then determined. Equilibration *in vitro* requires a long time. Blood is placed in a glass container, called a tonometer, and continuous rotation spreads the blood in a thin film on the tonometer walls. After several minutes the partial pressure of any gas is the same in the gas phase, in the plasma, and in the red blood cells. Oxygen and carbon dioxide pressures are measured, and the oxygen content of blood is determined with the Van Slyke apparatus. With this instrument, blood oxygen is extracted by vacuum, after which it is compressed to a known volume, and the pressure it exerts under these conditions is determined exactly. In order to calculate the amount of oxygen bound to hemoglobin, it is necessary to subtract from the total volume of oxygen extracted the amount dissolved, which can be calculated by applying Henry's Law. This makes it possible to establish the relationship between HbO_2 and P_{O_2} (at known temperature and P_{CO_2} values), which when plotted yields the oxyhemoglobin dissociation curve.

While the amount of dissolved oxygen is directly proportional to P_{O_2},

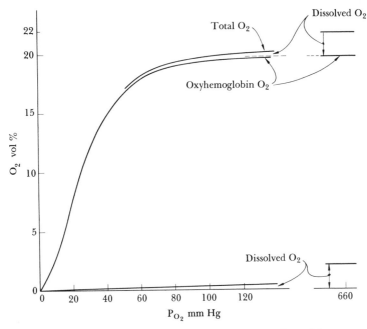

FIGURE 3.   Relationship between oxygen content and partial pressure
of oxygen in blood — the blood O_2 dissociation curve.

On the ordinate: oxygen content in volumes percent (ml of O_2 STPD in each 100 ml of blood). On the abscissa: partial pressure of oxygen, in mm Hg. The partial pressure of CO_2 is constant at 40 mm Hg. The figure shows that:

— the amount of dissolved oxygen is low and increases linearly with P_{O_2};

— the amount of oxygen present as oxyhemoglobin is relatively very important and the volume of oxygen chemically bound reaches a maximum (oxygen saturation of hemoglobin = 100%) when P_{O_2} is approximately 150 mm Hg. The relationship between HbO_2 and P_{O_2} is called the HbO_2–P_{O_2} relationship;

— the increase in blood oxygen content in hyperoxia, as compared to normoxia, is due essentially to dissolved oxygen.

the curve describing P_{O_2}–HbO_2 relationship has a sigmoid shape. This curve (Fig. 3) shows that:

a) half the total Hb is in HbO_2 form at a pressure of approximately 25–30 mm Hg;

b) the part of the curve between 10 and 60 mm Hg is very steep;

c) when the P_{O_2} exceeds 60 mm Hg, the rate of increase of O_2 saturation is progressively reduced, saturation being achieved at about 150 mm Hg. At a pressure of 600 mm Hg, blood contains more oxygen than at 150 mm

Hg, but the increase is due solely to the increase in dissolved oxygen, the quantity of oxyhemoglobin remaining unchanged. The maximal amount of O_2 that can be bound as HbO_2 is defined as the oxygen capacity.

The ratio of the O_2 bound to hemoglobin, in a given blood sample, to the oxygen capacity of that sample gives the O_2 saturation of the blood, S_{O_2}. If this saturation is expressed as a percentage rather than as an absolute number,

$$\%S_{O_2} = \frac{\text{Total } O_2 \text{ in sample} - \text{Dissolved } O_2 \text{ in sample}}{\text{Total } O_2 \text{ volume at 150 mm Hg} - \text{Dissolved volume at 150 mm Hg}} \cdot 100.$$

The relationship between HbO_2 and P_{O_2} applies only to the specific P_{CO_2}, pH, and temperature conditions under which it was determined.

EFFECT OF TEMPERATURE

An increase in temperature displaces the middle part of the oxyhemoglobin dissociation curve to the right. This means that, at the same P_{O_2}, the higher the temperature, the lower will be the O_2 content of blood. This is of importance when tissue or blood temperature changes, especially during physical exercise (or hypothermia).

P_{CO_2} AND pH EFFECT — THE BOHR EFFECT

In Figure 3, the relationship between P_{O_2} and HbO_2 has been shown at a constant P_{CO_2} of 40 mm Hg. A different P_{CO_2} would not affect the sigmoid shape of the dissociation curve, but would change the absolute values. The P_{O_2} value required to achieve a certain saturation is equal to the P_{O_2} read at the same saturation on the first curve multiplied by a certain factor. This factor is the same for all points of the dissociation curve, greater than unity when P_{CO_2} is above 40 mm Hg and lower than unity for P_{CO_2} below 40. Thus, for each P_{CO_2}, we will have a different P_{O_2}–HbO_2 relationship, and a whole family of O_2 dissociation curves can be obtained (Fig. 4). Note that the partial pressure of O_2 that corresponds to any saturation increases when P_{CO_2} increases. This is tantamount to stating that, at a given P_{O_2}, the O_2 saturation is decreased by an elevation in P_{CO_2}.

The increase in P_{CO_2} decreases the affinity of hemoglobin for oxygen. This is called the Bohr effect since it was first described in 1904 by the Danish physiologist of that name.

The variations in pH have the same effect on the dissociation curve as variations in P_{CO_2}, a drop in pH causing a shift to the right. The fact that an increase in P_{CO_2} lowers the pH may lead one to believe that CO_2 effects are due to changes in pH. However, it is generally accepted that the CO_2

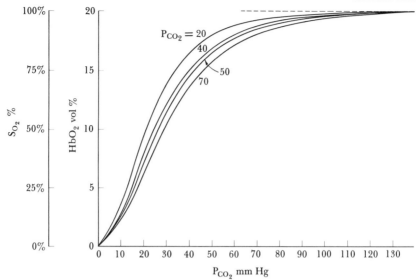

FIGURE 4.   Bohr effect.

On the ordinate, blood oxygen content as HbO_2 in vol%, and the corresponding O_2 saturation.   On the abscissa, partial pressure of O_2 in blood. Total, or maximal, hemoglobin O_2 capacity is shown by the horizontal broken line. The different curves represent the HbO_2–P_{O_2} relationship for different partial pressures of CO_2, expressed in mm Hg. The HbO_2–P_{O_2} curve for P_{CO_2} = 40 mm Hg is identical to that in Figure 3. The Bohr effect is an expression of the decrease in oxygen affinity of hemoglobin by P_{CO_2}: at the same oxygen pressure, the O_2 bound as HbO_2 is higher when P_{CO_2} is lower.

action is direct and is related to the fact that carbon dioxide combines with hemoglobin to form carbaminohemoglobin.

The relationship between HbO_2 on one hand and P_{O_2} and P_{CO_2} on the other can be shown on the O_2–CO_2 diagram of Fenn, Rahn, and Otis (1946) (Fig. 5). Each of the lines in this diagram corresponds to a given O_2 content and O_2 saturation. Had the relationship been completely independent of P_{CO_2} each of these isopleths (iso-content lines) would have been perpendicular to the abscissa. The fact that they are not, shows the effect of P_{CO_2} on the HbO_2 dissociation curve, the Bohr effect. In the figure, a point a, corresponding to a P_{O_2} of 88 and a P_{CO_2} of 41, has an O_2 content of 19.3 vol%, while the O_2 content at a point $\bar{v}$, determined by a P_{O_2} of 37 and a P_{CO_2} of 47.5, can be read as 13.5 vol%. The first set of values corresponds to an arterial blood, the second to a venous blood. The figure shows that in the absence of the Bohr effect, a decrease in O_2 content to the same value

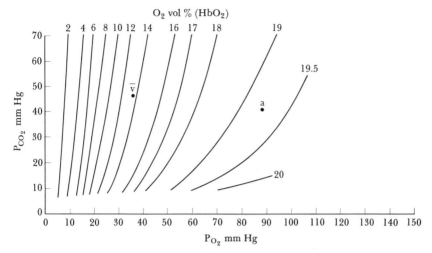

FIGURE 5.   Isopleths for HbO_2 saturation on the P_{O_2}–P_{CO_2} diagram, showing the relationship between P_{CO_2}, P_{O_2}, and the O_2 content in HbO_2 form.

Each HbO_2 curve corresponds to a given O_2 content, expressed in volumes per cent. The slope of these isopleths is due to the Bohr effect (at the same O_2 pressure, HbO_2 is higher when P_{CO_2} is lower). Point a is a representative arterial blood point ($P_{CO_2} = 41$ mm Hg, $P_{O_2} = 88$ mm Hg), and point v̄ corresponds to a mixed venous blood sample ($P_{CO_2} = 47.5$ mm Hg, $P_{O_2} = 37$ mm Hg).

of 13.5 vol% would have required a more considerable drop in P_{O_2} (to 34 instead of 37). The potential usefulness of the O_2–CO_2 diagram for graphic representation of various aspects of respiratory physiology will be explored subsequently.

PROPERTIES OF HEMOGLOBIN

Non-oxygenated hemoglobin is a purple pigment. Oxyhemoglobin is red. This explains the color difference between arterial and venous blood.

Hemoglobin contains 0.33% (by weight) of iron. Since one molecule of hemoglobin cannot contain less than one atom of iron (which has an atomic weight of 56) the minimal molecular weight of hemoglobin is $\dfrac{56 \times 100}{0.33}$ = 16,800. The hemoglobin molecule can be made by n such basic Hb molecules, that is $(Hb)n$. In all mammals, including man, n has been shown to have a value of 4. Natural hemoglobin would therefore be written Hb_4, but in many cases the simple statement $Hb + O_2 \rightleftharpoons HbO_2$ can adequately replace the more complex $Hb_4 + 4\,O_2 \rightleftharpoons Hb_4(O_2)_4$.

A gram of hemoglobin can bind 1.34 ml STPD of oxygen. A mole of elementary Hb will therefore have the ability to take up $16,800 \cdot 1.34$ = 22,400 ml STPD of oxygen, exactly one mole. If 15 grams of hemoglobin are present in 100 ml of a given blood, the oxygen capacity would be $15 \cdot 1.34 = 20.1$ vol%. The O_2 capacity could be determined by measuring blood hemoglobin concentration or blood iron content. However, it is better to determine directly the O_2 capacity because a certain fraction of the hemoglobin may not be functional, that is, may be unable to bind oxygen. For instance, blood may contain some forms of hemoglobin such as methemoglobin and carboxyhemoglobin which do not bind O_2. This inactive hemoglobin is normally less than 0.5% of the total, but in smokers may be as high as 8%.

The elementary Hb molecule is composed of two elements:

a) the heme, which has a molecular weight of 600 and which contains one Fe atom bound to 4 pyrrole groups;

b) the globin, bound to the Fe atom by its fifth valence.

Each basic molecule can bind one molecule of O_2, which is taken up by the sixth valence of the iron atom. Normally this iron is in the ferrous state, Fe^{++}, and only under this condition can hemoglobin combine with oxygen. Certain substances, such as ferricyanide, permanganate, aniline, etc., can change Fe^{++} to the ferric state, transforming hemoglobin into a brown pigment, methemoglobin, which cannot bind oxygen. Normally the concentration of methemoglobin in blood is extremely small, but in cases of intoxication by one of the chemicals listed above, and in a certain hereditary condition, known as idiopathic methemoglobinemia, this concentration may reach very high levels.

CARBOXYHEMOGLOBIN

The sixth valence of iron can also bind carbon monoxide, CO, forming a red pigment, carboxyhemoglobin (HbCO). The affinity of hemoglobin for carbon monoxide is extremely high since complete saturation of hemoglobin by CO will occur when blood is exposed to a gas mixture containing 0.1% CO in N_2 (with no oxygen). When oxygen is also present, as happens in carbon monoxide poisoning, the simple relationship which exists between the partial pressures of the two gases (P_{O_2} and P_{CO}) and the amounts of these gases that are combined (HbO_2 and $HbCO$), can be stated as:

$$\frac{[HbCO]}{[HbO_2]} = M \frac{P_{CO}}{P_{O_2}}.$$

In general, M has a value of about 250. This equation shows that if blood is exposed to a gas containing both oxygen and carbon monoxide, where P_{O_2}

is 100, half of the hemoglobin will be bound to CO if the partial pressure of this gas is 0.4 mm Hg. Such would be the case in alveolar gas if inspired air contained 1 part in 2000 of CO. The equation shows that it is beneficial to increase the alveolar partial pressure of oxygen (by breathing 100% O_2) in the event of carbon monoxide poisoning.

In anemia, where the level of blood hemoglobin is decreased, the shape of the O_2 dissociation curve is the same as that of a normal blood (curve 4 in Fig. 6). If HbO_2 was expressed in % saturation, both curves would be

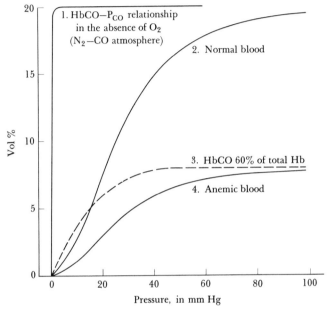

FIGURE 6. Comparison of the relationship between carboxyhemoglobin and oxy-hemoglobin on one hand and the carbon monoxide and oxygen pressures on the other.

Curve 1 shows blood carbon monoxide content as a function of carbon monoxide pressure, when carbon monoxide is mixed with pure nitrogen. At a very low CO pressure, below 1 mm Hg, the hemoglobin is completely saturated with CO.

Curve 2 shows the normal HbO_2–P_{O_2} relationship of blood at a P_{CO_2} of 40. This curve is identical to those shown in Figures 3 and 4.

Curve 4 shows the HbO_2–P_{O_2} relationship in a blood containing only 40% of the normal hemoglobin concentration. Curve 4 has exactly the same shape as curve 2, and is obtained by multiplying the ordinates of Figure 2 by 0.4.

Curve 3 shows the HbO_2–P_{O_2} relationship of functional hemoglobin (40%), when the other 60% are bound to carbon monoxide as HbCO. It is clear that the HbO_2–P_{O_2} relationship is affected by the presence of HbCO.

superimposed. Carbon monoxide intoxication also causes a decrease in functional hemoglobin, but an important feature of this intoxication is that it introduces a change in the shape of the O_2 dissociation curve. In this case, the hemoglobin that is not bound to CO exhibits a very high affinity for oxygen, this additional affinity being more pronounced when the amount of HbCO is increased (curve 3 of Fig. 6). For instance, when the blood contains 60% HbCO, 95% saturation with oxygen of the remaining hemoglobin is achieved at a P_{O_2} of 40, as opposed to approximately 100 under normal conditions. This explains why, for the same amount of functional hemoglobin, carbon monoxide poisoning is much more incapacitating than anemia, since in the former the tissues cannot fully utilize the oxygen that reaches the peripheral capillaries, O_2 being so tightly bound to hemoglobin (see Roughton, 1954).

FUNCTIONAL HEMOGLOBIN AND INTEGRITY OF THE GLOBIN

Although O_2 is bound only by the heme iron atom, the integrity of the complete hemoglobin molecule is required if Hb is to be changed into HbO_2. The heme group by itself, or fixed to other organic nitrogenous compounds (amino acids, albumin, etc.), does not accept O_2. On the other hand if it is recombined with natural globin, a hemoglobin molecule having all the original characteristics is obtained. Thus globin is an indispensable part of the molecule, and gives the heme the property of reacting with O_2.

The relationship between P_{O_2} and HbO_2 is remarkably constant in any one subject, but may differ from that found in another. In general, in women the curve has a more pronounced sigmoid shape than in men. Among human beings, the differences may be due to individual values of pH and P_{CO_2} rather than a real difference in the chemical structure of hemoglobin. At any rate, the fact that the curves *are* different precludes application of a standard curve to any given individual, although this standard curve is more than adequate for understanding most of the problems concerning gas transport by blood.

ORIGIN OF THE SHAPE OF THE O_2 DISSOCIATION CURVE

The law of mass action can be applied to the reaction $Hb + O_2 \rightleftharpoons HbO_2$, yielding:

$$\frac{[HbO_2]}{[Hb] \cdot P_{O_2}} = K,$$

but since $[Hb] = [\text{total hemoglobin}] - [HbO_2]$, this can be modified into:

$$S_{O_2} = \frac{K \cdot P_{O_2}}{1 + K \cdot P_{O_2}},$$

where S_{O_2} is again the oxygen saturation. The graphical relationship between S_{O_2} and P_{O_2} is a rectangular hyperbola. Thus the sigmoid shape of the O_2 dissociation curve cannot be explained by the equation $Hb + O_2 \rightleftharpoons HbO_2$.

Adair's theory explains this shape by the fact that we are really dealing with Hb_4, and postulates different compounds, Hb_4O_2, $Hb_4(O_2)_2$, $Hb_4(O_2)_3$, and $Hb_4(O_2)_4$, with several intermediate equations, such as $Hb_4(O_2)_2 + O_2 \rightleftharpoons Hb_4(O_2)_3$. If each of these has its own equilibrium constant, a combination of these equations can explain the shape of the dissociation curve. However, the existence of these intermediary compounds has not yet been demonstrated (see references and discussions in Roughton, 1954).

II. CARBON DIOXIDE TRANSPORT IN BLOOD

A. The P_{CO_2}–C_{CO_2} relationship

Blood contains an important volume of carbon dioxide, in various forms. The Van Slyke apparatus allows one to extract from normal blood approxi-

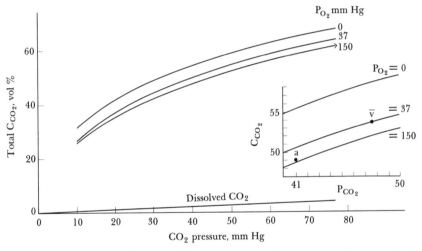

FIGURE 7. Relationship between blood carbon dioxide content, C_{CO_2}, and the partial pressure of carbon dioxide, P_{CO_2} — the blood CO_2 dissociation curve.

The carbon dioxide content of blood does not depend only on P_{CO_2} but also on the oxygen pressure. Three different relationships between C_{CO_2} and P_{CO_2} are given: one for an O_2 pressure of zero, the second for 37 mm Hg, and the third for 150 mm Hg. The figure shows that, at a given P_{CO_2}, the blood contains less carbon dioxide if the oxygen pressure is higher (Haldane effect).

In the insert, the same curves appear on an enlarged scale. Point a corresponds to arterial blood, point $\bar{v}$ to mixed venous blood. This insert shows the importance of the Haldane effect in the change from arterial to venous blood.

mately 60 vol% of CO_2, through the combined action of an acid and a vacuum.

The relationship between carbon dioxide content of blood, C_{CO_2}, and the partial pressure of that gas in blood, P_{CO_2}, has been established with the tonometric technique described for O_2, and can be plotted as a carbon dioxide dissociation curve (Fig. 7). The CO_2 content increases with its partial pressure, but the curve does not flatten out in the physiological range (P_{CO_2} values between 20 and 60) and thereby differs from the O_2 dissociation curve.

B. Effect of the partial pressure of oxygen — Haldane effect

The relationship between P_{CO_2} and C_{CO_2} is extremely sensitive to variations in oxygen saturation of blood (Fig. 7). The carbon dioxide pressure required to establish a given CO_2 content increases with the partial pressure of O_2. In other words, at any CO_2 partial pressure, the CO_2 content will decrease when the partial pressure of O_2 becomes higher. This phenomenon has been described by Christiansen, Douglas, and Haldane (1914) and is usually called the Haldane effect.

The relationship between C_{CO_2} on one hand and P_{CO_2} and P_{O_2} on the other can be shown on the O_2–CO_2 diagram (Fig. 8).

Each of the points of this diagram is defined by the combination of

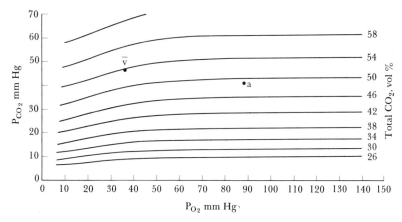

FIGURE 8.   Graphical representation of blood CO_2 content on the P_{O_2}–P_{CO_2} diagram.

Each of the lines corresponds to a given CO_2 content. Points a and $\bar{v}$ correspond to arterial and venous blood respectively, and are identical to those shown in Figures 5 and 7.

specific values for P_{O_2} and P_{CO_2} and corresponds to a certain C_{CO_2}. The different curves that appear on the diagram are drawn through points having the same CO_2 content, and are iso–CO_2 content lines, or CO_2 content isopleths. The inflection of the curves down and to the left is an expression of the Haldane effect. Had this effect not existed, the isopleths would have been parallel to the abscissa.

Note that the Haldane effect is practically absent at high oxygen pressures, because this effect is due to the fact that Hb and HbO_2 are not identical in terms of carbon dioxide transport, and, at high P_{O_2}, variations in oxygen pressure affect very slightly the relative concentrations of HbO_2 and Hb. If the arterial and venous points previously considered are again plotted, the CO_2 content of the first ($P_{O_2} = 88$ mm Hg, $P_{CO_2} = 41$ mm Hg) is 49 vol%, while that of the latter ($P_{O_2} = 37$ mm Hg, $P_{CO_2} = 47.5$ mm Hg) is 54 vol%.

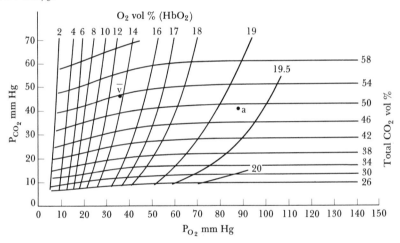

FIGURE 9.   Graphical representation of O_2 and CO_2 blood content isopleths on the P_{O_2}–P_{CO_2} diagram.

This representation allows one to see at one glance the changes that blood undergoes in the tissues (a − v̄ difference) or in the lungs (v̄ − a difference).

The two families of curves from Figures 5 and 8 can be drawn in the same diagram, and the resulting figure (Fig. 9) shows both the O_2 and the CO_2 content of blood as a function of P_{O_2} and P_{CO_2}. This diagram enables one to see the changes in oxygen and carbon dioxide tensions and content that blood undergoes in the lungs where gas exchange converts venous blood into arterial blood, or in the tissues where the opposite process takes place.

C. Forms of carbon dioxide transport

Study of carbon dioxide transport in blood requires an answer to two questions. The first pertains to the different forms in which CO_2 is present in blood; while the second deals with the extent to which each of these forms participates in loading in the tissues (and unloading in the lungs) the *additional* volume of CO_2 supplied by metabolism. All the reactions are reversible, and the CO_2 gained by blood at the tissue level is identical to the CO_2 lost in the lungs (only the sign is reversed). The addition of CO_2 to blood as it flows through the peripheral capillaries will be considered next.

1. DISSOLVED CARBON DIOXIDE

Dissolved carbon dioxide is found in plasma and in red blood cells, and the partition between the two depends on the CO_2 solubility in each as well as on the hematocrit. The volume of dissolved carbon dioxide exceeds by far that of dissolved oxygen. For instance, in arterial blood, at a CO_2 pressure of 41 mm Hg, 2.67 vol% of dissolved CO_2 will be found. In the venous blood, where P_{CO_2} is 47.5 mm Hg, the content is 3.07 vol%. This means that, in this example, the difference between the amounts dissolved in venous and arterial blood is 0.40 vol%. Since the overall venous-arterial CO_2 difference (expressed as $C\bar{v}_{CO_2} - Ca_{CO_2}$) is of the order of a few volumes percent, it is obvious that the change in dissolved CO_2 represents a sizeable fraction of the CO_2 exchange. In the case of oxygen (see p. 46 and Table VI), the arterio-venous difference in dissolved gas constitutes a much smaller fraction of the total exchange.

2. COMBINED CARBON DIOXIDE

BICARBONATE ION. The CO_2 molecules which diffuse into the blood dissolve, and most of these dissolved molecules combine with water to form carbonic acid:

$$CO_2 + H_2O \rightleftharpoons H_2CO_3 \tag{1}$$

Carbonic acid dissociates readily yielding bicarbonate ions and hydrogen ions.

$$H_2CO_3 \rightleftharpoons HCO_3^- + H^+ \tag{2}$$

BICARBONATE ION IN RED BLOOD CELLS. Reaction (1) is very slow in plasma, while the CO_2 that diffuses into the red cells is exposed to an enzyme, carbonic anhydrase, which enhances reaction (1). Part of the HCO_3^- ion that is subsequently formed combines with K^+ ion, which is present in large amounts as in all cells.

In fact, the amount of available K^+ ions increases because of the transformation of HbO_2 into Hb, which occurs at the same time as CO_2 is gained. Since Hb is less acid than HbO_2, transformation of HbO_2 into Hb frees K^+ ions. Part of the H^+ ions formed in reaction (2) is bound to hemoglobin:

$$HbO_2 + H^+ \rightleftharpoons H \cdot Hb + O_2.$$

BICARBONATE ION IN PLASMA. Only a small amount of bicarbonate ions is formed in the plasma because of the absence of carbonic anhydrase. Nevertheless, when blood absorbs carbon dioxide, plasma HCO_3^- increases appreciably, as part of the bicarbonate ions formed in the red cells diffuse into the plasma through the cellular membrane, which allows diffusion of anions.

Since electrical equilibrium must prevail, this migration of HCO_3^- ions into the plasma would be exceedingly small unless it was accompanied by either simultaneous diffusion of a positively charged particle in the same direction or by movement of a negative charge in the opposite direction. Since the cellular membrane is rather impermeable to positive charges, the K^+ ion of the red cells cannot move into the plasma with the HCO_3^-, thus precluding the first of the two possibilities. On the other hand, the unimpeded movement of negatively charged ions allows Cl^- to diffuse into the cells, replacing the HCO_3^- ions that are diffusing out. This migration of Cl^- ions is known as the Hamburger effect or chloride shift. The movement of HCO_3^- and Cl^- are regulated by the Gibbs-Donnan equilibrium, which is expressed here by:

$$\frac{Cl^- \text{ in plasma}}{Cl^- \text{ in R.B.C.}} = \frac{HCO_3^- \text{ in plasma}}{HCO_3^- \text{ in R.B.C.}}$$

CARBAMINOHEMOGLOBIN. Even when carbonic anhydrase is inhibited by cyanide or acetazolamide, blood can rapidly bind a large volume of carbon dioxide. This cannot result from the formation of bicarbonate since in the absence of carbonic anhydrase, this formation is extremely slow. CO_2 is bound directly and rapidly, without need of enzymes, to certain amine radicals in the globin part of the hemoglobin:

$$Hb \cdot NH_2 + CO_2 \rightleftharpoons Hb \cdot NH \cdot COOH.$$

The reaction yields carbaminohemoglobin. This reaction is coupled with transformation of HbO_2 into Hb. Non-oxygenated hemoglobin can bind more CO_2 in the carbamino form than oxygenated hemoglobin.

Figure 10 summarizes O_2 and CO_2 exchange in the peripheral capillaries. The relative importance of the various forms in which O_2 and CO_2 are

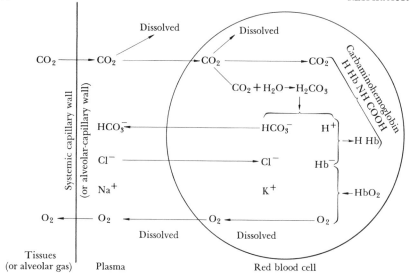

FIGURE 10.   Schematic representation of O_2 and CO_2 exchange in the tissues.

This exchange occurs between capillary blood and tissues. The circle on the right represents a red blood cell. Plasma is interposed between tissues and red cell.

Part of the CO_2 molecules dissolves in the plasma. A part also dissolves in the cellular water.

A second fraction of CO_2 is bound to hemoglobin, forming carbaminohemoglobin. This reaction is enhanced by simultaneous de-oxygenation of oxyhemoglobin ($HbO_2 \rightarrow Hb$).

A third fraction of CO_2 is hydrated, because of the presence of carbonic anhydrase in the red cells. Carbonic acid dissociates in H^+ ions and bicarbonate ions. Part of the H^+ ions associate, with hemoglobin, particularly de-oxygenated hemoglobin which is being formed at the same time. A fraction of the HCO_3^- ions remains in the cell, the rest diffusing into the plasma. Since no positively charged ion can accompany the HCO_3^- ion (the cell membrane is poorly permeable to positive ions), electrical neutrality of plasma and red cells is maintained by migration of Cl^- ions from plasma to red cells (Hamburger effect). As a consequence of this "chloride shift," the Na^+ ion of plasma, freed from its equilibrium with Cl^- now balances the HCO_3^- ion. The Cl^- ions, which enter the cells as well as the HCO_3^- ions which have been formed inside the cells and have not migrated, balance the K^+ ions which have been liberated by the change of HbO_2 into Hb because Hb is less acid than HbO_2.

Table VI gives a numerical example of the different volumes of O_2 and CO_2 in exchange, and of the extent to which dissolved and combined fractions of O_2 and CO_2 come into play.

In the lungs, the molecules undergo the same movements but in the opposite directions. All arrows would have to be oriented the other way.

TABLE VI

	RED BLOOD CELLS			PLASMA			WHOLE BLOOD		
	a	v̄	(a − v̄)	a	v̄	(a − v̄)	a	v̄	(a − v̄)
Oxygen									
P_{O_2}, mm Hg............	88	37		88	37		88	37	
Dissolved, vol%........	0.11	0.04	+0.07	0.11	0.04	+0.07	0.22	0.08	+0.14
HbO_2, vol%...........	19.3	13.5	+5.8				19.3	13.5	+5.8
Total, vol%..........	19.41	13.54	+5.87	0.11	0.04	+0.07	19.52	13.58	+5.94
Carbon dioxide									
P_{CO_2}, mm Hg...........	41	47.5		41	47.5		41	47.5	
Dissolved, vol%........	1.1	1.3	−0.2	1.6	1.8	−0.2	2.7	3.1	−0.4
HCO_3^-, vol%...........	12.9	13.7	−0.8	31.0	33.3	−2.3	43.9	47.0	−3.1
$HbCO_2$, vol%.........	2.4	3.9	−1.5				2.4	3.9	−1.5
Total, vol%..........	16.4	18.9	−2.5	32.6	35.1	−2.5	49.0	54.0	−5.0
pH..................	7.19	7.17	+0.2	7.40	7.37	+0.03			
Hematocrit, %.........	44.8	45.1							

found in plasma, red cells, and whole blood is shown in Figure 11. However, this figure does not show adequately in what form the additional CO_2 introduced by the tissues is carried to the lungs. For example, the volume of CO_2 bound as carbaminohemoglobin in arterial blood is relatively small, but it increases considerably as the blood flows through the tissues (in fact *relatively* more than bicarbonate), and in addition carbaminohemoglobin plays an important role in the gas exchange in tissues and lung. This example spotlights the fundamental difference between volume of gas in blood and volume of gas exchanged.

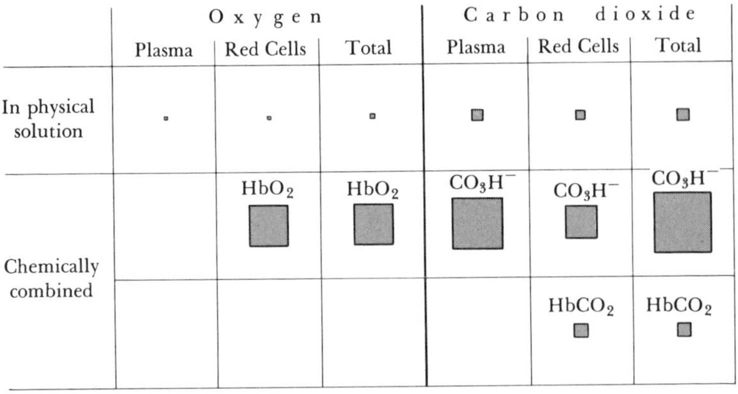

	Oxygen			Carbon dioxide		
	Plasma	Red Cells	Total	Plasma	Red Cells	Total
In physical solution	▫	▫	▫	▢	▢	▢
Chemically combined		HbO_2 ▨	HbO_2 ▨	CO_3H^- ▨	CO_3H^- ▨	CO_3H^- ▨
					$HbCO_2$ ▢	$HbCO_2$ ▢

FIGURE 11.   The different forms in which carbon dioxide and oxygen are found in arterial blood (P_{CO_2} = 41 mm Hg; P_{O_2} = 88 mm Hg).

The surface of the shaded areas is proportional to the oxygen and carbon dioxide volumes. This table is based on the data appearing in Table VI.

Table VI shows on one hand the absolute volumes of CO_2 and O_2 in the R.B.C., plasma, and whole blood, and on the other the extent the different forms change as arterial blood is transformed into mixed venous blood. The table indicates changes in the tissues, where blood loses O_2 and gains CO_2. The phenomena that take place in the lungs are exactly the opposite, quantitatively (during the steady state) as well as in terms of direction of the biochemical reactions, and all that is needed to study the exchange in the lung is to change the signs of the figures in the $(\bar{v} - a)$ column.

Table VI, adapted from Dill, Edwards, and Consolazio (1937), is based on values obtained from twelve resting normal men, of adult age, at sea level. These authors presented their data in a convenient nomogram. Dill, Talbott, and Consolazio (*J. Biol. Chem.*, 1937, **118**, 649–666) constructed a similar diagram for subjects living at high altitude. A nomogram is valid only for subjects living at a given altitude. The isopleths which appear on the O_2–CO_2 diagram of Figure 9 have been drawn by Fenn and Rahn on the basis of this nomogram.

Table VI shows the relative importance of the different forms in which CO_2 is transported in the exchange in lung and in the peripheral tissues. Some of the important points should be emphasized.

1) Although the absolute amount of CO_2 in plasma considerably exceeds the amount in the cells, the volume of CO_2 lost to the alveolar gas (which is also the quantity supplied by the tissues) is divided almost equally between plasma and red blood cells.

2) The volume of dissolved CO_2 is not negligible, while for oxygen, both the dissolved volume in absolute terms and the extent to which this volume participates in gas exchange are negligible under normal conditions.

3) Carbaminohemoglobin plays an important role in CO_2 exchange.

4) The CO_2 exchange affects mainly the bicarbonate form, and mostly its plasmatic component. We have seen that the increase in plasma HCO_3^- is due to transfer of that ion from the red cells, where the presence of carbonic anhydrase allows hydration of CO_2 into carbonic acid, a required step in the formation of the bicarbonate ion. Diffusion of a bicarbonate ion into the plasma is always accompanied by a migration of one Cl^- ion in the opposite direction.

5) The transfer of ions between plasma and red cells leads to a small change in osmotic pressure. During gas exchange at the tissular level, the osmotic pressure of the cells tends to increase while that of the plasma tends to decrease. Water flows into the cells, and their volume (as measured by the hematocrit) is slightly higher in the venous than in the arterial blood, as shown by the last line of Table VI.

6) Red cells and hemoglobin play a considerable role in the transport of carbon dioxide. When plasma obtained by centrifugation of whole blood (separated plasma) is subsequently equilibrated at various P_{CO_2} values, its CO_2 content changes very little. On the other hand, the CO_2 content of plasma obtained by equilibrating whole blood followed by centrifugation (true plasma) varies considerably when P_{CO_2} is changed (Fig. 12). This is due to the fact that only the red cells are able to form a large quantity of HCO_3^- ions which then diffuse into the plasma.

7) The transformation of HbO_2 in Hb is of considerable importance. When this takes place, some "oxylabile" amine groups can bind CO_2 as a carbamine. Moreover, since Hb is less acid than HbO_2, the basic K^+ ion is liberated when hemoglobin passes from the oxygenated to the non-oxygenated form, and K^+ reaches equilibrium with HCO_3^- and Cl^- ions (the latter coming from the plasma).

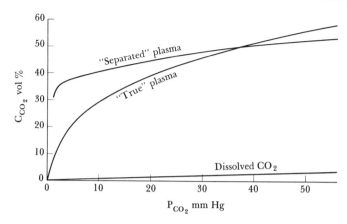

FIGURE 12. CO_2 content, C_{CO_2}, of "separated" plasma and "true" plasma
as a function of partial pressure of CO_2, P_{CO_2}.

The curve labeled "separated" plasma shows the relationship between C_{CO_2}
and P_{CO_2} in plasma obtained by centrifugation of whole blood, *then equilibrated* at
different CO_2 pressures.

The curve labeled "true" plasma shows the relationship between C_{CO_2} and P_{CO_2}
in plasma of whole blood equilibrated at different CO_2 pressures, and *then separated*
by centrifugation.

The figure shows that in the part of the curve pertaining to the normal P_{CO_2}
values, the C_{CO_2}–P_{CO_2} curve of "separated" plasma is much less steep than that of
"true" plasma. This shows the importance of the red cells and of hemoglobin in the
ability of blood to bind CO_2.

8) In the absence of the reaction $HbO_2 \rightleftharpoons Hb$, blood can bind the same
volume of CO_2 only at the cost of an important change in pH in the acid
direction, and of a more pronounced increase in P_{CO_2}. The small variation
in pH is due in part to the buffering action of hemoglobin (and of the other
blood buffers) but mainly to the transformation of HbO_2 into Hb. As pointed
out before, Hb is less acid than HbO_2, and as a consequence Hb can bind
more hydrogen ions than HbO_2, and Hb requires less of the available K^+
ions.

Whatever the mechanism of acid-base balance may be, the plasma pH *
is defined by the Henderson-Hesselbalch equation, which as applied to
respiratory gases can be set as:

---

* When the term "blood pH" with no additional details is used, it always refers, by
definition, to plasma pH. This is the value that is determined when measuring pH in
whole blood.

$$pH_{plasma} = 6.10 + \log \frac{C_{CO_2} \text{ of plasma in mM/l} - 0.03\ P_{CO_2}}{0.03\ P_{CO_2}, \text{ mm Hg}}$$

$$= 6.10 + \log \frac{[HCO_3^-] \text{ plasma, mM/l}}{0.03\ P_{CO_2}, \text{ mm Hg}}$$

or

$$= 6.10 + \log \frac{[HCO_3^-] \text{ plasma, vol\%}}{0.067\ P_{CO_2}, \text{ mm Hg}}$$

9) *Partial pressures and total pressure of gases in the alveolar gas and in the arterial and venous blood.*

TABLE VII

		ALVEOLAR GAS	ARTERIAL BLOOD	VENOUS BLOOD
P_{N_2},	mm Hg	569	569	569
P_{O_2},	mm Hg	103	88	37
P_{CO_2},	mm Hg	41	41	47.5
P_{H_2O},	mm Hg	47	47	47
Total pressure mm Hg		760	745	700.5

Table VII assumes 1) that alveolar and arterial P_{N_2} are equal, although it is currently believed that arterial P_{N_2} exceeds the alveolar value by a few millimeters of mercury (see Rahn, 1961), and 2) that arterial P_{CO_2} equals alveolar P_{CO_2} (see p. 120).

The table shows that the total pressure of gases in blood is lower than that in the alveoli, because arterial P_{O_2} is always lower than alveolar P_{O_2} (see p. 124). The total pressure of venous blood is even lower than that in arterial blood because, following gas exchange in the tissues, there is a considerable drop in P_{O_2}, while P_{CO_2} increases by only a few millimeters of mercury. This explains why no gas is released in the pleural space (although the partial pressure is normally lower than the barometric pressure by a few millimeters of mercury, for instance 755 as opposed to 760 mm Hg). If the total pressure of blood gases was higher or equal to that in the pleura, gases would accumulate in the latter and create a pneumothorax.† The fact that the pleural pressure is lower than the total gas pressure in blood explains also why air introduced in the pleural cavity disappears progressively. How-

† There is no liquid in the pleural cavity for almost the same reason as there is no gas (Agostoni and coworkers, 1957). The absence of liquid is due to the fact that the osmotic pressure of the plasma proteins, directed outwards, is higher than transmural capillary pressure — that is, capillary pressure minus pressure in the pleural cavity — which is directed into the pleural space.

ever, pneumothorax resorption requires several weeks because of the low solubility of nitrogen in blood. The rate at which gas is resorbed depends mainly on the blood flow. For example, when a bronchus loses its patency, and the corresponding lung volume is not ventilated, gas resorption leads rapidly to atelectasis (see W. A. Dale and Rahn, *Am. J. Physiol.*, 1952, **170**, 606–615).‡

‡ Several articles dealing with resorption of gases from body cavities can be found in the *Handbook of Physiology. Section 3: Respiration, Volume II*, edited by Fenn and Rahn (Baltimore: Williams & Wilkins, 1965) and in an article by Rahn (1961).

NORTHEASTERN JUNIOR COLLEGE
LIBRARY 29624
STERLING COLORADO

5
Mechanics of Ventilation

I. ANATOMICAL AND HISTOLOGICAL CONSIDERATIONS

From the standpoint of ventilation, the thorax can be considered to be an elastic closed container in communication with the environment through the respiratory airways, and to have a shape that is affected by the forces exerted by the respiratory muscles.

Besides the mediastinal viscera, the thorax contains the lungs, separated from the thoracic wall, diaphragm, and mediastinal structures by a serosa, with the visceral pleura lining the lungs while the parietal pleura covers the thoracic wall and the mediastinal viscera. The whole complex, to which we shall refer as the "thorax," includes the lungs and the "chest wall," the latter corresponding to all the thoracic structures except the lung, and including all the elements that surround the lungs and create or transmit forces which act on the lungs. The chest wall is the container that can be affected by the action of the respiratory muscles and the lung is the content.

Intralobular bronchi, which have a diameter of about one millimeter, lead to the terminal bronchioles, which are less than one millimeter long and possess in their walls smooth muscle fibers, known as the Reissessen muscles. These bronchioles lead to the transitional bronchioles or respiratory bronchioles which in turn end as alveolar ducts.

Pulmonary alveoli open into the respiratory bronchioles and alveolar ducts, with a few smooth muscle fibers around the opening. The complex alveolar duct + alveoli constitutes a primary lobule (diameter 1 to 5 mm) arising from a respiratory bronchiole. Fifty to one hundred and fifty primary lobules form the secondary lobule.

There are approximately 500 million alveoli, with a mean diameter of 0.2 mm. Assuming the alveoli to be spherical, the total area can be calcu-

51

lated to be of the order of 60 m² (approximately 650 sq ft). The wall that separates the capillary blood from the alveolar gas is extremely thin, and never exceeds 0.15 to 0.3 μ in thickness. On the gas side, it is lined by a continuous liquid film.

The work of Miller (1950), von Hayek (1953), and Policard (1955) gives precise information on pulmonary anatomy and histology, while the papers of Weibel and Gomez (1962) and of Staub and Storey (1962) should be consulted for histophysiology.

II. VENTILATORY CYCLE AND FLOW

The ventilatory cycle

Ventilation is a periodic phenomenon, in which inspiratory movements, when a certain volume of air enters the lungs, alternate with expiratory movements, when gas is expelled from the lungs into the atmosphere. The volume of air inspired and subsequently expired defines the amplitude of the cyclic air movement and is called *tidal volume*.

The beginning of the cycle is usually considered to be the time immediately preceding inspiration, and the duration of each cycle, given by the time separating the start of two successive inspirations, is the period of the ventilatory phenomenon. The inverse of the period is the frequency. The shorter the period, the higher the frequency. Usually the period, P, is expressed in seconds, and the frequency, f, in cycles per minute.

P, sec	10	6	4	2
$f = \dfrac{1}{P} \cdot 60$, per minute	6	10	15	30

The characteristics of the ventilatory cycle, in terms of frequency, tidal volume, and wave form of the respiratory movements, vary considerably even in the normal subject, in response to changes in body position, passage from wakefulness to sleep, variations in the level of energy expenditure and of gas exchange. In addition, even under identical conditions, the characteristics of ventilation differ from subject to subject, which leads to the concept of a ventilatory "personality."

At rest, the tidal volume of a normal adult may vary from 400 to 1500 ml, and the respiratory frequency from 5/minute to 22/minute. The ventilatory flow rate, or minute volume of ventilation, varies less than either tidal volume or frequency, which means that subjects with a low frequency have a high tidal volume and vice versa. If the resting minute volume is expressed as a function of the body area, or of the subject's weight, its range of values decreases somewhat.

During *muscular exercise*, both tidal volume and respiratory frequency increase, and a new minute volume is achieved through one of an infinite number of combinations of frequency and tidal volume. In severe exercise, the tidal volume may exceed 3 l and the frequency 40/minute.

Ventilatory flow

1) DEFINITION OF VENTILATORY FLOW

Ventilatory flow is the volume of air ventilated per unit time. This flow, $\dot{V}$, is equal to the product of the tidal volume, V_T, by the respiratory frequency, f.

$$\dot{V} = V_T \cdot f$$

For instance,

	VENTILATORY FLOW V, in l/min BTPS	TIDAL VOLUME V_T, in l BTPS	RESPIRATORY FREQUENCY f, in times/min
At rest	7.2	0.6	12
During moderate exercise	40.0	1.6	25

In man, two factors normally affect ventilation:

a) Variations in energy expenditure of the body (muscular exercise, thermoregulation, digestion). Ventilatory flow and energy expenditure vary in the same direction. In the most strenuous exercise, ventilatory flow may exceed 150 l/min, BTPS and can be 20 times as high as that prevailing at rest.

b) Altitude: during exposure to altitude, ventilation increases.

c) In addition, certain animals (dog, rabbit) placed in a hot environment exhibit a very high respiratory frequency, coupled with a reduced tidal volume, an example of thermal tachypnea.

In order to estimate the maximal ventilatory capacity of a subject, two methods are currently used.

2) MAXIMAL VOLUNTARY VENTILATION (MVV)

(This is also called maximum breathing capacity, abbreviated MBC.) The subject is asked to ventilate as hard and as fast as he can, and generally chooses the optimal tidal volume-frequency combination. This procedure is extremely tiring and cannot be maintained for more than 20 seconds, which is however adequate to obtain the required measurement. Flows of more than 200 l/min can be obtained. The MVV values depend on the subject's build, age, and sex. For men, Baldwin, Cournand, and Richards (1948) have suggested the following relationship:

MVV, l/min, BTPS = (86.5 − 0.522 × age in years) × body surface area in square meters.

For women:

MVV, l/min, BTPS = (71.3 − 0.474 × age in years) × body surface area in square meters, with a variation coefficient of about 20%, which indicates a high degree of scatter. Therefore a determined MVV can be said to be decreased only if it is reduced by more than 40% of the predicted mean value.

3) FORCED EXPIRATORY VOLUME (FEV)

The maximal voluntary ventilation test is tiring and sometimes difficult to perform. Measurement of forced expiratory volume does not have these disadvantages. In this maneuver a single rapid expiration is studied. The subject inspires maximally and then expires as rapidly as possible, and the expiratory curve is recorded on a kymograph moving at an appropriate speed. In order to expire a volume equal to the vital capacity, several seconds are required. The volume expired during the first second is measured and is designated as FEV_1. It is expressed in l BTPS/s. Normally it represents at least 80% of the vital capacity, a fact stated as:

$$\frac{FEV_1, \text{ in } l/s}{VC, \text{ in } l} \cdot 100 > 80\%.$$

The ratio has the dimension of frequency. According to Cara (1953) it corresponds to the optimal frequency of the maximal voluntary ventilation.

The significance of this ratio is not simple. If it has a very low value, it usually indicates an abnormally high resistance to gas flow in the airway. In asthma and pulmonary emphysema, the ratio has often a value of less than 50%. However, inhalation of a bronchodilator aerosol increases this ratio substantially in the asthmatic subject, but has no effect on the emphysematous patient. In an asthmatic, during a symptom-free interval, aerosolization of a very dilute acetylcholine solution causes bronchoconstriction and lowers the FEV as well as the $\frac{FEV_1}{VC}$, while the same aerosol has no effect on a healthy subject.

Distribution of inspired gas

Is the air that enters the lungs during inspiration distributed to each anatomical entity (lobes, segments, lobules, etc.) in proportion to the volume of gas these elements contained at the end of expiration?

Several methods have been applied to the study of the problem of proportional (or even) distribution of air in the lungs. The simplest one is ausculation: a pulmonary zone that is poorly ventilated will produce less sound than one that is well ventilated. The problem of distribution can also be studied radiologically. Normally, during voluntary hyperventilation, the opacity of the lungs changes, the lungs being more opaque during expiration. The transparency of an area which is poorly ventilated, especially during a rapid expiration (like cough) or rapid inspiration (like sniff) varies less than that of well-ventilated areas. However these methods will detect only important and widespread abnormalities of distribution and cannot show whether, during normal breathing, inspired air is distributed to each element in proportion to its volume.

If this distribution was even, inhalation of a certain volume of gas would cause an identical dilution of the gas initially present in each of the pulmonary units. If, on the other hand, inspired gas is not distributed in proportion to the respective volumes of the elements it reaches, the alveolar gas of the poorly ventilated alveoli will be less diluted than that of well-ventilated elements.

Several methods (see Fowler, 1952; Bouhuys and Lundin, 1959) enable one to study the distribution of inspired gas. One of these is based on the analysis of elimination of alveolar nitrogen (nitrogen washout) during prolonged O_2 breathing (Fig. 13). Successive inspirations of oxygen dilute progressively the pulmonary nitrogen and each expiration vents into the atmosphere a certain amount of nitrogen until all the N_2 is eliminated from the air spaces. If the inspired gas, oxygen, was distributed to all alveoli in proportion to their volume, it would be simple to predict the N_2 washout curve, since it is easy to foresee that in this case the nitrogen fraction in the expirate would decrease gradually as an exponential function of time. If, on the other hand, the distribution is not even, the well-ventilated elements will be rapidly depleted of N_2 while the poorly ventilated alveoli will be washed out at a slower rate. A great number of such rates may exist simultaneously, but in general nitrogen washout in the lungs behaves as if the lung was made up of two components, one well ventilated and the other not, each having its own exponential washout curve, the slower corresponding obviously to the poorly ventilated compartments.

A certain uneven distribution of the inspired gas can be demonstrated in the normal subject. In disease, this unevenness may be considerable, and complete washout of N_2 from the lungs would require a very long time. In some cases, at the end of 7 minutes, as required in the test designed by Darling, Cournand, and Richards (1940), the nitrogen fraction is still high, whereas in normals it falls below 0.025 or 2.5%. This abnormality occurs when there is a regional disturbance in inspiratory expansion (as would occur in a localized paralysis, such as that of a hemidiaphragm or in cases where there

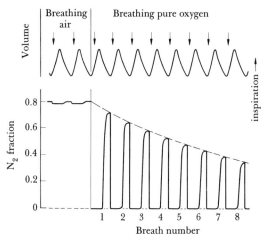

FIGURE 13.   Elimination of nitrogen from the lungs
during oxygen breathing (schematic).

Upper diagram is a spirogram (lung volume changes versus time).

Lower diagram shows the nitrogen fraction at the mouth sampled continuously from the mouthpiece or the respiratory mask, and analyzed with a rapid response analyzer.

As long as the subject breathes air, the nitrogen fraction in the ventilatory gas is nearly constant. If the respiratory quotient is below unity, as is the general rule, nitrogen is slightly higher in the expired gas than in the inspired air.

When the subject breathes oxygen rather than air, lung nitrogen is eliminated, and the fraction in expired gas decreases progressively. A study of the nitrogen elimination curve allows one to see whether inspired air distribution to the different parts of the lungs is proportional to their volume or not.

is local rigidity of the chest wall or of the pulmonary parenchyma) or when certain airways present an abnormally high resistance to air flow (emphysema, exudates, tumors, compression of airways, etc.).

III.   LUNG VOLUMES

A subject breathing spontaneously will inhale during each inspiration a certain volume of air, expelled during the following expiration. This volume is what we have called tidal volume. Thus, during the respiratory cycle, the thorax volume varies between two volumes, that which is reached at the end of expiration, called the expiratory position of the thorax, and the other reached at the end of inspiration, which corresponds to the inspiratory position of the thorax. The difference between the two represents the tidal volume, provided no change in thoracic blood volume has occurred.

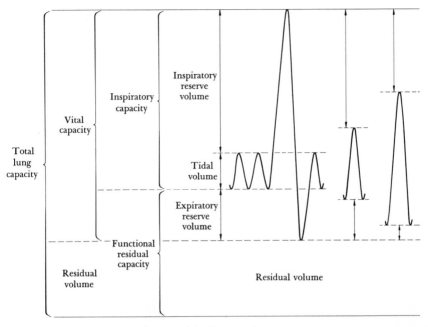

FIGURE 14.   Lung volumes.

At the end of a spontaneous expiration, the subject, by performing a voluntary, forced, expiratory movement, can expel an additional air volume, called *expiratory reserve volume*. Similarly, at the end of a normal inspiration, a forced inspiratory movement allows the subject to inhale an additional volume of air which constitutes the *inspiratory reserve volume*.

The subject can therefore take in a maximal inspiration and follow this with a maximal expiration, a maneuver which will expel his inspiratory reserve volume, tidal volume, and expiratory reserve volume. This is called *vital capacity*, and represents the maximal volume of gas the subject can move voluntarily during a single respiratory movement.

During spontaneous ventilation, even when this is extremely high, the subject never brings into play his whole vital capacity. The tidal volume rarely exceeds half the vital capacity.

A given tidal volume does not occupy a fixed segment of the vital capacity. As an example, in the supine position, the expiratory reserve volume is much smaller than when standing or sitting and, as a consequence, the inspiratory capacity (which is the sum of the tidal volume and the inspiratory reserve volume) is much higher while lying down than while sitting. Even for a given body position, the respective importance of the three volumes which constitute the vital capacity varies considerably from one subject to the other. However, at rest, the expiratory reserve volume is always much smaller than the inspiratory reserve volume.

On the other hand, since the tidal volume itself varies at rest (depending on the position and on whether the subject is awake or asleep) and can also be increased considerably during activity, such as muscular exercise — where the tidal volume can be up to six times higher than the resting volume — the inspiratory reserve volume and, to a lesser extent, the expiratory reserve volume, can also vary considerably.

Nevertheless, vital capacity is relatively constant in a given subject. It decreases at altitude, in reference to its value at sea level, and it also decreases in the supine position. Vital capacity is dependent on different factors, more specifically height, age, and sex. For adults, Baldwin, Cournand, and Richards (1948) have established the following relationships:

In males:

V.C. in ml BTPS = [27.63 − (0.112 × age in years)] × height in cm.

In females:

V.C. in ml BTPS = [21.78 − (0.101 × age in years)] × height in cm.

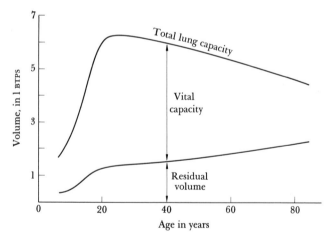

FIGURE 15.   Total lung capacity, vital capacity, and residual volume
as function of age, for subjects of average build.

The coefficient of variation of these relationships is about 15%. Figure 15 shows the influence of age on vital capacity.

After having exhaled maximally, a certain volume of air is left in the lungs. This volume which cannot be expired is called *residual volume*. Thus, at the end of a spontaneous expiration, the thorax contains a volume of gas called *functional residual capacity*, which is the sum of the expiratory reserve volume (which could have been expired during forced expiration) and of the residual volume (which cannot be expired by a forced expiratory maneuver). Finally, the sum of the vital capacity and of the residual volume gives us the *total lung capacity*, that is the maximal volume of air that the lungs can contain, and which is in fact in the thorax when it is in a forced inspiratory position.

As opposed to the volumes that constitute vital capacity, and to vital capacity itself, all of which can be measured directly, the residual volume can be measured only indirectly. In practice this volume is measured by dilution of a poorly soluble gas such as nitrogen or helium.

As an example, in the closed circuit dilution method using nitrogen (Christie, 1932), the subject, after a spontaneous expiration (in which case one measures the functional residual capacity) or a forced expiration (in which case one measures the residual volume), is connected to a closed circuit containing pure oxygen and a carbon dioxide absorber. In this closed system, the absolute amount of nitrogen does not change; but while at the beginning of the test the nitrogen was to be found only in the lungs, at the end of the test, the same nitrogen is evenly diluted, that is, it will be found at the same concentration in the gas of the lung and in the gas of the external circuit.

At the beginning of the test, the fraction of nitrogen in the residual volume is 80% and thus the total volume of nitrogen must be $V_R \times 0.8$. At the end of the test, a certain nitrogen fraction, F_{N_2}, is found in a volume which is the sum of the residual volume V_R and of the volume of the external circuit, V_C, the latter being known. The nitrogen volume in this closed circuit has not changed between the beginning and the end, and as a consequence:

$$V_R \cdot 0.8 = (V_R + V_C) \cdot F_{N_2}$$

and

$$V_R = V_C \frac{F_{N_2}}{0.8 - F_{N_2}}$$

Thus, if the volume of the external circuit is 2 liters and if the final nitrogen fraction is 0.36, the residual volume can be calculated to be 1.64 l. In practice a certain number of precautions must be taken during the test and some corrections must be applied to the calculations.

With age, the residual volume normally increases, and at the same time the vital capacity decreases. However, the decrease in vital capacity exceeds the increase in residual volume, so that the total pulmonary volume decreases with age.

In certain lung diseases, in particular pulmonary emphysema, the residual volume is abnormally increased.

IV. THE VENTILATORY MUSCLES

It would be helpful to sketch here the anatomy of the thoracic cage and of the diaphragm, indicating how the capacity of the thorax can change. The volume of the thorax can increase in all directions, vertical, transversal, and antero-posterior. It is the vertical diameter which varies most, mainly because of the contraction of the diaphragm.

Anatomy

The upper orifice of the thorax is formed by the spine, the first ribs, their cartilages, and the upper edge of the sternum. The plane of this ring slopes down in the forward direction. The first ribs can rotate around a transversal axis passing through their necks, which leads to a vertical movement of the anterior end of the ribs and of the sternum. This elevation increases the antero-posterior diameter of the thorax.

The upper ribs (second to sixth) rotate around two axes. The first is the transversal axis passing through the necks of opposed ribs, and since the general direction of the ribs is forward and downward, the elevation of these ribs leads to an increase in the antero-posterior diameter.

The second axis of rotation passes through the rib tubercle and the costosternal joint. Since the middle part of the ribs is below this axis, the elevation of the ribs leads to an increase in the transverse diameter.

The lower part of the thorax (seventh to tenth ribs) behaves essentially as the top part, the main difference being that the antero-posterior diameter varies very little.

The lower surface of the thorax is formed by a muscular membrane, the diaphragm. Although the diaphragm is a continuous anatomical unit, its right and left halves have their own innervation through the right and left phrenic nerves. Section of one of these nerves leads to a paralysis involving almost exclusively the homolateral part of the diaphragm. The diaphragm is tendinous in its central part, but muscular all along its periphery. The muscular fibers are inserted along the lower orifice of the thorax, that is, on the lumbar vertebrae and on the psoas muscle posteriorly, on the lower six ribs laterally and on the xiphoid process of the sternum anteriorly. The shape of the diaphragm is that of a cupola. An antero-posterior section shows a convexity directed upward and backward, while a frontal section shows an upward convexity. When the thorax is in expiratory position, the lateral and posterior parts of the diaphragm rise nearly vertically from their costal insertions, forming a very sharp angle with the thoracic wall.

Action of the respiratory muscles

It would appear at first that knowledge of the anatomical features of the ventilatory muscles and of the range of movement of the structures where these muscles have their insertion would lead to an easy understanding of their action on the various thoracic diameters and therefore of their inspiratory or expiratory action. Actually, the action of the respiratory muscles is often very complex, and it is possible to visualize that a given muscle may be inspiratory or expiratory according to the prevailing mechanical conditions (see Intercostal muscles). In this respect, electromyographic techniques (see Taylor, 1960) enable one generally to recognize at what moment in the respiratory cycle a given muscle contracts. However, the fact that a muscle contracts during a specific phase of the cycle, during inspiration for instance, enables one to state that it plays some role during this phase of inspiration, but not that the muscle is partly responsible for the increased thoracic volume. A movement is caused by a force vector which may be the resultant of antagonistic force vectors. For instance, all that is required for inspiratory movements to occur is that the force developed by inspiratory muscles exceed that developed by expiratory muscles. Under these conditions it becomes easy to see why the role and importance of respiratory muscles have been the center of numberless controversies and why some phenomena are not clearly understood.

1. DIAPHRAGM

The diaphragm is an inspiratory muscle. As it contracts its curvature decreases slightly. It has been stated that the diaphragm uses the abdominal viscera as fulcrum and thus elevates the ribs (the muscular fibers rise nearly vertically from their costal insertion), and conversely, that it uses the ribs as fulcrum and contracts downwards, lowering the abdominal viscera. Under usual conditions both these mechanisms take place, as shown by fluoroscopy: lowering of the dome of the diaphragm, and hence increase in the vertical diameter of the thorax, and expansion of the lower ribs with increase in the transversal diameter of the thorax.

At rest, when the tidal volume is a few hundred milliliters, the dome of the diaphragm undergoes a vertical movement of 1 to 1.5 cm. During a forced expiration the dome rises high in the thorax, and during forced inspiration, the dome is lower and the diaphragm is less convex. The distance between the position of the dome in forced inspiration and in forced expiration is normally 6 to 10 cm.

The position of the diaphragm varies considerably with body position. In the supine position, the diaphragm is displaced several centimeters toward the head of the subject, and as a result the vital capacity decreases considerably because of a decrease in expiratory reserve volume. When the subject is lying on his side, the diaphragm is quite asymmetric, the upper half being somewhat flattened and the convexity of the lower half being increased. Under these conditions it is in the lower half that the respiratory movements are the most apparent.

During each inspiration the descent of the diaphragm pushes down the abdominal viscera and, as a result, the anterior wall of the abdomen moves slightly forward. When the diaphragm is paralyzed, the abdominal wall remains almost motionless.

When unilateral paralysis of the diaphragm is present, the corresponding hemidiaphragm is several centimeters higher than the contralateral hemidiaphragm, and shows only minimal movement during respiration. Sometimes during inspiration, especially when this is rapid, the paralyzed hemidiaphragm rises instead of moving downward. This is due to the fact that during inspiration the intrathoracic pressure drops, while the intra-abdominal pressure remains the same or increases.

2. INTERCOSTAL MUSCLES

The external intercostal muscles are placed so that they slope downward and forward. The internal intercostal muscles slope downward and backward. With this knowledge of the direction of the muscle fibers and of the axis of rotation of the bony structures it would seem simple to predict the action of the intercostal muscles. However this reasoning overlooks two facts. The first is that the intrathoracic pressure is lower than atmospheric pressure, and that the shape and position of the thoracic wall are different in living man than in the open chest cadaver. The second is that the position and the latitude of movement of the chest wall are modified by the concomitant action of other respiratory muscles, mainly the diaphragm. These considerations explain why there is so much discussion as to the action of the intercostal muscles.

Hamberger's theory, generally accepted, states that (a) contraction of the external intercostal muscles and of the intercartilaginous portion of these muscles elevates the ribs. These muscles normally contract during inspiration, even at rest; and (b) the internal intercostal muscles have a tendency to move the ribs closer to one another and to lower them.

The intercostal muscles play an important role in ventilatory mechanics. When they are paralyzed, movement of the thoracic wall is greatly decreased. Their action is especially important when the diaphragm is paralyzed. Furthermore, the intercostal muscles are of considerable importance during forced expiratory movements, especially coughing.

3. ABDOMINAL MUSCLES

Contraction of the abdominal muscles has two effects: it lowers the lower ribs and pushes on the abdominal viscera. The resulting increase in abdominal pressure moves the diaphragm upwards.

In the erect subject these muscles are often contracted continually and seem to play a role in maintaining body posture and supporting the abdominal viscera. When this is the case, there is generally some rhythmic fluctuation in the degree of contraction, with an increase during expiration.

Their action is especially marked when ventilation is high, and, in this case, the muscles relax during inspiration and contract during expiration and this contraction causes an important increase in abdominal pressure. Finally these muscles contract forcefully during acts where an increased abdominal pressure is required (cough, defecation, vomiting).

4. OTHER RESPIRATORY MUSCLES

Contraction of the scalene muscles elevates the first two ribs: these are inspiratory muscles. In some subjects they are active almost continually, in others only during inspiration. In any case they contract forcefully when ventilation is increased.

The sterno-cleido-mastoid muscles elevate the sternum and are therefore inspiratory.

Several additional muscles may contract during the respiratory cycle. However, because of their small dimension, or because they are but seldom brought into play, or simply because of insufficient knowledge, they will not be studied. We shall only note that the nares muscles, unimportant in man, can contract rhythmically during the respiratory cycle, and are responsible for the flaring of the nares sometimes observed during dyspnea.

5. SUMMARY

Inspiration is due primarily to diaphragmatic action. The intercostal and scalene muscles contract during inspiration in most resting subjects, and in all cases when ventilation is increased. Furthermore, in the erect subject, whenever there is continuous contraction of the abdominal wall, this decreases during inspiration.

When ventilation exceeds 50 l/m or thereabout, the sterno-cleido-mastoid muscles and the extensors of the vertebral column are also active.

Expiratory mechanisms are not as simple (see p. 80). Four complicating factors come into the picture:

a) At end-inspiration, the increase in thoracic volume corresponds to a certain amount of potential energy, due to the elastic properties of the thorax, similar to the potential energy stored in a spring under tension (see p. 69). This potential energy would be sufficient to ensure expiration, even at high ventilatory flow. In this case, expiration should be passive (type I, p. 80). This type of expiration, although theoretically possible, is never encountered.

b) When the inspiratory act is completed, the inspiratory muscles do not cease contracting instantaneously, but their activity decreases gradually during expiration and thereby controls the rate at which expiration takes place. In this case, expiration is braked (type II, p. 81).

c) The expiratory muscles contract (type III, p. 82), in which case expiration is active.

d) Expiration could possibly be controlled by a change in airway diameter, the latter being regulated by the degree of contraction of the bronchial muscles. This possibility has aroused little interest. It assumes that the speed of contraction and relaxation of the smooth muscles is rapid enough to produce changes in bronchial diameter during the course of a single respiratory cycle.

Maximal forces exerted by the respiratory muscles (Fig. 16)

The maximal force that a muscle can develop increases when the muscle is stretched. As a result, the maximal forces that the inspiratory and expiratory muscles can exert depend on the thoracic volume, which determines the degree of stretch of these muscles. In Rahn's method (1946) the subject expires maximally and inspires immediately thereafter a certain volume of air. Following this, he exerts for a few seconds a maximal inspiratory or expiratory effort through a mouthpiece connected to a mercury manometer. Since this is a closed system, no actual inspiration or expiration occurs. As a result of the muscular effort, the pressure in the lungs is increased or decreased, in relation to atmospheric pressure.

1) MAXIMAL EXPIRATORY FORCE

Following a forced inspiration, a maximal expiratory effort can increase the intrapulmonary pressure by approximately 100 mm Hg. However, this increase in pressure compresses the lung gases and the point describing the

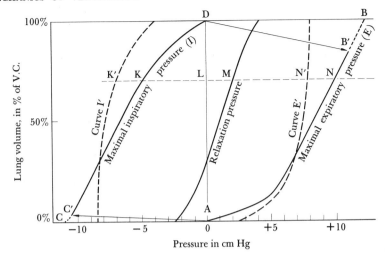

FIGURE 16.   Maximal forces of the ventilatory muscles.

Thoracic pressure-volume diagram.

Volume is expressed as % of V.C., or vital capacity. On the abscissa is mouth pressure in relation to barometric pressure. For technique, see text.

Curves E and I denote maximal intrapulmonary positive (E) and negative (I) pressures that can be recorded when a subject contracts maximally his expiratory or inspiratory muscles for a few seconds. The figure shows that the maximal expiratory pressure increases with lung volume.

The curve labeled "relaxation pressure" shows the pressure inside the lungs at different lung volumes, when the subject relaxes completely his ventilatory muscles with either a closed glottis or a closed measuring system.

The maximal expiratory pressure NL is the sum of a force ML due to thorax elasticity and of a force NM due to contraction of the expiratory muscles. The LN' segment is equal to MN. The curve joining all N' points, curve E', shows the maximal pressures developed by contraction of expiratory muscles at different lung volumes. The same reasoning can be applied to maximal inspiratory pressures, and gives curve I'.

(From H. RAHN, A. OTIS, L. E. CHADWICK, W. O. FENN, *Am. J. Physiol.*, 1946, **146**, 161–178.)

maximal expiratory pressure to volume relationship is not B but B'. When the thorax is reduced to its smallest possible volume by a forced expiration, the representative point, A, is such that both volume and expiratory pressure are zero. Between points B' and A, the maximal expiratory pressure curve, labeled E, shows what relationship exists between pulmonary volume and maximal expiratory force.

2) MAXIMAL INSPIRATORY FORCE

If the subject performs a maximal inspiratory effort following a forced expiration, i.e. when the lungs contain only the residual volume, the pressure
of the gas in the respiratory system is brought to about 100 mm Hg below
atmospheric pressure. Because of this pressure drop, the residual volume is
increased and the representative point is C' and not C. When the thorax,
following a forced inspiration, contains as much air as possible, it is obvious
that an inspiratory effort will not cause any drop in pressure, and the point
representing this condition appears as D. Curve I shows the relationship
between lung volume and maximal inspiratory forces.

Actually the maximal inspiratory or expiratory forces are not due exclusively to the maximal effort of the inspiratory or expiratory muscles.
For instance, when the lung volume represents 70% of the vital capacity,
the maximal expiratory pressure NL is due to the action of two forces:
that exerted by the expiratory muscles, shown as NM, and secondly by
the elastic properties of the thorax, represented by ML.

At the same lung volume, the maximal forces developed by the inspiratory musculature do not correspond to the pressure read on the manometer,
that is to LK, but rather to MK; for the thorax exerts the pressure ML,
which is in the opposite direction and therefore must be subtracted from
the pressure due to muscular force, which must therefore have been MK.

The pressure arising from maximal contraction of the respiratory muscles
can therefore be represented at any volume by a segment MK for maximal
inspiratory effort and by NM for maximal expiratory effort. It is easy to add
or subtract in each case the pressure due to the elastic properties of the
thorax and to obtain thereby the two curves I' and E' which show the pressure due solely to the maximal contraction of the inspiratory or expiratory
muscles at different lung volumes.

Movements of the bronchi

Two factors can considerably change the bronchial diameter: variations
in the pressure difference between the inside and the outside of the bronchi,
and variations in bronchial muscle contraction.

1) DIFFERENCE BETWEEN INTRABRONCHIAL AND PERIBRONCHIAL PRESSURES

Variations in diameter due to this mechanism are passive.

The *intrabronchial* pressure is variable. The changes in pressure are synchronous with ventilation. The pressure is negative (in relation to barometric pressure) during inspiration and positive during expiration. The

changes in pressure are more pronounced in the parts of the bronchial tree that are further away from the trachea.

The *peribronchial* pressure is also variable, due to two causes (see p. 77). On one hand the thoracic volume changes, and the extent to which the intrathoracic pressure is lower than barometric pressure is related to thoracic volume (see p. 73). The other cause is the resistance to air flow in the bronchial tree. Since part of this resistive airway is interposed between a point of the conductive system and the perialveolar and peribronchial spaces, the variations in peribronchial pressure due to airway resistance are always higher than the variations in intrabronchial pressure.

As a result:

a) The bronchioles are constantly subjected to a distending force.

b) Since the peribronchial pressure is more negative in the inspiratory than in the expiratory position, the bronchial diameter must vary in the same direction as lung volume. However, the inspiratory increase in lung volume stretches the bronchi. This would tend to narrow their lumen and oppose the increase in diameter that would result from the drop in peribronchial pressure.

c) During inspiration and expiration, the variations in peribronchial and intrabronchial pressures are such that the difference between these two pressures is not the same at a given lung volume. At the same lung volume, the difference between peribronchial and intrabronchial pressures must be less negative during expiration than during inspiration, and therefore, at any lung volume, the bronchial caliber must be less during expiration than during inspiration.

This difference is very conspicuous when the bronchial diameter is abnormally low. This decrease in diameter may be due either to contraction of the smooth bronchial muscles (bronchial spasm encountered in asthma) or to a decrease in negative peribronchial pressure, due in turn to a decrease in pulmonary elasticity (as would occur in pulmonary emphysema).

2) THE BRONCHIAL MUSCLES

The muscular system is especially developed at the bronchiolar level, where cartilage is absent, the bronchial wall is pliant, and the patency of the bronchioles is due to the fact that peribronchial pressure is lower than intrabronchial pressure.

Contraction of the bronchial muscles decreases the bronchial diameter and, if the pressure difference between upstream and downstream is maintained, causes a decrease in air flow.

Bronchial muscles have a double innervation (see Wyss, 1952):

— there are cholinergic, parasympathetic fibers coming from the vagus nerves, which, when excited, cause bronchoconstriction. Inhalation or injection of acetylcholine has the same effect. In addition, histamine is a powerful bronchoconstrictor acting directly in the muscle fibers;

— there are also adrenergic fibers of sympathetic origin that innervate the bronchial muscles. Stimulation of these fibers, as well as inhalation of an aerosol or injection of epinephrine and norepinephrine, cause the relaxation of previously contracted bronchial muscles.

Bronchospasm which is present during asthmatic attacks, can be reversed by epinephrine. In the asthmatic patient, during an attack-free interval, an increased sensitivity to acetylcholine can be demonstrated by the use of acetylcholine aerosols (see p. 54).

Bronchial muscles are, through their innervation, under the influence of the higher vegetative centers. It is believed that bronchomotor activity of central origin is dependent on some factor, acting directly or indirectly on the vegetative centers: excitation of carotid and aortic chemoreceptors (by a decrease if the partial pressure of oxygen in the arterial blood) can reflexly cause bronchodilation. On the other hand, excitation of the carotid and aortic baroreceptors by elevation of arterial blood pressure causes bronchoconstriction (Daly and Schweitzer, 1951, and Widdicombe, 1962).

Bronchial muscles are normally tonically contracted. Administration of atropine, by aerosol for instance, decreases the airway resistance and increases anatomical dead space.

Although analytical physiology of the bronchial muscles is well known, the problem of how this musculature is brought into play is still not solved. Does the degree of contraction vary during the respiratory cycle? It has been reported that bronchial muscles contract during inspiration and thereby oppose the mechanical increase in diameter discussed above, while the opposite occurs during expiration. Are there bronchial peristaltic movements toward the hilum, initiated by excitation of the mucosa by foreign bodies (dust, exudate)? Do these muscles play a role in the distribution of inspired gas in the lungs? This role may be coupled with the regulation of distribution of blood flow in the lungs, since, as will be discussed later (p. 119), it is the relation between air flow and blood flow in the different areas which determines quantitatively the alveolar-capillary gas exchange.

Bronchial diameter depends therefore on mechanical factors involving the variations of intrabronchial and peribronchial pressures, and variations of lung volume, as well as on physiological factors which appear as changes in tension of the bronchial muscles. Briscoe and Du Bois (1958) have shown that, as a final result, the airway resistance decreases when lung volume increases.

V. ELASTIC PROPERTIES OF THE THORAX, OF THE CHEST WALL, AND OF THE LUNGS. INTRAPLEURAL PRESSURE

Elastic properties of the thorax

The respiratory muscles exert forces which change the shape of the thorax, which is an elastic cavity. A body is said to be elastic when, following deformation under the influence of an outside force, its initial shape is restored when the outside force disappears. Deformation of an elastic body is by definition reversible. In the case of a coil spring, the increase in length of the spring is proportional to the force that is applied to it. As long as the force and the increase in length do not exceed a certain value, the ratio of increase in length to force is constant (Hooke's Law) and characterizes the "distensibility" of the spring. The inverse of this ratio, that is the ratio of force to change in length, indicates the elastance of the spring.

When the respiratory muscles are relaxed and the glottis is open, the thorax has a certain shape and contains a certain volume of air, designated as the relaxation volume, V_R. Under these conditions, the intrapulmonary or intra-alveolar pressure is the same as the barometric pressure (Fig. 17, point 0 on the abscissa). This volume corresponds to an expiratory reserve of approximately 30%, the value shown in Figure 17.

An additional expiration brings the lung volume to a value that is lower than the relaxation volume. If the muscles are then relaxed, the thorax has a tendency to expand, exerting a force directed outwards. If the subject is connected to a manometer before he relaxes, and the glottis is open, the manometer will show a pressure P_1, negative in reference to ambient pressure. If air is allowed to enter the lungs, a volume of air $V_R - V_1$ is inspired passively, and the lungs regain their relaxation volume V_R.

On the other hand, when the thorax is expanded, following an inspiration, a force directed inward is exerted by the thorax, and at this volume V_2, a pressure P_2, higher than ambient, is read on the manometer. When the airway is opened, a certain volume of air equal to $V_2 - V_R$ is expired and the thorax returns to its relaxation volume.

The intrapulmonary pressure can be measured in this fashion at different lung volumes between forced expiration and forced inspiration. The ratios

$$\frac{V_2 - V_R}{P_2} \quad \text{and} \quad \frac{V_R - V_1}{P_1}$$

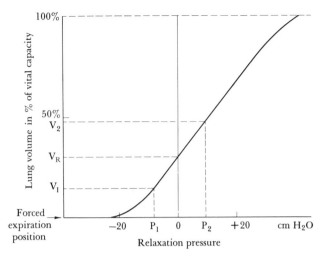

FIGURE 17.   Thorax relaxation curve.

To each lung volume (expressed as % of the V.C.) shown on the ordinate there is a corresponding pressure, shown on the abscissa. In practice, the subject, connected to a manometer, relaxes completely his ventilatory muscles. The pressures P_1, 0, and P_2 (difference between the pressure in the airways and the barometric pressure) correspond to volumes V_1, V_R, and V_2. At the relaxation volume, V_R, the relaxation intrapulmonary pressure is equal to ambient pressure. At volume V_1, which is less than V_R, the relaxed thorax, because of its elastic properties, tends to resume volume V_R, and this creates in the airways of the relaxed thorax a pressure that is negative in respect to barometric pressure (point P_1). The slope of the relaxation curve, expressed in absolute volume (and not, as in the figure, as percent of the vital capacity), is the thoracic or total respiratory compliance, which is the inverse of thoracic elastance.

indicate the average distensibility or average *compliance* of the thorax between V_2 and V_R and between V_R and V_1, respectively. In general, the ratio $\dfrac{dV}{dP}$ indicates this compliance and corresponds to the slope of the relaxation volume-pressure curve. This compliance is maximal in the middle part of the vital capacity, that is in the region in which the normal tidal volume is represented. The compliance expresses the pliability of the thorax and is considerably decreased in some pulmonary diseases (e.g. in pulmonary fibrosis).

The inverse of compliance, that is the ratio $\dfrac{dP}{dV}$, indicates the elastance of the thorax, that is the change in intrapulmonary pressure caused by a certain variation of the thoracic volume.

These physical definitions go against common usage where the elasticity of the body indicates how much it can be deformed by a certain force. In physics, if the shape of a body is very much affected by outside forces, its elastance is said to be low.

Elastic properties of the chest wall

The thorax relaxation pressure, which is an index of the elasticity of the whole thorax, has a double origin: the elasticity of the chest wall — that is to say the whole respiratory system excluding the lungs — and the elasticity of the lungs.

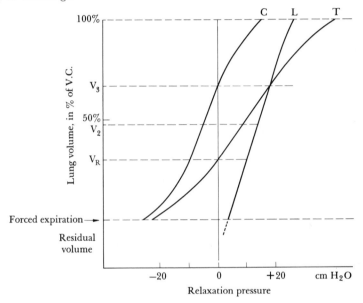

FIGURE 18. Pressure-volume curves for the thorax (total), lung, and chest wall.

On the ordinate, relative lung volumes; on the abscissa, pressure (relative to barometric pressure) in centimeters of water.

Curve T: thorax (total) relaxation curve. At volume V_R, the relaxation pressure is zero.

Curve L: pressure-volume curve of the lungs.

Curve C: pressure-volume curve of the isolated chest wall.

At any volume the thorax relaxation pressure is equal to the algebraic sum of the pressure originating in the chest wall and that originating in the lung. At volume V_R, the pressure originating in the lungs is equal in magnitude and of opposite sign to the pressure originating in the chest wall. At volume V_3, the chest wall pressure is zero, and the thorax relaxation pressure is due solely to lung elasticity.

The chest wall and the lungs do not have the same elastic properties, the main difference being that their relaxation volumes differ (Fig. 18).

The relaxation volume of the chest wall is larger (volume 3) than the relaxation volume of the thorax, V_R, and corresponds to 60 to 70% of the vital capacity. A higher or lower volume will cause forces directed inward or outward and therefore create pressures that are negative or positive. Thus, there is a relaxation curve pertaining only to the chest wall, which appears as curve C in Figure 18. The elasticity of the chest wall depends on the elasticity of the various elements of the thoracic cage (tendons, ligaments, muscles, etc.), which produce stretch or torsional forces. Insofar as the respiratory muscles are concerned, only the elastic forces are developed during relaxation, while the activity of the respiratory centers is voluntarily inhibited. However, this inhibition of motor activity does not abolish a possible tonic activity which, if at all present, can be suppressed by curarization.

Elasticity of the lungs

The relaxation volume of the lungs is much smaller than that of the chest wall. It is in fact less than residual volume, and thus under the 0% of vital capacity, or, in other words, below the maximal expiratory position. As was the case with the chest wall, a pressure-volume curve for the lungs alone can be drawn, and appears as L in Figure 18.

The pulmonary elasticity depends mainly on two factors:

a) the elastic fibers in the pulmonary parenchyma. The increased force they exert decreases when the lung volume decreases.

b) the surface tension of the liquid film that covers the alveolar epithelium (see the discussion by Mead, 1961). Any surface having a surface tension tends to decrease in area. In the case of a sphere (as, for instance, a soap bubble), the pressure inside the sphere is higher than the pressure outside (Laplace's Law).

Intrapleural pressure

The pulmonary elasticity explains why the pressure within the pleural cavity, which separates the lungs from the other anatomical structures of the ventilatory system, is negative in respect to the intrapulmonary or alveolar pressure. In Figure 18, the pressure exerted by the lungs is positive. Since the lungs have a tendency to contract, the alveolar pressure is positive in relation to that in the pleura. As a consequence, the intrapleural pressure is lower than alveolar pressure. This means that, as the lung volume increases, the intrapleural pressure decreases and becomes more negative in relation to alveolar pressure. As an example, it is −10 cm of water when measured at the relaxation volume, V_R, and −13 cm of water at volume 2, after 700 ml have been inspired.

MEASUREMENT OF INTRAPLEURAL PRESSURE

It is possible to introduce needles in the pleura of animals. The intrapleural pressure is probably not the same in all parts of the pleura, because the lungs do not seem to be isotropic (a term applied to bodies in which the elastic properties are identically distributed in all directions).

In practice, intrapleural pressure is never measured directly in man, except when a pneumothorax is present. However, the pressure inside the esophagus approximates closely the intrapleural pressure, especially in the sitting or standing position. This pressure is measured with a balloon made of very pliable material, about 12 cm in length and 1.5 cm in diameter. This balloon is swallowed until it reaches the lower third of the esophagus and moderately inflated, so that the walls are not under tension. It is usually accepted (see Mead and Whittenberger, 1953) that the variations in intra-esophageal pressure, synchronous with the respiratory cycle, enable a quantitative estimate to be made of the variations in intrapleural pressure and therefore the elastic properties of the lungs, as well as the variations in pressure due to the mechanical resistance of the lungs and airways.

Thorax, chest wall, and lung compliance values

It is possible to measure directly the relaxation pressure of the thorax (p. 69) although it is not easy to relax the respiratory muscles. The intra-esophageal pressure (see above) can be considered as representative of mean intrathoracic pressure. Since the total relaxation pressure, shown as T in Figure 18, is the algebraic sum of the pressure due to the elastic properties of the lungs (curve L) and that of the chest wall (curve C), it is possible to calculate the latter by difference.

At the thorax relaxation volume, V_R, the intrapulmonary pressure is zero. At this volume, the retractile elastic force of the lung balances exactly the tendency of the chest wall to expand.

At the 0% volume, the lungs exert a minimal retractile force and the chest wall a maximal outward force.

At volume 3, the thoracic wall is at its relaxation volume and therefore exerts no force. The relaxation pressure of the thorax is due entirely to lung elasticity.

Above volume 3, chest wall *and* lungs exert inward forces on the air contained in the lungs.

In the middle part of the vital capacity, compliance of the whole thorax is about 100 ml/cm H_2O. This means that a 100 ml increase in the gas volume contained in a relaxed thorax increases the intrapulmonary pressure by 1 cm of water. The compliances of the chest wall and of the lungs are higher (in Figure 18 the values are 177 ml/cm H_2O and 230 ml/cm H_2O respectively in the middle zone of the vital capacity, if the latter is about 5 l). It is easy to see why these compliances are higher than the total thoracic compliance since lungs and chest wall are similar to two springs in parallel. Two such springs, subjected to a certain force, will stretch less than either one of them taken separately and subjected to the same stretching force.

There is a simple relationship between the various compliances. If the symbols ΔP_T, ΔP_L, and ΔP_C are used to designate the variations in the pressures exerted by the thorax, lung, and chest wall when a change in volume ΔV takes place, it can be stated that:

$$\Delta P_T = \Delta P_L + \Delta P_C,$$

and hence

$$\frac{\Delta P_T}{\Delta V} = \frac{\Delta P_L}{\Delta V} + \frac{\Delta P_C}{\Delta V}.$$

The ratio $\frac{\Delta P}{\Delta V}$ indicates elastance, which is the inverse of compliance (see p. 70). As a consequence, total thoracic elastance is the sum of lung elastance and chest wall elastance.

VI. ANALYTICAL STUDY OF THE FORCES EXERTED BY THE RESPIRATORY MUSCLES
(Rohrer, 1925; Otis, Fenn, and Rahn, 1950)

The forces exerted by the respiratory muscles displace the thoracic wall and the lungs, and therefore perform a certain amount of work. The magnitude of the forces required to produce a given displacement depends essentially on two factors:

1) Elastance and resistance to deformation of the thoracic wall and of the lungs;

2) The resistance to air flow in the airway.

The forces required to accelerate and decelerate the thorax and air during the respiratory cycle are very small and can be neglected (Mead, 1956).

Forces required to deform the thorax

1) THORACIC ELASTANCE

The chest wall and the lungs are endowed with elastic properties (p. 69). Insofar as the work performed by the muscles of respiration is concerned, the elastic properties of the chest wall and of the lungs can be considered together. The thorax relaxation pressure-volume curve establishes what force must be exerted to overcome the elastance when the thorax volume changes, for instance, from volume V_R to volume V_2 (Fig. 18). At volume V_2, with the muscles relaxed and the glottis closed, the thorax exerts on the lung gases a pressure which is positive in relation to ambient pressure. If the glottis was opened, with the muscles still relaxed, a volume of air equal to $V_2 - V_R$ would be expired passively. However, if the subject is to maintain the same lung volume in spite of the opening of the glottis, the inspiratory muscles have to contract and exert a pressure equal to the relaxation pressure P_2, but in the opposite direction. This is why in Figure 19, the line eiR is directed toward negative pressures and not toward positive pressures as in Figure 17.

During inspiration, the muscles stretch the thoracic "spring" and store in it a certain potential energy, which could ensure passive expiration without additional energy expenditure. This does not mean that expiration is normally passive, but simply that passive expiration is theoretically possible (see p. 80).

In general, the force exerted by the inspiratory muscles to overcome thoracic elastance and bring the lung volume to a value V is:

$$P = K(V - V_R) \qquad (1)$$

where P is the thorax relaxation pressure, $V - V_R$ the change in lung volume, and K is a constant, the elastance of the system (albeit a constant only in the middle part of vital capacity).

Following an inspiration up to volume Vi, the pressure becomes equal to $K(Vi - V_R)$.

At the end of a normal, resting, spontaneous expiration, the lung volume is generally V_R and the pressure P is zero.

However, when the end-expiratory volume is smaller than V_R the expiratory muscles must exert forces to counterbalance the elastic properties of the thorax which would have tended to restore the volume V_R.

2) RESISTANCE TO DEFORMATION OF THE TISSUES

In addition to the above, the inspiratory muscles must overcome the friction that takes place in the tissues (lung, thoracic cage, diaphragm, and abdominal muscles) during respiratory movements. The forces that must be exerted for this purpose depend on the speed of the movement and therefore on the rate of air flow at that particular instant. The relationship between pressure and rate of air flow, $\dfrac{dV}{dt}$, is:

$$\Delta P = K_1 \left(\frac{dV}{dt}\right) + K_2 \left(\frac{dV}{dt}\right)^2 \tag{2}$$

where K_1 and K_2 are constants.

This frictional resistance in the tissues is much smaller than the one discussed below and is sometimes neglected.

Forces required to overcome resistance to air flow in the airways

Airways resistance causes variations in the gas pressure in the alveoli during the respiratory cycle. These variations are such that the alveolar pressure is negative during inspiration and positive during expiration (in reference to the atmosphere). The ventilatory muscles must exert a certain force to overcome this resistance. Air flow in different parts of the airway may be laminar (streamlined) or turbulent.

a) When the flow is laminar, the difference in pressure between two points is directly proportional to the flow rate $\dfrac{dV}{dt}$,

$$\Delta P = K_3 \left(\frac{dV}{dt}\right) \tag{3}$$

The factor K_3 depends, among other things, on the viscosity of the gas. It is often called viscous resistance to air flow.

b) In other parts of the airway, especially at the level of bends or bifurcations, the drop in pressure ΔP along the airway is proportional to the square of the flow rate, and

$$\Delta P = K_4 \left(\frac{dV}{dt}\right)^2 \tag{4}$$

The factor K_4, which defines turbulent flow resistance, depends on gas density.

To sum up, the variation in pressure ΔP that is required to ensure a flow $\dfrac{dV}{dt}$ across the airways can be written as:

$$\Delta P = K_3 \left(\frac{dV}{dt}\right) + K_4 \left(\frac{dV}{dt}\right)^2 \tag{5}$$

The constants K_3 and K_4 do not depend only on gas viscosity and density, but also on the geometry of the airways. As an example, K_3 is 16 times smaller when the airway diameter is doubled (Poiseuille's Law). It is therefore obvious that an increase in bronchial caliber makes ventilation much easier.

The fact that airway resistance is related to gas viscosity and density leads to some therapeutic considerations. In the emphysematous subject, for instance, the bronchial diameter is decreased, especially during expiration. In these narrowed bronchi, air flow is rapid and turbulent. The drop in pressure due to turbulent resistance is much higher than that due to laminar resistance, since the turbulent resistance is proportional to the second power of flow (equation 4). When this subject breathes a helium-oxygen mixture instead of air, ventilation is easier and maximal voluntary ventilation increases. This is due to a considerable decrease of turbulence in the airways, since the density of helium is much lower than that of nitrogen. A minor increase in laminar resistance also takes place, since helium is more viscous than nitrogen (see Otis and Bembower, 1949).

Variations in ambient pressure also change gas density. Furthermore, although theoretically pressure changes do not affect gas viscosity, during exposure to altitude the change in respiratory gas composition (whose components each have a different viscosity) actually causes a small decrease in expired air viscosity, while the viscosity of inspired air remains unchanged. In summary, the difference between alveolar and ambient pressures required to produce a certain flow is less at altitude than at sea level. On the other hand, under increased pressure (compression chambers, diving) this pressure difference increases and consequently the work required of the respiratory muscles also increases. On this basis alone, ventilation may cause some distress (Marshall, Lanphier, and Dubois, 1956).

VII. FORCES EXERTED DURING THE VENTILATORY CYCLE. TYPES OF VENTILATION

During inspiration

The forces have to overcome:

a) the elastance of the thorax (chest wall and lungs) which depends only on the volume $(V - V_R)$ as shown in equation 1;

b) the resistance of the tissues to deformation (Eq. 2). This resistance is relatively small;

c) the resistance to air flow in the airway (Eq. 5).

The mechanical resistances b) and c) depend on the speed at which changes take place and therefore on the rate of air flow, $\dfrac{dV}{dt}$.

At any time during inspiration, when the volume inspired is $(V - V_R)$ and the flow is $\dfrac{dV}{dt}$, the total force developed, expressed as a pressure ΣP,

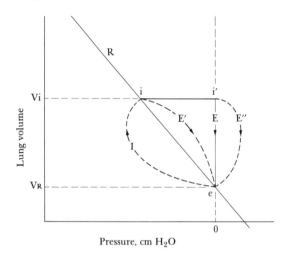

FIGURE 19.   Schematic representation of lung volume as a function of the pressure exerted by the respiratory muscles. Different theoretical types of ventilation.

The pressure, relative to the barometric pressure, expresses the force developed by the ventilatory muscles.

V_R is the relaxation volume; V_i is the lung volume after inspiration of a volume $V_i - V_R$.

The eiR line is the total thoracic relaxation curve.

The eIi line corresponds to the pressures developed by the inspiratory muscles during inspiration of the tidal volume $V_i - V_R$. The area eIie is the dynamic work of inspiration. Area eii'e represents the elastic work of inspiration, and is a source of the potential energy available during expiration.

If expiration is entirely passive, the work of the expiratory muscles is zero, and all the energy required for expiration comes from the potential energy eii'e (ventilatory type I). The total work performed during one ventilatory cycle is given by area eIii'Ee.

The iE'e line corresponds to the case where the inspiratory muscles relax progressively during expiration, and expiration is braked (ventilatory type II).

The iE''e line corresponds to the case where expiratory muscles contract during expiration, and expiration is active (ventilatory type III). In this case, the mechanical energy required for expiration corresponds to the area eii'E''e, and originates partly from the elastic potential energy eii'e, stored during inspiration, and partly from energy supplied by contraction of the expiratory muscles, corresponding to area ei'E''e.

Figure 20 shows spirograms and pneumotachograms obtained from these three *theoretical* types.

which is the only pressure that can actually be measured, is the sum of the pressures given in equations 1, 2, and 5.

$$\Sigma P = K(V - V_R) + K' \left(\frac{dV}{dt}\right) + K'' \left(\frac{dV}{dt}\right)^2 \qquad (6)$$

where $K' = K_1 + K_3$ and $K'' = K_2$ and K_4.

This equation gives the force that must be developed by the respiratory muscles at any time at which the volume is V and the flow rate is $\frac{dV}{dt}$.

At end expiration, intrapulmonary or intra-alveolar pressure, P_A, is equal to the barometric pressure P_B. If the volume of air in the lungs is equal to the relaxation volume, V_R, the respiratory muscles are at rest. If inspiration was very slow and consequently $\frac{dV}{dt}$ was very small, the forces exerted would have to overcome only elastance and would follow the line eiR (Fig. 19). In fact, because of the resistance to air flow, more force is required (henceforth we shall not take into account the tissue resistance to deformation which, as discussed on page 76, is negligible) and the alveolar pressure is negative. The pressure-volume curve does not follow eiR but eIi. The horizontal distance between curve eIi and the eiR line indicates the difference between pressure in the alveolar air and the atmosphere, $P_A - P_B$.

The different steps are in this order: contraction of the inspiratory muscles; increase in lung volume; decrease in intra-alveolar pressure, P_A, in relation to barometric pressure, P_B; because of this difference in pressure, air flows from the area of high pressure (ambient air, P_B) to that of low pressure (i.e. the intra-alveolar air where the pressure is P_A). At end inspiration, P_A is again equal to P_B.

During expiration

Expiration can be either passive, braked, or active. The three theoretical types that may be described are probably only rarely found in this simple form.

TYPE I: PASSIVE EXPIRATION

At end inspiration, the inspiratory muscles cease to contract, and the expiratory muscles do not contract.

The energy required for expiration comes only from the potential energy stored in the thorax during inspiration. Expiration is passive. The airways exert a certain resistance to flow of air to the atmosphere, and the alveolar

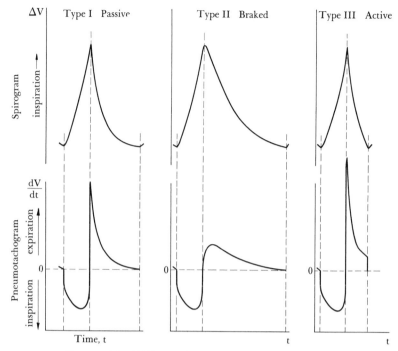

FIGURE 20.   Different theoretical types of ventilation.

On the ordinates: upper curve — volume of ventilation; lower curve — flow rate, $\frac{dV}{dt}$. On the abscissae: time. The upper diagram is therefore a spirogram, and the lower a pneumotachogram.

These types differ in terms of the expiratory forces that are exerted, and can be identified by the character on the figure on the pressure-volume diagram, as seen in Figure 19. However, in the *normal* subject, the different ventilatory types can be estimated by the characteristics of the spirogram and pneumotachogram.

In type I, contraction of the inspiratory muscles ceases abruptly and expiration is passive. The expiratory rate (pneumotachogram) rises rapidly, then decreases rapidly, more or less exponentially. On the spirogram, this is shown by a lung volume decrease which is rapid at first and becomes gradually slower.

In type II, expiration is braked by the progressive relaxation of the inspiratory muscles. Expiratory flow rate increases progressively, then decreases progressively, but the decrease in $\frac{dV}{dt}$ does not reach the zero line exponentially (unless the last part of expiration is passive). On the spirogram, the expiratory part of the excursion has a lesser slope than in types I and III.

In type III, the expiratory muscles contract. The flow rate increases abruptly at the beginning of expiration, and the expiratory phase ends rather suddenly. The mean expiratory flow rate is high and the expiratory part of the spirogram is more nearly rectilinear and has a steep slope.

In certain patients, in whom expiratory air flow resistance is high, spirograms and pneumotachograms may look like those seen in type I, although expiration is active. This example shows that in order to diagnose the ventilatory type accurately, it is necessary to use the pressure-volume diagram (see Fig. 19), but plotting such a diagram is difficult.

pressure, P_A, is higher than the ambient pressure, P_B. The expiratory pressure-volume curve is represented by ii'Ee on Figure 19. Expiration is prolonged and the lung volume returns gradually to the relaxation volume (Fig. 20).

The respiratory centers exhibit a discontinuous activity, showing phases during which inspiratory activity occurs, separated by phases during which no activity can be detected and passive expiration takes place.

TYPE II: BRAKED EXPIRATION

The inspiratory muscles do not cease contracting abruptly; they relax progressively. Expiration starts as soon as the force exerted by the inspiratory muscles drops below the opposed force exerted by the thoracic elasticity. Thus the inspiratory muscles oppose a purely passive and elastic expiration and perform resistive "work." This resistive "work" slows and brakes expiration. The air flow will therefore be slower than during passive expiration, and the alveolar pressure P_A, required to make air flow out, will be less elevated. On the pressure-volume diagram (Fig. 19) this condition is represented by iE'e.

In this case, the respiratory centers exhibit continuous inspiratory activity, the intensity of which varies rhythmically.

This continual contraction of decreasing strength during expiration has been verified by electromyography of certain intercostal muscles and of the diaphragm using esophageal electrodes, which are swallowed till they reach the level of the diaphragm (Agostoni, 1960; Petit, 1960; Taylor, 1960). Progressive relaxation of the inspiratory muscles and of the diaphragm is a common occurrence, at least in resting subjects. If this did not take place, the expiratory flow would rapidly reach a maximum and then decrease gradually. This is indeed what happens in type I, but this type is very rare in normal awake subjects (compare type I and II in Fig. 20).

In type II, time required for expiration is longer than that required for inspiration.

TYPE III: ACTIVE EXPIRATION

The expiratory muscles contract. Alveolar pressure is higher in this case than in types I and II where expiration is passive or braked. The expiratory pressure volume curve follows the path ii′E″e (Fig. 19). Expiration is not much longer than inspiration.

The respiratory centers are continuously active, with alternation of inspiratory and expiratory phases.

Thus, in type I, the activity of the respiratory centers (manifested by respiratory muscle contraction) is discontinuous. On the other hand, in types II and III, activity is continuous.

At rest, expiration is usually braked. During mild exercise, type II can still be found, but the "braking" is less pronounced than at rest. During heavy muscular exercise, ventilation is of type III and requires the alternate contraction of inspiratory and expiratory muscles. In other words, if expiratory flow is moderate, the potential energy stored in the thorax during inspiration may be sufficient to overcome airway resistance during expiration, but if high flow is required, active expiration is necessary.

In practice, it is very difficult to class ventilation in these three types. Classification requires knowledge of the spirogram, the pneumotachogram (Fleisch, 1925), and esophageal pressures (from which the forces exerted by respiratory muscles can be deduced). When all these are known, it is possible to establish a pressure volume diagram, similar to that shown in Figure 19.

Intrathoracic pressure variations during the respiratory cycle (Fig. 21)

The variations in intrapulmonary (intra-alveolar) pressure due to resistance to gas flow in the airways are transmitted to the whole thorax. For example, if we assume that at a given lung volume, and in the absence of ventilatory movement, with the chest fixed in that position, the intrathoracic (intrapleural or esophageal) pressure is -8 cm H_2O in relation to P_B, then, at the same lung volume, during inspiration, the intrathoracic pressure may be -9 cm H_2O and the alveolar pressure -1 cm H_2O.

We have seen (p. 76) that variations in alveolar pressure depend on two factors: airway resistance and flow rate. In the normal resting subject, positive or negative pressure changes represent at most a few centimeters of water. However, when the rate of air flow is increased (as would happen during muscular exercise), the changes are more pronounced (Fig. 21).

In a subject exhibiting abnormally high resistance to flow, as seen during certain forms of laryngitis (croup), tracheal or bronchial compression,

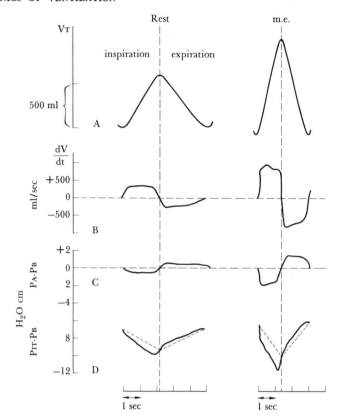

FIGURE 21.   Alveolar and intrathoracic pressures during the ventilatory cycle.

A, spirogram (ventilatory volume as a function of time).

B, pneumotachogram (instantaneous flow rate $\dfrac{dV}{dt}$, as a function of time).

C, alveolar pressure, P_A, relative to P_B, as a function of time. Alveolar pressure is negative in respect to P_B during inspiration and positive during expiration. The differences in pressure $P_A - P_B$ are necessary to overcome the airways resistance to gas flow.

D, intrathoracic or intrapleural (approximated by esophageal) pressure, P_{IT}, in reference to P_B, as a function of time.

The broken lines show the probable variations in intrathoracic pressure due to lung elastance in the absence of mechanical resistances. The continuous curves show the actual intrathoracic pressure. In this case, in addition to the negative pressure due to elastic forces, one must add the algebraic value of the variations in pressure required to overcome mechanical resistances (these are by and large localized in the airways; there is also a certain resistance to deformation of the lung tissue, due to friction taking place in the tissues during volume changes, but this lung resistance to deformation is rather small).

The left column corresponds to resting ventilation (V_T = 600 ml, f = 12/min), and the right corresponds to ventilation during moderate muscular exercise (V_T = 1100 ml, f = 20/min). The figure shows that when ventilation is relatively high, the energy loss in the airways and the pressure oscillation are more marked.

bronchospasm (contraction of bronchial smooth muscles during asthma), intrapleural pressure variations are much higher and may reach several tens of centimeters of water. Since all the changes in alveolar pressure that occur during respiration are transmitted to the whole thorax, a marked drop in alveolar pressure, and therefore in intrathoracic pressure, may be observed in subjects in whom the airway resistance is abnormally elevated during inspiration. As a result the soft parts of the chest walls are pulled inward and a depression of the supraclavicular fossae may be observed. During expiration, the huge increase in intrathoracic pressure causes a rise in venous pressure and produces bulging of the veins (for instance, the external jugular veins).

VIII. WORK AND ENERGY EXPENDITURE OF THE RESPIRATORY MUSCLES

Mechanical work (Rohrer, 1925; Otis, Fenn, and Rahn, 1950)

The mechanical work (force × displacement = F × L) performed by the respiratory muscles during inhalation of a tidal volume V_T is the product of the pressure multiplied by the volume inspired. The dimensional equation of this product is:

$$P \cdot V = \frac{F}{L^2} \cdot L^3 = F \cdot L.$$

If we consider equation 6 which shows the pressure required at a lung volume V to ensure a flow of $\frac{dV}{dt}$ and if we assume that flow is a sine function of time, the following equation, obtained by integration, permits calculation of W_I, the work required to perform one inspiration:

$$W_I = aKV_T^2 + bK'V_T (fV_T) + cK''V_T (fV_T)^2 \tag{7}$$

in which V_T is the tidal volume, f is the respiratory frequency, a, b, and c are constants and K, K', and K'' are coefficients of elastance, viscous resistance, and turbulent resistance.

More simply, W_I corresponds to area eIii'e of Figure 19.

If expiration is passive (ventilatory type I), W_I also represents total work. Since the work done for one cycle is repeated f times per minute (f being the frequency), by multiplying both sides of equation 7 by f, one obtains the mechanical power, the power supplied by the respiratory muscles. Tidal volume being the sum of dead space volume and alveolar tidal volume, it is possible with a few assumptions to express the mechanical power as a function of $\dot{V}_A$, the alveolar ventilation.

In order to obtain a given alveolar ventilation, it is possible to ventilate the lungs with a large tidal volume at low frequency or alternatively to use a smaller volume and increase the frequency. The mechanical power required varies with frequency, and it can be shown that there is a frequency at which the mechanical work performed is minimal. There should be therefore an optimal frequency, a particular ventilatory pattern which would require a minimal mechanical power. This can well be understood in view of the fact that at low frequency — and therefore high tidal volume — the work required to overcome elastance increases considerably. At high frequency, with a smaller tidal volume, the elastic work is smaller, but the relatively high flow increases the work required to overcome both viscous and turbulent resistance.

The mechanical power equation to which we have just referred enables one to determine theoretically what is the best ventilatory pattern (for a given alveolar ventilation) for which the mechanical power required is minimal. With an assumed constant, mechanical efficiency of the respiratory muscles, it becomes possible to predict the most economical ventilatory pattern. It has been suggested that this could be the basis on which each subject naturally selects his respiratory pattern. However, this selection depends not only on the mechanical properties of the thorax and on the economy of work required for ventilation, but also to a large extent on the functional properties of the whole ventilatory system (see p. 146) and on the nature of the respiratory stimuli.

If the expiratory muscles also contract (ventilatory type III), the mechanical work is increased and corresponds to the area eIii'E''e of Figure 19, in which eIie is the dynamic inspiratory work and eii'E''e is the dynamic expiratory work. Part of the latter is supplied by the elastic potential energy stored in the thorax during inspiration, and this corresponds to the area eii'e. Therefore only the difference between eii'E''e and eii'e, that is, area eEi'E''e, represents mechanical work performed by expiratory muscles.

Energy expenditure of the respiratory muscles

The energy expended by the respiratory muscles can be determined by measuring the increase in oxygen consumption caused by hyperventilation.

The latter can either be voluntary or brought about by inhalation of carbon dioxide or addition of an external dead space. Figure 22 shows that the energy expenditure of the respiratory muscles, expressed per liter of ventilation, is lower at moderate ventilation than during hyperventilation. At rest, the oxygen uptake required to ventilate 1 liter of air is of the order of 0.5 ml STPD. Therefore, the oxygen uptake of the ventilatory muscles represents 1 to 2% of the total consumption of the resting body. On the

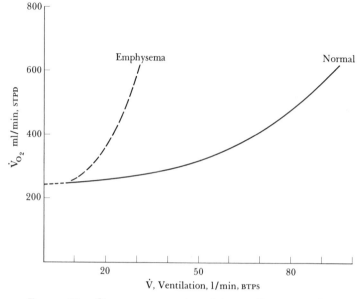

FIGURE 22.   Oxygen consumption of the ventilatory muscles.

On the ordinate, total body oxygen consumption, $\dot{V}_{O_2}$. On the abscissa, ventilation.

Hyperventilation may be voluntary, or be caused by breathing a CO_2-enriched gas mixture, the body remaining at rest. Therefore, the $\dot{V}_{O_2}$ increase can be attributed entirely to the activity of the ventilatory muscles. The figure shows that as ventilation increases, the energy expenditure per liter ventilation also increases. In certain lung diseases the energy expenditure of the respiratory muscles is relatively very high.

other hand, at the high ventilatory levels found during muscular exercise, the respiratory muscles require several milliliters of oxygen for each liter of ventilation. As a result, the fraction of the oxygen consumption available to the other muscles decreases when the ventilation is increased. Theoretically, there is a critical value above which any increase in ventilation, and therefore in the activity of the respiratory muscles, would require an increase in metabolism which would use all the additional oxygen delivered to the body by this increase in ventilation. This critical value is never reached by the normal subjects, but, in certain diseases, the energy cost of ventilation can be increased considerably (see Otis, 1954).

The way in which the mechanical work of ventilation can be estimated has already been discussed. From these data, it is possible to calculate the mechanical efficiency of the respiratory muscles. This efficiency is of the order of 5 to 10%, much lower than that of most muscles, which often exceeds 20%. However, this calculation assumes that activity of the respiratory muscles has no other function than that of ensuring a given ventilation. This is probably not the case, because variations in intrathoracic pressures which occur during ventilatory movements play a role in circulation. When calculating the efficiency of the respiratory muscles, the circulatory as well as the respiratory work should be taken into account.

6

Pulmonary Gas Exchange

I. COMPARISON OF INSPIRED AND EXPIRED GAS COMPOSITION

Atmospheric air

The top row of figures in Table VIII shows the gas fractions in dry atmospheric air, and the bottom row shows the corresponding partial pressures. These are calculated at a mean barometric pressure at sea level, that is 760 mm Hg, and assuming a water vapor pressure of 47 mm Hg, which is the saturation pressure at 37 °C. This humidified air is sometimes called "tracheal air," indicating that air that reaches the alveoli from the tracheobronchial tree is at BTPS conditions (p. 12).

TABLE VIII

	O_2	CO_2	N_2	H_2O	TOTAL
Fraction............	0.210	0.000	0.790	0	1.00
(Dry ambient air).....	(0.2099)	(0.003)	(0.7898)		
Partial pressure mm Hg ("tracheal" air).....	150	0	563	47	760

From the standpoint of animal physiology, the CO_2 fraction in atmospheric air is essentially zero, and very often ambient air is used as CO_2-free standard gas to calibrate carbon dioxide analyzers. The term N_2 includes here not only nitrogen (which constitutes 78.03% of the atmosphere) but all the inert gases (argon is 0.95%, helium, etc.), a simplification based on the fact that all these gases take no part in any active body process (see p. 5).

The composition of air is the same not only at any point on the surface

of the earth but at any altitude. However, altitude affects the total barometric pressure and hence the partial pressures of O_2 and N_2. The composition of inspired air is altered only in the following exceptional circumstances:

a) in experimental conditions where the subject inspires an artificial
gas mixture, hypoxic, hyperoxic, or hypercapnic (rich in CO_2);

b) in certain cases where the natural atmosphere contains an important
fraction of CO_2;

c) when breathing in confined atmospheres, where the fraction of oxygen drops and that of CO_2 increases, an exceedingly rare case. The composition of the atmosphere in cities is essentially normal in terms of O_2 and
CO_2. The atmosphere is polluted but not confined.

Expired gas

Lavoisier has shown that expired gas contains less oxygen and more carbon
dioxide than atmospheric air (see p. 4). Expired gas is also generally warmer
and more humid than inspired air. Therefore, in order to calculate the
volumes of O_2 and CO_2 taken up from and added to air by respiration, it
is necessary to compare inspired and expired gas under the same conditions.
In practice, dry gas compositions are used for this purpose.

TABLE IX

GAS FRACTION	INSPIRED GAS, I (dry)	EXAMPLE I, Expired gas, E (dry)	R = 1.00 Difference	EXAMPLE II, Expired gas, E (dry)	R = 0.80 Difference
F_{CO_2}	0.000	0.040	+0.040	0.037	+0.037
F_{O_2}	0.210	0.170	−0.040	0.166	−0.044
F_{N_2}	0.790	0.790	0.000	0.797	+0.007

EXAMPLE I

When the respiratory quotient is unity, the number of molecules of O_2
taken up by blood is equal to the number of molecules of CO_2 eliminated
by the circulation. The volumes of inspired gas and of expired gas (both
reduced to the same temperature and humidity conditions) are equal, and
the nitrogen fraction of expired gas $F_{E_{N_2}}$ is equal to that of inspired air, $F_{I_{N_2}}$.

EXAMPLE II

If, as is usually the case, the respiratory quotient is below 1, the volume of
oxygen taken up by blood in the lungs exceeds the volume of CO_2 elimi-

nated, and the expired volume is lower than the inspired volume (the opposite would occur if the respiratory quotient was higher than 1). Since there is no nitrogen exchange between body and environment, the same number of N_2 molecules are to be found in an expired volume smaller than the inspired volume; then $F_{E_{N_2}}$ is higher than $F_{I_{N_2}}$. If the respiratory quotient is higher than 1, $F_{E_{N_2}}$ is smaller than $F_{I_{N_2}}$.

Carbon dioxide production (or output), $\dot{V}_{CO_2}$

If the volumes of CO_2 inspired and expired per unit time are shown by $\dot{V}_{E_{CO_2}}$ and $\dot{V}_{I_{CO_2}}$ respectively,

$$\dot{V}_{CO_2} = \dot{V}_{E_{CO_2}} - \dot{V}_{I_{CO_2}} \tag{1}$$

Under normal conditions, inspired air does not contain any CO_2 and hence,

$$\dot{V}_{CO_2} = \dot{V}_{E_{CO_2}} = \dot{V}_E \cdot F_{E_{CO_2}} \tag{2}$$

EXAMPLE (during moderate exercise, $P_B = 760$ mm Hg, t = 23 °C)

$\dot{V}_E$ = 27.6 l/min, ATPS

$F_{E_{CO_2}} = 0.045$

Factor for reducing ATPS to STPD = 0.875 (see p. 20).

$\dot{V}_{CO_2} = 27.60 \times 0.045 \times 0.875 = 1.09$ l/min, STPD

Oxygen consumption (or uptake), $\dot{V}_{O_2}$

Oxygen consumption = amount of oxygen inspired − amount of oxygen expired,

$$\dot{V}_{O_2} = \dot{V}_{I_{O_2}} - \dot{V}_{E_{O_2}}$$

from which

$$\dot{V}_{O_2} = \dot{V}_I \cdot F_{I_{O_2}} - \dot{V}_E \cdot F_{E_{O_2}} \tag{3}$$

The respiratory quotient is only rarely equal to one and hence expired volume usually differs from inspired volume. Therefore, when it is proposed to assess $\dot{V}_{O_2}$ by measuring only one ventilatory flow rate (usually expiratory), the difference between $\dot{V}_E$ and $\dot{V}_I$ must be taken into account. When R is smaller than one, $\dot{V}_E$ is smaller than $\dot{V}_I$ and consequently $F_{E_{O_2}}$ is higher than it would have been if no change in volume had taken place. $F_{E_{O_2}}$ must therefore be corrected in order to be compared properly to $F_{I_{O_2}}$. A simple calculation enables one to obtain the following equation, from which $\dot{V}_{O_2}$ can be calculated:

$$\dot{V}_{O_2} = \dot{V}_E \frac{F_{I_{O_2}} - F_{E_{O_2}} - F_{I_{O_2}} \cdot F_{E_{CO_2}}}{1 - F_{I_{O_2}}} = \dot{V}_E \frac{F_{I_{O_2}} - F_{E_{O_2}}}{1 - F_{I_{O_2}}(1 - R)} \tag{4}$$

When the respiratory quotient is unity, that is when $F_{IO_2} - F_{EO_2}$ = F_{ECO_2}, the equation becomes $\dot{V}_{O_2} = \dot{V}_E(F_{IO_2} - F_{EO_2})$.

When the respiratory quotient differs from unity, the ratio

$$\frac{F_{IO_2} - F_{EO_2}}{1 - F_{IO_2}(1 - R)} \text{ replaces } (F_{IO_2} - F_{EO_2}).$$

This ratio, sometimes known as "true" oxygen, can be calculated directly from F_{EO_2} and F_{ECO_2} using tables or nomograms (Consolazio, 1951).

EXAMPLE (resting subject)

P_B = 760 mm Hg, t = 23 °C
Factor for reducing ATPS to STPD = 0.897 (see p. 20)
Factor for converting ATPS to BTPS = 1.085 (see p. 13)
$\dot{V}_E$ = 5.8 l/min, ATPS
F_{ECO_2} = 0.037
F_{EO_2} = 0.166
$\dot{V}_E$ = 5.80 × 1.085 = 6.29 l/min, BTPS
$\dot{V}_{CO_2}$ = 5.80 × 0.897 × 0.037 = 0.192 l/min, STPD
$\dot{V}_{O_2}$ = 5.80 × 0.897 × 0.046 = 0.239 l/min, STPD
R = 0.80

It can be seen that the difference between F_{IO_2} and F_{EO_2} is 0.044 and that the calculations are based on a value 0.046, representing "true oxygen," that is the difference between inspired and expired oxygen which would have prevailed had the respiratory quotient been 1 instead of 0.80. Had this correction been neglected, an error of 4% would have been introduced in the computed oxygen uptake. The more R differs from unity, the higher the error.

Relationship between P_{CO_2} and P_{O_2} in expired gas

The relationship between P_{ECO_2} and P_{EO_2} is:

$$P_{ECO_2} = \frac{R \cdot P_{IO_2}}{1 - F_{IO_2}(1 - R)} - \frac{R}{1 - F_{IO_2}(1 - R)} P_{EO_2} \tag{5}$$

When breathing air, $F_{IO_2} = 0.21$.
Equation (5) is a linear equation of the form

$$y = a - bx$$

where both a and b depend on the value R.

A certain slope, $-b$, corresponds to each value of R, and consequently it is possible to label each of these lines with the respiratory quotient to which it pertains (Fig. 23). The line having a slope of -1 corresponds to an R of 1. For this reason, these lines are called R lines.

All those lines fan out from Pi_{O_2}, a value taken on the abscissa, since ambient air contains no CO_2, and this point corresponds to atmospheric air.

The slope of the R lines fan is not affected by the changes in barometric pressure. At sea level, with a barometric pressure of 760 mm Hg, Pi_{O_2} is 150 mm Hg (Fig. 23, point I). The normal variations in barometric pressure

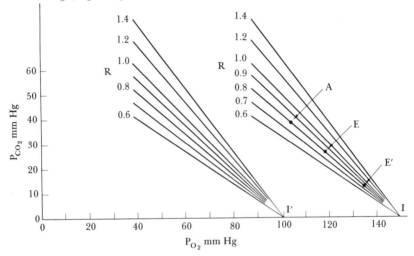

FIGURE 23.   Inspired air, expired gas, and respiratory quotient lines on the $P_{O_2}-P_{CO_2}$ diagram.

Point I corresponds to inspired air at sea level ($\text{Pi}_{CO_2} = 0$, $\text{Pi}_{O_2} = 150$ mm Hg). Diverging from point I is a fan of straight lines, called respiratory quotient lines or R lines. As an example, any point on the 0.8 line is such that comparison of the values which define this point and of the values for point I would allow one to calculate a respiratory quotient value of 0.8. In the examples given in the text, points E and E′ correspond to the same O_2 consumption and CO_2 production (and therefore the same respiratory quotient) but to two different ventilations, one of which (E′) is twice as high as the other (E). For the same oxygen consumption, expired gas composition is nearer that of inspired air, if ventilation is higher.

Point I′ corresponds to P_{CO_2} and P_{O_2} of inspired air at an altitude of 3000 meters (10,000 feet), where barometric pressure is 526 mm Hg. Note that the slopes of the respiratory quotient lines are not affected by the change in barometric pressure. A change in altitude simply moves the respiratory quotient lines. On the other hand, a change in fractional concentration of oxygen in inspired gas (see equation 5), which produces what is called an equivalent altitude, changes the fan of respiratory quotient lines.

Point A corresponds to an alveolar gas sample.

at any point cause a change in oxygen pressure in ambient and "tracheal" air. If, for instance, P_B is 750 mm Hg, $P_{IO_2}=$ 148 mm Hg. In this case point I is at 148 on the abscissa and the R lines fan out of this point.

At an altitude of 3000 meters (10,000 ft), P_B is 526 mm Hg and P_{IO_2} is 101 mm Hg (Fig. 23, point I'). The R lines fan out from this point, without change in slope.

On the other hand, an increase in the oxygen fraction of inspired gas decreases the difference in slope and "closes" the fan. When inspiring 100% O_2, the point representing the O_2 and CO_2 composition of expired gas will be on a line having a slope of -1, regardless of the value of the respiratory quotient.

The value of R, the respiratory quotient, can be obtained from equation 5 and is:

$$R = \frac{P_{ECO_2}(1 - F_{IO_2})}{P_{IO_2} - P_{EO_2} - (P_{ECO_2} \cdot F_{IO_2})}$$

The nomograms of Consolazio (1951) and of Rahn and Fenn (1955) allow P to be measured directly from the values of P_{EO_2} and P_{ECO_2} without need for calculations.

Changes in expired gas composition

In the preceding example (p. 91), $\dot{V}_E = 5.80$ l/m, $F_{ECO_2} = 0.037$ ($P_{ECO_2} = 26.4$ mm Hg), $F_{EO_2} = 0.166$ ($P_{EO_2} = 118$ mm Hg). The same O_2 uptake and CO_2 output would have been calculated if $\dot{V}_E$ had been 11.60 l/m and if $F_{ECO_2} = 0.0185$ (13.2 mm Hg) and $F_{EO_2} = 0.188$ (134 mm Hg), in which case the ventilation would be doubled, but the difference between inspired and expired gas reduced by half. On the O_2–CO_2 diagram (Fig. 23), the point representing the first example is at E, and the point for the second example is at E', half way down the IE line. It is obvious that for a given O_2 uptake and CO_2 output, the difference between expired and inspired gas decreases as the ventilation increases.

When in equation 4 $\dot{V}_{O_2}$ is expressed at STPD conditions, and $\dot{V}_E$ at BTPS, the factor by which $\dot{V}_E$ is multiplied is the fraction of oxygen utilized, F_{UO_2}. This is the product of the factor required to reduce BTPS values to STPD times the difference between inspired and expired oxygen fraction corrected for respiratory quotient effects (true oxygen).

$$\dot{V}_{O_2}, \text{ l/min, STPD} = \dot{V}_E \text{ l/min, BTPS} \times F_{UO_2}$$

In the preceding example:

$$0.239 \text{ l/min, STPD} = 6.29 \text{ l/min, BTPS} \times 0.038$$

in which case the body takes up 38 ml STPD of oxygen from each liter of air ventilated.

The inverse of this value is the ventilatory equivalent, that is the number of liters of air at BTPS the body must ventilate in order to obtain 1 liter of oxygen. In the preceding example, the ventilatory equivalent is 26.3 l.

The composition of expired gas is quite variable, and changes with body position, sleep, and metabolic rate. It also varies from one subject to another. The fraction of oxygen utilized varies from 0.025 to 0.050 and the ventilatory equivalent from 40 to 20.

II. COMPARISON BETWEEN INSPIRED, EXPIRED, AND ALVEOLAR GAS COMPOSITION. DEAD SPACE AND ALVEOLAR VENTILATION

Inhomogeneity of expired gas

In the preceding section, expired air was considered as a homogeneous mixture of oxygen, carbon dioxide, and nitrogen. However, during expiration, the composition of expired gas is not constant. If the dry gases are considered, the first part of the expiration has the same composition as ambient air, and the following fraction is low in O_2 and high in CO_2. The expired gas collected in a spirometer is in fact a mixture of these two components in variable proportions.

Figure 24 shows how O_2 and CO_2 vary in expired gas collected at the mouth. We now have measuring instruments (infrared CO_2 analyzers and mass spectrometers which can measure simultaneously CO_2, O_2, and other gases) that are rapid enough to determine continuously the composition of the different parts of expired gas. The first part of the expired volume contains no CO_2, but as expiration proceeds, the fraction of CO_2 in expired gas increases rapidly and reaches approximately 0.05. From that point on, the fraction of CO_2 increases gently under resting conditions and more rapidly during muscular exercise. A similar change takes place for oxygen, but in the opposite direction. The ratio between the difference in the two CO_2 levels during expiration and the difference in O_2 levels corresponds to the respiratory quotient.

This indicates that only part of the inspired gas undergoes gas exchange. It is obvious that the last part of the inspired gas does not reach the alveolar spaces, where O_2 is taken up and CO_2 is eliminated. This part of inspiration remains in the tracheobronchial tree where the thick walls do not allow any gas exchange and inspired air composition will therefore be maintained. The last part of inspiration constitutes perforce the first part of expiration,

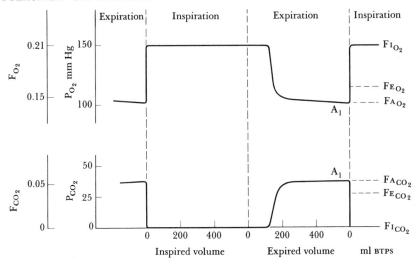

FIGURE 24.   Fractions and partial pressures of O_2 and CO_2 in gas sampled at the mouth during normal ventilation.

On the ordinates, fractions and partial pressures of O_2 (upper curve) and CO_2 (lower curve).

On the abscissae, inspired and expired volumes.

During inspiration, the O_2 and CO_2 fractions and partial pressures are those of ambient air.

The first part of the expiration comes from the anatomical dead space. The second part comes from the alveolar spaces. The gas sampled at A_1 may be considered, to a certain extent, to represent mean alveolar gas.

and this is followed by air coming from the alveoli, rich in CO_2 and relatively poor in O_2.

Although rapid, the change in expired gas composition is not abrupt, as is the change taking place at the beginning of inspiration; this can be explained by the following three reasons:

a) Air flow in an airway is not uniform. The central part of the moving air moves more rapidly than the elements near the walls.

b) The various parts of the lungs do not supply alveolar gas at the same time. During expiration, one bronchus may supply alveolar gas while inspired air is still coming out of another.

c) During the respiratory cycle, some CO_2 molecules diffuse from the alveoli into the terminal bronchioles while some oxygen molecules diffuse from the bronchioles into the alveoli. There is a transition from inspired to alveolar gas rather than an abrupt change.

Anatomical dead space

The volume of inspired gas that does not undergo gas exchange is called
dead space. The notion of dead space is in fact very complex and does not
seem to be very precisely defined (see p. 98).

The preceding description indicates that there is a very distinct anatomical dead space. This is the volume of the airways in which no gas exchange
takes place. It includes all the airways without alveoli and not provided
with a surface across which gas exchange can take place. This volume includes all the respiratory system volume between mouth and terminal
bronchioles.

There are several ways of measuring this anatomical dead space (see
Fowler, 1952). In a cadaver, the length and diameter of different segments
of the airways can be measured and the volume calculated. Even better,
the volume of a cast of the airways can be measured.

In vivo, anatomical dead space can be measured from the composition
of expired gas during expiration (either in terms of O_2 and CO_2 or alternatively N_2 following inspiration of 100% O_2). The method consists in

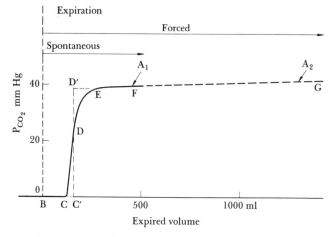

FIGURE 25. Measurement of anatomical dead space.

On the ordinate, partial pressure of CO_2 in the expired gas, sampled at the
mouth. On the abscissa, expired volume.

The continuous curve BCDEF shows the variation in P_{CO_2} during expiration
of a normal tidal volume. The extension of this line to G is found only during forced
expiration. The total volume of expired CO_2 would have been the same if instead of
following the curve BCDEF, expired P_{CO_2} had followed BC'DD'F. Areas CC'D and
DD'E are equal. The volume BC' represents the anatomical dead space volume.

measuring the volume that would have been expired if instead of curve BCDEF of Figure 25, the expired gas could be plotted as BC'DD'EF, so that areas CC'D and DD'E were equal. The volume read on the abscissa at a point C' corresponds to the anatomical dead space.

This anatomical dead space is of the order of 150 ml in the adult male at rest. It increases with increasing functional residual capacity. This change may be up to a hundred milliliters. It also increases when tidal volume increases, as is the case during muscular exercise.

This notion of anatomical dead space and knowledge of its volume are still not sufficient to explain the composition of alveolar gas with which the capillaries exchange. The composition of alveolar gas depends also on the *physiological* dead space volume. The complexity of this problem requires first a study of what alveolar gas is and how its composition can be determined.

Alveolar gas

DEFINITION

This gas is to be found in the alveolar spaces, that is near the alveolar capillary walls. This gas supplies O_2 molecules to the capillary blood and receives CO_2 molecules.

At end inspiration, the gas contained in the lungs is not all alveolar gas, since a part of the lungs does not have alveoli. This part is the tracheobronchial tree, which constitutes the anatomical dead space. By the end of inspiration, this dead space is filled with ambient air. During expiration, ambient air is swept out by gas coming from the alveoli, and as soon as this alveolar gas enters the tracheobronchial tree, it stops exchanging O_2 and CO_2 with the alveolar capillaries.

At the end of a normal expiration, the volume of air present in the lungs (functional residual capacity) may be 2.5 liters, of which 2.35 liters would be in the alveolar spaces and 0.15 liter in the dead space.

COMPOSITION

Alveolar gas contains carbon dioxide (about 5 percent) and oxygen (a few percent less than atmospheric air). Table X gives an example of the O_2 and CO_2 composition of inspired air, expired gas, and alveolar gas. Partial pressures are calculated assuming a barometric pressure of 760 mm Hg.

A point representing alveolar gas composition can be plotted on the O_2–CO_2 diagram (point A of Fig. 23). This point must be on the same R line as E, since the respiratory quotient measured in the mixed expired gas

TABLE X

	AMBIENT AIR		EXPIRED GAS		ALVEOLAR GAS	
	CO_2	O_2	CO_2	O_2	CO_2	O_2
Fraction, F (dry gas).....	0.000	0.210	0.037	0.166	0.054	0.146
Partial pressure, P $P = (P_B - 47) \times F....$	0	150	26.4	118.4	38.5	104.1

depends only on the changes that have taken place in the fraction that is actually being exchanged, that is, alveolar gas. The only effect of the addition of dead space gas (which is identical in composition to inspired air) is a dilution of alveolar gas and change in the same proportion $P_{A_{CO_2}}$ and $(P_{I_{O_2}} - P_{A_{O_2}})$. The greater the contribution of dead space gas to expired gas, the more the latter will differ from alveolar gas.

Equation 5 for expired gas can also be applied to alveolar gas. This can be done by replacing the O_2 and CO_2 partial pressures in expired gas by those found in the alveolar gas.

$$P_{A_{CO_2}} = \frac{R \cdot P_{I_{O_2}}}{1 - F_{I_{O_2}}(1 - R)} - \frac{R}{1 - F_{I_{O_2}}(1 - R)} P_{A_{O_2}} \qquad (6)$$

MEAN ALVEOLAR GAS COMPOSITION

Any value of $P_{A_{CO_2}}$ and of $P_{A_{O_2}}$ can only be a mean value, for two reasons:

1. Alveolar gas does not have the same composition in all parts of the lung. It is easy to visualize that if two areas have the same blood flow, the composition of alveolar gas in the one in which ventilation is higher will be nearer atmospheric (see p. 119). The exact fashion in which alveolar O_2 and CO_2 vary in different areas of the lungs is not known precisely, but this variation seems to be quite important. It seems logical to believe that
— at any given time, certain parts of the lung receive no blood flow. As a consequence, the air that reaches them will not undergo gas exchange (areas ventilated and not perfused);
— other parts of the lungs have a normal circulation but are not ventilated (areas perfused but not ventilated). The gas found in these alveoli will be relatively rich in CO_2 and poor in O_2.

These are extreme cases. Several areas of the lungs are relatively well perfused in respect to their ventilation, or vice versa; so one can speak of areas well perfused and poorly ventilated and areas well ventilated and poorly perfused. The alveolar gas composition will differ in areas which do not have the same perfusion-ventilation ratio (see p. 119).

2. Alveolar gas composition varies during the respiratory cycle (Fig. 26) (see DuBois, 1952). This happens because ventilation is a cyclic phenomenon, while blood circulation in the pulmonary capillary and exchange between capillary blood and alveolar gas are continuous (but not constant, since capillary blood flow is pulsatile and can vary during the respiratory cycle [see DuBois, 1952]).

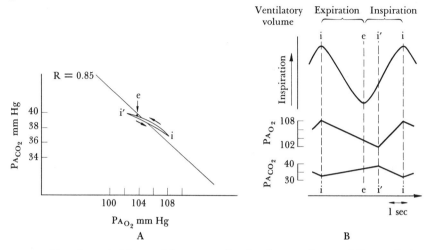

FIGURE 26. O_2 and CO_2 partial pressures in alveolar gas, $P_{A_{O_2}}$ and $P_{A_{CO_2}}$, during the ventilatory cycle, shown on the left on a $P_{O_2}-P_{CO_2}$ diagram (curve A) and on the right as a function of time (curve B).

Point i: end inspiration.

Point i to e: expiration. P_{CO_2} increases and P_{O_2} decreases.

From e to i': inspiration of anatomical dead space gas. This gas is the last part of the gas expired by the alveoli during the preceding expiration. P_{CO_2} continues to increase and P_{O_2} continues to decrease.

From i' to i: fresh air enters the alveoli and dilutes the alveolar atmosphere. P_{CO_2} decreases and P_{O_2} increases.

The point representing mean alveolar gas must be on the respiratory quotient line calculated from the mean composition of expired gas (0.85 in the case shown in this figure).

(Schema from DuBois, 1952.)

Atmospheric air enters the alveoli only during inspiration. During expiration $P_{A_{O_2}}$ decreases and $P_{A_{CO_2}}$ increases from a value i to value e (Fig. 26, B). During inspiration, the first gas to reach the alveoli comes from the anatomical dead space, gas vented from the alveoli during the preceding expiration. During this phase of inspiration, $P_{A_{O_2}}$ continues to decrease and

$P_{A_{CO_2}}$ continues to increase reaching the values shown at i′. After this gas has been washed out of the tracheobronchial tree, fresh air enters the alveoli, and $P_{A_{O_2}}$ increases and $P_{A_{CO_2}}$ decreases to values shown at i. There is therefore a cyclic change in alveolar gas composition, that can be drawn as a loop on the O_2–CO_2 diagram (Fig. 26, A). The alveolar point moves along the loop i e i′i, but its rate of movement along this loop is not constant (Fig. 26, B shows an example in which the time required to move from i to i′ is longer than the time required to move from i′ to i).

Several factors can affect these cyclic changes, in terms of both extent and speed:

a) When the lung volume increases, the alveolar pressure oscillations decrease. A large lung volume cushions the oscillations of $P_{A_{O_2}}$ and $P_{A_{CO_2}}$ and, as a consequence, minimizes the oscillations of partial pressure in the arterial blood. During expiration, the lung volume decreases and, if the gas exchange proceeds at the same rate, the rate of change in alveolar gas composition must increase progressively.

b) Amplitude (and frequency) of the variations in alveolar pressures is also affected by the ventilatory pattern, the amplitude being higher in subjects where ventilation is achieved by the combination of low frequency and high tidal volume.

c) Changes in pulmonary capillary blood flow during the respiratory cycle (when present) also influence the variations in alveolar pressures, an increase in flow speeding up these variations. Pulmonary blood flow is constant in some resting subjects, but not in those who have a low respiratory frequency or those whose pattern includes respiratory pauses (DuBois and Marshall, 1957). It probably varies also during muscular exercise.

d) During muscular exercise, the magnitude of the gas exchange during a single respiratory cycle increases considerably and the oscillations in $P_{A_{O_2}}$ may exceed 10 mm Hg.

In summary, the composition of alveolar air varies in different parts of the lung and at different times of the cycle. These two factors, poorly defined at present, must be taken into account when mean alveolar gas is to be defined. There are at least two such definitions. The composition of this gas may be:

— that of a mixture of the different gases *leaving* the various alveoli during expiration. This alveolar gas can be sampled and analyzed;

— or alternatively that of a mixture of the different gases *contained* in the various alveoli. This is obviously an imaginary mixture. However, gas exchange actually takes place between the blood and the gas contained in the different alveolar spaces, and not between blood and gas expired by the alveoli, which corresponds to the first definition.

Obviously, these theoretical problems make it difficult to evaluate the composition of alveolar gas, and cast some doubts on the interpretation of small differences between the alveolar and arterial partial pressures of O_2 and CO_2.

Methods for determining alveolar gas composition

1. DIRECT SAMPLING OF ALVEOLAR GAS

a) CONTINUOUS ANALYSIS OF ALVEOLAR GAS COMPOSITION. This method has been described on page 94. The alveolar values are usually read on the "plateau," that is the flat part of the tracing which follows complete washout of the anatomical dead space, as for example at points A_1, on Figures 24 and 25. This requires the existence of a well-defined "plateau," which implies a tidal volume sizeable enough to wash out completely the dead space. Otherwise, even the last part of the expired gas is made of a mixture of alveolar gas and dead space air. This "plateau," which has a slight slope, even at rest, shows a pronounced rise when alveolar gas exchange is increased, as is the case in muscular exercise.

b) END-EXPIRATORY SAMPLING. Several methods, among them that of Rahn and Otis (1949), allow a sample to be withdrawn automatically from the last part of the expired gas (point A of Figs. 24 and 25). These methods are acceptable if the conditions indicated for the previous technique are fulfilled, and if ventilation is regular.

It is therefore advantageous to deal with an anatomical dead space which is as small as possible. This is facilitated by using mouthpieces (or masks) and respiratory valves of as small a volume as possible. The additional dead space is called "apparatus dead space." In some cases, the sampling catheter can be placed in the mouth or in the trachea.

c) SAMPLING BY THE HALDANE-PRIESTLEY METHOD. In order to ensure withdrawal of a sample originating entirely from the alveolar spaces, Haldane and Priestley (1905) have suggested collection of the terminal part of a forced expiration (point A_2 in Fig. 25), which takes place either immediately following an inspiration (end-inspiratory sample) or immediately following a normal expiration (end-expiratory sample). Haldane and Priestley had originally suggested taking the mean of the values obtained from these two samples. The great advantage of this method is that there is no doubt that the sample originates entirely in alveolar spaces (see Bannister, 1954). On the other hand, it has often been pointed out that this method gives values which are too high for CO_2 and too low for O_2, because gas exchange continues during the prolonged expiration, causing a drop in $P_{A_{O_2}}$ and a rise in $P_{A_{CO_2}}$. This drawback is especially apparent when gas exchange is increased by muscular exercise. In addition, this technique disturbs respiration temporarily and therefore does not allow sampling at very short intervals.

2. INDIRECT METHOD

a) BASED ON ARTERIAL BLOOD P_{CO_2} (Enghoff, 1938). This method is based on the assumption that the partial pressures of CO_2 in arterial blood, Pa_{CO_2}, and in alveolar gas, PA_{CO_2}, are equal (it should be noted that proper sampling and analysis of arterial blood are not easy). This value of PA_{CO_2} enables PA_{O_2} to be calculated by the use of equation 6, in which the respiratory gas exchange R is computed from the composition of expired gas.

The validity of this method rests on the assumption that PA_{CO_2} is equal to Pa_{CO_2}. This assumption was unquestioned until recently, but it is now thought that a difference between PA_{CO_2} and Pa_{CO_2} exists, a concept based more on theoretical considerations than on experimental findings. In the normal subject, this difference, small as it may be, is not negligible if *physiological* dead space and alveolar tidal volume are to be calculated exactly (p. 103). At any rate, the arterial-alveolar P_{CO_2} difference may be sizeable in certain diseased conditions.

This method is based on the definition of mean alveolar gas composition as the mean value obtained from the composition of alveolar gas (taking into account the complex cyclic variations during the respiratory cycle) in the alveolar areas that are perfused. The gas in alveoli which are not perfused — if they exist — cannot affect arterial P_{CO_2}.

b) BY APPLICATION OF BOHR'S EQUATION. It has been stated above that since expired gas is a mixture of alveolar gas and inspired air (see p. 94) its composition will depend on the relative importance of these two volumes, the sum of which constitutes the expired volume:

$$V_T = V_D + V_A \qquad (7)$$

where V_T is the tidal volume, V_D is the dead space volume, and V_A is the alveolar tidal volume, these three volumes having different gas compositions.

If a gas is found at a fractional concentration F_E in the expired gas, at a fractional concentration F_I in the inspired and dead space gas and at a fractional concentration F_A in the alveolar gas, these fractions will be related since the quantity of that gas present in V_T must be the sum of the quantities in the two volumes which make up V_T.

$$V_T \cdot F_E = V_D \cdot F_I + V_A \cdot F_A$$

Since $V_A = V_T - V_D$,

$$F_A = \frac{V_T \cdot F_E - V_D \cdot F_I}{V_T - V_D}$$

Multiplying by $(P_B - 47)$ yields:

$$P_A = \frac{V_T \cdot P_E - V_D \cdot P_I}{V_T - V_D} \tag{8}$$

The following form of this equation is called Bohr's equation (Bohr, 1890):

$$V_D = V_T \frac{P_A - P_E}{P_A - P_I} \tag{9}$$

When dealing with oxygen, the subscript O_2 can be added to the pressure terms. When considering CO_2, the inspired CO_2 can be neglected if air is inspired. This simplifies the equation to:

$$P_{A_{CO_2}} = P_{E_{CO_2}} \frac{V_T}{V_T - V_D} \tag{10}$$

In order to determine P_{CO_2} and P_{O_2} in the mean alveolar gas, the *physiological* dead space, V_D, must be known. However, since this physiological dead space is determined by using in Bohr's equation (equation 9) alveolar pressure values obtained by other methods, this technique is no more or less valid than the others.

The notion of alveolar gas is therefore very complex. A precise definition is nevertheless required in order to evaluate the methods used to measure the composition of this mean alveolar gas. At present, all the methods only enable one to estimate $P_{A_{CO_2}}$ and $P_{A_{O_2}}$ with a reasonable degree of accuracy. The measurements are quite adequate in the normal resting subject, but there can be an error of several millimeters of mercury under other conditions.

Physiological dead space

If the $P_{A_{CO_2}}$ term of equation 10 represents P_{CO_2} of mean alveolar gas, the calculated V_D corresponds to the *physiological* dead space. The calculated V_D value varies according to the value of $P_{A_{CO_2}}$ used in equation 10. Knowing the conceptual (p. 98) and technical (p. 101) difficulties involved in determining the mean alveolar gas composition, it is easy to understand that the values of the physiological dead space are open to controversy.

Physiological dead space is normally larger than anatomical dead space (except in a few unusual cases, such as a respiratory pattern characterized by a very high frequency and a very low tidal volume). It is sometimes stated that physiological dead space is the sum of the anatomical dead space and of an "alveolar" or "parallel" dead space, also occasionally called "distribution" dead space (related to differences in distribution patterns of ventilation and perfusion and unevenness of alveolar gas composition in different parts of the lungs) (see Folkow and Pappenheimer, 1955; Asmussen and Nielsen, 1956; Severinghaus and Stupfel, 1957).

It is generally accepted that resting physiological dead space only slightly exceeds anatomical dead space. For instance, in male subjects, anatomical V_D is approximately 150 ml and physiological V_D is 160 ml. In females, both values are somewhat lower.

Physiological dead space decreases during voluntary apnea.

Both anatomical and physiological dead space values increase when lung volume increases.

Both dead space values are higher in the erect than in the supine position (Bjurstedt, 1962).

Physiological dead space is markedly increased during muscular exercise and is the larger the more severe the exercise. At peak exercise, the physiological dead space may be as high as 500 ml. This increase is due mainly to alveolar factors, because anatomical dead space increases only slightly.

Alveolar tidal volume. Alveolar ventilation

The interest of the notion of physiological dead space is linked with the notion of alveolar ventilation and alveolar gas exchange. Equation 7

$$V_T = V_D + V_A$$

indicates that physiological dead space volume and alveolar tidal volume are complementary. The alveolar tidal volume is therefore that volume of atmospheric air which participates in alveolar gas exchange and is transformed into mean alveolar gas during the course of one single respiratory cycle.

Multiplying each of the terms of equation 7 by respiratory frequency, f, yields:

$$V_T \cdot f = V_D \cdot f + V_A \cdot f$$

or

$$\dot{V} = V_D \cdot f + \dot{V}_A$$

The over-all ventilatory flow is equal to the sum of physiological dead space ventilation and alveolar ventilation.

This equation enables one to understand how respiratory frequency affects alveolar ventilation. Certain conclusions can be drawn from the examples of Table XI (the last line is only theoretical).

TABLE XI

$\dot{V}$ ml/min, BTPS	f/min	V_T ml	V_D ml	$f \times V_D$ ml/min	$\dot{V}_A$ ml/min
6,000	10	600	200	2,000	4,000
12,000	10	1,200	200	2,000	10,000
12,000	30	400	200	6,000	6,000
12,000	60	200	200	12,000	0

(The assumption of a constant physiological dead space does not alter the conclusions.)

1) Alveolar ventilation depends on frequency and tidal volume, the product of which gives the total ventilation. For a given total ventilation, alveolar ventilation (the essential factor in alveolar gas exchange) increases when frequency decreases and tidal volume increases (lines 2, 3, and 4).

2) Theoretically, if frequency of ventilation was very high and tidal volume became equal to dead space volume, alveolar ventilation would be zero (line 4). This is not absolutely correct, because when this ventilatory pattern is present, physiological dead space decreases and a certain alveolar ventilation is maintained.

3) As a result of the two preceding conclusions, it is possible to state that if the total ventilation is to be increased in order to obtain a higher alveolar ventilation, it would be "advantageous" to increase tidal volume rather than frequency.

Alveolar ventilation equations (See Rahn and Fenn, 1955.)
Alveolar ventilation is that flow which brings about mean alveolar air composition. A number of exact quantitative relationships exist between the CO_2 production, $\dot{V}_{CO_2}$, the oxygen uptake, $\dot{V}_{O_2}$, and the partial pressures of O_2 and CO_2, $P_{A_{O_2}}$ and $P_{A_{CO_2}}$.

The alveolar ventilation equation for oxygen is:

$$\dot{V} = \frac{863\dot{V}_{O_2}[1 - F_{I_{O_2}}(1 - R)]}{P_{I_{O_2}} - P_{A_{O_2}}}$$

or

$$P_{A_{O_2}} = P_{I_{O_2}} - 863\frac{\dot{V}_{O_2}}{\dot{V}_A}[1 - F_{I_{O_2}}(1 - R)] \tag{11}$$

For carbon dioxide, the relationship is

$$\dot{V}_A = 863\frac{\dot{V}_{CO_2}}{P_{A_{CO_2}}} = \frac{863 \cdot R \cdot \dot{V}_{O_2}}{P_{A_{CO_2}}}$$

or

$$P_{A_{CO_2}} = 863\frac{\dot{V}_{CO_2}}{\dot{V}_A} \tag{12}$$

In these equations, $\dot{V}_A$ is in l/min, BTPS, $\dot{V}_{O_2}$ and $\dot{V}_{CO_2}$ are in l/min, STPD, and $P_{A_{O_2}}$ and $P_{A_{CO_2}}$ are in mm Hg. The factor 863 is derived from the use of these units of measurement and physical conditions $\left(863 = 760 \times \dfrac{310}{273}\right)$.

Equations 11 and 12 enable the following fundamental facts to be grasped:

1) If CO_2 production and alveolar ventilation are increased proportionately, $P_{A_{CO_2}}$ does not vary. This is *more or less* what happens during muscular exercise. If the values for a normal subject, breathing spontaneously, are applied to equation 12, the resultant $P_{A_{CO_2}}$ is normal by definition. The condition is called alveolar normocapnia (which is somewhat variable, according to subjects and conditions, see p. 160).

The same relationship exists for oxygen, and in a normal subject, breathing spontaneously, alveolar normoxia prevails. The values for alveolar normocapnia and normoxia correspond to point A in Figure 27.

2) When there is *alveolar hypoventilation* with an unchanged CO_2 production, and in more general terms when the ratio $\dfrac{\dot{V}_{CO_2}}{\dot{V}_A}$ increases, $P_{A_{CO_2}}$ increases. This condition can be defined as a *"relative"* alveolar hypoventilation (relative in reference to CO_2 production) and results in *hypercapnia*.

The same phenomenon can be described for $P_{A_{O_2}}$, in which case relative alveolar hypoventilation increases the difference between $P_{I_{O_2}}$ and $P_{A_{O_2}}$ by lowering $P_{A_{O_2}}$, the result being alveolar hypoxia. If the respiratory quotient has not changed (as would occur in maintained and prolonged hypoventilation) the new alveolar gas point will be on the same R line as the normal alveolar point, for instance at A_1. The higher the degree of relative hypoventilation, the more pronounced alveolar hypercapnia and hypoxia will be. As an example, point A_1 corresponds to a 25% decrease in alveolar ventilation and point A'_1 to a 33% decrease.

These changes can be produced experimentally by voluntary *prolonged* hypoventilation (which is not easily maintained) or by adding an external dead space (breathing through a tube of a few hundred milliliters volume). In diseased states, this condition of relative hypoventilation can be found in cases where ventilatory insufficiency is present (emphysema, obesity, respiratory muscle paralysis, etc.), and accompanied by a relative alveolar hypoventilation, causing respiratory acidosis (see p. 160).

3) When there is *alveolar hyperventilation* with no change in CO_2 production or, more generally, when the ratio $\dfrac{\dot{V}_{CO_2}}{\dot{V}_A}$ decreases, $P_{A_{CO_2}}$ drops. This condition corresponds to a relative alveolar hyperventilation and results in hypocapnia. In terms of oxygen, relative hyperventilation causes a decrease in the difference between $P_{I_{O_2}}$ and $P_{A_{O_2}}$ by increasing $P_{A_{O_2}}$, the result being

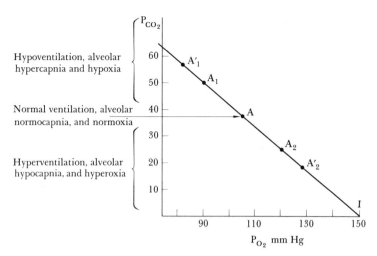

FIGURE 27.   Variations in alveolar gas composition as a result of maintained changes in alveolar ventilation, at constant metabolic level.

Point A corresponds to normal O_2 and CO_2 pressures. In this case, alveolar ventilation is in normal proportion to CO_2 production and O_2 consumption. This condition can be defined as alveolar normoxia and normocapnia.

Points A_1 and A_1' show hypercapnia and hypoxia. These alveolar pressure values can be observed when there is hypoventilation, that is insufficient ventilation in relation to the gas exchange. Hypoventilation is more marked at point A_1' than at point A_1.

Points A_2 and A_2' (hypocapnia and hyperoxia) can be observed in the case of relative hyperventilation. This hyperventilation is more marked at point A_2' than at point A_2.

alveolar hyperoxia. If the respiratory quotient has not changed (maintained and prolonged hyperventilation), the alveolar point will be located on the same R line as the normal alveolar point, for instance at A_2. The more marked the hyperventilation, the further away from A the alveolar point will move. As an example, point A_2 corresponds to a relative hyperventilation of 50% and point A_2' to a hyperventilation of 100%.

This relative hyperventilation can be obtained experimentally by a voluntary increase in ventilation. It is also encountered in some pulmonary or cardiac diseases, and is not uncommon in patients ventilated artificially (respirator cases, anesthesia) when the artificial ventilation exceeds that required by the gas exchange. Relative alveolar hyperventilation causes respiratory alkalosis (see p. 160).

Constancy and variability of alveolar gas composition

At sea level, and under resting conditions, the composition of alveolar gas (sampled correctly) varies between certain limits: $P_{A_{O_2}}$ between 90 and 115 mm Hg, and $P_{A_{CO_2}}$ between 32 and 45 mm Hg. In other conditions these values may differ markedly from the above. Some of the causes are:

1) FOOD INTAKE

a) DIGESTION. During the two hours following ingestion of food, an increase in $P_{A_{CO_2}}$ can be observed. It is the consequence of metabolic alkalosis (gastric juice secretion frees Na^+ ions which bind CO_2 as bicarbonate). During the third and fourth hour the opposite change is usually observed, probably due to the secretion of bile, which is alkaline.

b) TYPE OF DIET. A vegetarian diet leads to metabolic alkalosis, and relative hypercapnia. On the other hand, diets rich in animal protein bring about metabolic acidosis and relative hypocapnia (Hasselbalch, 1912).

2) METABOLIC RESPIRATORY QUOTIENT

It is obvious that if the respiratory quotient changes, at least one of the two alveolar partial pressures considered must vary. For instance, if $P_{A_{CO_2}}$ is maintained, an increase in respiratory quotient corresponds to an increase in $P_{A_{O_2}}$ (a decrease in the difference between $P_{I_{O_2}}$ and $P_{A_{O_2}}$). On the other hand, when the respiratory quotient is maintained, any change in $P_{A_{CO_2}}$ must be accompanied by a change in $P_{A_{O_2}}$ in the opposite direction and to a proportionate extent (see p. 107).

3) BODY POSITION

In the erect position, $P_{A_{CO_2}}$ is a few millimeters of mercury lower than in the supine position (see Rahn, 1954).

4) DURING SLEEP

$P_{A_{CO_2}}$ increases by several millimeters during sleep (see Reed and Kellogg, 1958). While falling asleep, ventilation is often very irregular and major changes in alveolar gas composition can sometimes be observed.

5) MENSTRUAL CYCLE AND PREGNANCY

During ovulation, $P_{A_{CO_2}}$ reaches a maximum. It decreases progressively during the second phase of the menstrual cycle and is 4 mm Hg below the maximum during menses (see Rahn, 1954).

During pregnancy, there is a marked hypocapnia: 6 to 8 mm Hg (see Winterstein, 1955). The origin of the hyperventilation that is observed during pregnancy is complex, and the fact that steroid hormone injection causes hyperventilation (see Loeschcke, 1954) must be taken into account.

6) MUSCULAR EXERCISE

Two factors influence alveolar gas composition:

a) Change in the metabolic respiratory quotient. During exercise, the proportion of carbohydrates oxidized, and consequently the respiratory quotient, increases. In exercise of very long duration, a drop in respiratory quotient occurs, probably because of a decrease in carbohydrate oxidation (exhaustion of carbohydrate reserves) and an increased oxidation of fats.

b) In moderate exercise, there is generally a slight hypercapnia. On the other hand, during severe exercise, in which metabolism produces an abnormally high amount of fixed acid (lactic acid), the resulting metabolic acidosis causes relative hyperventilation and hypocapnia.

7) EXPOSURE TO ALTITUDE

The main change is that of $P_{A_{O_2}}$ which drops by several of millimeters of mercury. Both acute exposure to altitude of a non-acclimatized subject and prolonged exposure (acclimatized subjects) cause overall and alveolar hyperventilation and alveolar hypocapnia, the extent of which increases as the barometric pressure decreases (see p. 191).

Conclusions

Numerous factors can affect the partial pressures of CO_2 and O_2 in alveolar gas. The variations in pressure are less than they might be since these pressures can be regulated. Equations 11 and 12 show the relationship between those pressures, the O_2 and CO_2 exchange and alveolar ventilation. The magnitude of O_2 and CO_2 exchange is extremely variable, and can be ten to fifteen times larger during exercise than at rest. However, $P_{A_{O_2}}$ and $P_{A_{CO_2}}$ vary relatively little, and this relative constancy indicates that the partial pressures are regulated.

On the other hand, if none of the causes of variations listed above are operative (as occurs during the steady state) the variations in alveolar gas composition are minimal. In particular, $P_{A_{CO_2}}$ probably varies by less than 1 mm around its mean value, and it is in this context that the rule of constant composition of alveolar gas must be understood.

In everyday life, alveolar gas composition varies somewhat under the influence of the factors listed above. In addition, transient changes are imposed by swallowing, straining, talking, sighing, or yawning.

All these factors must be kept in mind when determining whether a given alveolar gas composition is normal or not. A value of 40 mm Hg for P_{CO_2} may not necessarily be normal nor a value of 37 mm Hg abnormal or technically faulty. Interpretation of alveolar gas composition must always take into account the various factors which affect this composition under normal conditions.

III. GAS EXCHANGE BETWEEN ALVEOLAR GAS AND BLOOD

Schematic description of gas exchange in the lungs

The mixed venous blood of the pulmonary artery reaching the pulmonary capillaries is separated from the alveolar gas by the alveolar-capillary membrane. This membrane is less than 1 μ thick and has a surface area of 60 sq m. The O_2 and CO_2 molecules in the capillary blood do not exert the same pressure as those in the alveolar gas. Since the alveolar wall is permeable, this pressure difference causes a movement of molecules from the point of high pressure to the point of low pressure, by simple physical *diffusion* (A. Krogh, 1910), a purely passive phenomenon.

1) CARBON DIOXIDE TRANSFER (Fig. 28)

The partial pressure of CO_2 in the mixed venous blood, $P\bar{v}_{CO_2}$, is higher than that of CO_2 in the alveolar gas and, as a result, CO_2 molecules pass from the blood into the alveolar gas. In the first part of the capillary, the capillary-alveolar pressure difference is maximal and the molecules pass rapidly. As more and more molecules leave the venous blood, the content and pressure of CO_2 in blood decrease. The capillary-alveolar pressure difference and the rate of transfer decrease progressively, and finally pressure equilibrium on both sides of the membrane is reached and transfer stops. The P_{CO_2} of blood leaving the capillary is equal to the alveolar P_{CO_2}.

Carbon dioxide is very soluble in body fluids, and thus diffuses rapidly (see p. 17). Therefore pressure equilibrium is achieved long before the blood reaches the end of the capillary. Even when the amount of CO_2 which must diffuse is high (as in the case of muscular exercise), the CO_2 diffusion rate is such that pressure equilibrium across the capillary wall is achieved. At the end of the capillary, blood P_{CO_2} cannot, under any condition, be lower than alveolar P_{CO_2}. This could have occurred only if active transport of CO_2

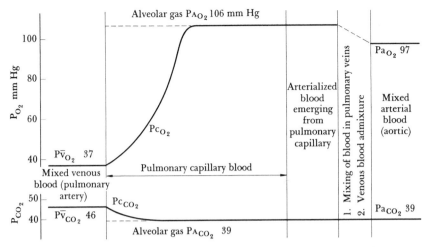

FIGURE 28.   Schematic drawing of gas exchange between capillary blood
and alveolar gas (in normoxia).

$P\bar{v}_{O_2}$ and $P\bar{v}_{CO_2}$ are the O_2 and CO_2 partial pressures in mixed venous blood.
PA_{O_2} and PA_{CO_2} are the O_2 and CO_2 partial pressures in alveolar gas.
Pc_{O_2} and Pc_{CO_2} are the O_2 and CO_2 partial pressures in capillary blood.
Pa_{O_2} and Pa_{CO_2} are the O_2 and CO_2 partial pressures in mixed arterial blood.
All pressures are in mm Hg.
The figure shows that the gas partial pressures in blood at the end of the capillary
are in equilibrium with the gas pressures in alveolar gas.
The right-hand side of the drawing shows that Pa_{CO_2} in the final mixed arterial
blood, that is in the left ventricle and in the aorta, is equal to PA_{CO_2}. On the other
hand, Pa_{O_2} is lower than PA_{O_2} for two reasons: 1) mixing of different arterialized
blood components, having different partial pressures (see p. 120), and 2) admixture
of a small amount of blood coming from the venous-arterial shunts (see p. 122).

molecules against a pressure gradient was taking place; there is no evidence
of any active role of the alveolar-capillary wall in terms of gas exchange for
either oxygen or carbon dioxide.

2) OXYGEN TRANSFER (Figs. 28 and 29)

At the beginning of the capillary, blood P_{O_2} is lower than alveolar P_{O_2} and
O_2 molecules diffuse from alveolar gas into the blood. As is the case for
CO_2, the rate of diffusion decreases gradually along the capillary. However,
oxygen, with its low solubility, is 20 times less diffusible than carbon dioxide.
The oxygen pressure in the blood leaving the capillary is not in all cases in
equilibrium with alveolar P_{O_2}. When the pressures are not equal, it is

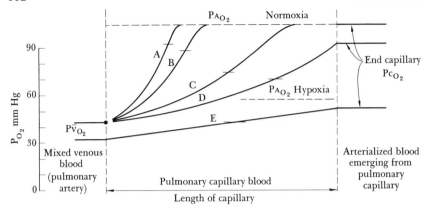

	PA_{O_2}	$P\bar{c}_{O_2}$	$(PA_{O_2}-P\bar{c}_{O_2})$	$D_{O_2} = \dfrac{\dot{V}_{O_2}}{PA_{O_2}-P\bar{c}_{O_2}}$	End capillary P_{O_2}	$(PA_{O_2}-Pa_{O_2})$
A	104	92	12	20	104	0
B	104	88	16	15	104	0
C	104	74	30	8	104	0
D	104	60	44	5.5	92	12
E	57	42	15	16	51	6

FIGURE 29.   Effects of changes in diffusing capacity and of hypoxia
on oxygen exchange in the lungs.

Pc_{O_2} is the partial pressure of oxygen in mm Hg in the pulmonary capillary blood, between its initial value as it enters the capillary (that of the mixed venous blood contained in the pulmonary artery, $P\bar{v}_{O_2}$) and its value at the end of the capillary. The horizontal line on each curve shows the level of the mean capillary pressure, $P\bar{c}_{O_2}$.

Curves A, B, C, and D pertain to normoxia. On curves A and B, the oxygen diffusing capacity, D_{O_2}, is normal. On curve C, D_{O_2} is below normal. In cases A, B, and C, Pc_{O_2} reaches equilibrium with alveolar oxygen pressure, but this equilibration occurs later along the capillary as D_{O_2} decreases.

In curve D, D_{O_2} is very low and equilibrium between Pc_{O_2} and PA_{O_2} does not occur. As the blood leaves the capillary, Pc_{O_2} is below PA_{O_2}. There is an alveolar-capillary block.

Curve E pertains to hypoxia (altitude). Although D_{O_2} is normal, the decrease in alveolar-capillary pressure difference does not allow end-capillary Pc_{O_2} to reach equilibrium with PA_{O_2}.

The table under the figure gives the numerical data for the different curves. The oxygen consumption is the product of D_{O_2} times $(PA_{O_2} - P\bar{c}_{O_2})$, (equation 13). In all five cases, $\dot{V}_{O_2}$ is 240 ml/min, STPD. D_{O_2} is expressed in ml STPD/min/mm Hg.

obvious that the blood leaving the pulmonary capillary must have a P_{O_2} below that of the alveolar gas (a value higher than alveolar gas would have indicated the existence of an oxygen-secreting mechanism).

At present, it is accepted that P_{O_2} of blood leaving the pulmonary capillary and P_{O_2} of alveolar gas are essentially the same in normoxia, either at rest or during moderate exercise. This equilibration is possible, in spite of the fact that oxygen diffusibility is low, because the pressure difference at the beginning of the capillary is much higher for O_2 than for CO_2.

On the other hand, in hypoxia, the difference in alveolar-capillary pressures is decreased, and the O_2 diffusion is less rapid than during normoxia. The P_{O_2} of blood leaving the capillary is lower than alveolar P_{O_2} (Fig. 29). This difference is especially apparent during muscular exercise, when the amount of oxygen that must be transferred increases considerably while the contact time between blood and capillary wall can drop to 0.3 to 0.4 seconds (at rest, contact time is 0.75 second).

Gas diffusion between alveolar gas and blood

DEFINITION OF PULMONARY DIFFUSING CAPACITY

The molecules of O_2 and CO_2, which are transferred because of the difference in partial pressures between blood and alveolar gas, cross a number of membranes and liquid interphases which present a certain resistance to their passage. This resistance limits the rate of diffusion from one side of the alveolar wall to the other.

The simple relationship between the quantity of a gas diffusing from one medium into the other per unit time, $\dot{V}_X$, and the difference between partial pressure of the gas in the alveolar gas, P_{AX}, and the mean pressure of the gas in the capillary, $P\bar{c}_X$, is given by:

$$\dot{V}_X = D_X(P_{AX} - P\bar{c}_X) \tag{13}$$

D_X is the diffusing capacity of the lungs for gas x. When $\dot{V}_X$ is in ml/min, STPD, and the pressures are in mm Hg, D_X becomes the volume of gas which diffuses between blood and gas per minute and per mm Hg pressure difference.

$$D_X, \text{ml STPD/min/mm Hg} = \frac{\dot{V}_X, \text{ml/min, STPD}}{(P_{AX} - P\bar{c}_X) \text{ in mm Hg}} \tag{14}$$

When equation 14 is written as

$$P_{AX} - P\bar{c}_X = \frac{1}{D_X} \cdot \dot{V}_X \tag{15}$$

the analogy with Ohm's Law becomes apparent:

Potential difference = Resistance × Current.

The term $\dfrac{1}{D_X}$ is indeed analogous to a resistance to gas transfer. The lower the diffusing capacity, D_X (which is analogous to a conductance), the higher $\dfrac{1}{D_X}$ or resistance becomes.

METHODS FOR MEASURING DIFFUSING CAPACITY

Among the factors that must be measured in order to calculate the diffusing capacity of the lungs for a given gas (see Eq. 14) is $\bar{Pc}_X$, the mean capillary pressure. Partial pressure of the gas and diffusion rate decrease progressively along the capillary. The mean capillary pressure of a gas in the pulmonary capillary is the theoretical pressure which, if maintained all along the capillary, would cause the gas to diffuse across the alveolar wall at the rate which is actually found. In order to determine $\bar{Pc}$, the time course of the partial pressure along the capillary must be determined. It is not possible to do this directly, but if the partial pressures at the beginning and at the end of the capillary are known, the curve showing the partial pressure versus time can be drawn and integrated in order to determine the mean pressure. However, this is possible only if the partial pressure of the blood leaving the capillary, end-capillary Pc, differs from alveolar gas pressure PA. When the two are equal, it is impossible to know how much time has elapsed since they reached equilibrium, and it is impossible to draw the partial pressure-time curve. This requirement (inequality of PA and end-capillary pressure) limits the choice of gases available to measure D_X. In general, gases which are very diffusible as CO_2, as well as gases which can be carried by blood only in small amounts (such as acetylene or ethyl-iodide), reach equilibrium across the alveolar wall long before the blood leaves the capillary and therefore cannot be used to determine diffusing capacity.

Only two gases fulfill the condition, namely oxygen and carbon monoxide.

1. OXYGEN METHOD (Bohr, 1909). The measurement is impossible in normoxia because Pc_{O_2} at the end of the pulmonary capillary is equal to PA_{O_2}. On the other hand, on the basis of theoretical and experimental reasons, it is accepted that in hypoxia the terminal Pc_{O_2} is not equal to PA_{O_2}. Measurement of P_{O_2} in the arterial blood of a subject in hypoxia allows the end-capillary P_{O_2} to be estimated. If $P\bar{v}_{O_2}$ (partial pressure of oxygen in the mixed venous blood which enters the pulmonary capillary) is known or assumed, the values of P_{O_2} at the beginning and at the end of the pulmonary capillary are known, and it becomes possible to treat these data by a mathematical procedure known as Bohr's integration (Bohr, 1909). This enables

one to reconstitute the curve describing the course of P_{O_2} along the capillary and to calculate the mean pressure, $\overline{Pc}_{O_2}$. The other terms of the equation present little difficulty: the measurement of $\dot{V}_{O_2}$ raises no problem, while the determination of $P_{A_{O_2}}$ is more difficult, but possible (see p. 101).

This method requires a long and delicate technique (see Riley, Cournand, and Donald, 1951; Comroe, 1955) and it measures the oxygen diffusing capacity only in hypoxia. However, the method has considerable importance from the historical point of view, and is the only one which is based on a respiratory gas — oxygen.

2. CARBON MONOXIDE METHODS. These are the only methods used in practice. The affinity of hemoglobin for carbon monoxide is such that it is usually accepted that its pressure in blood is negligible when compared to alveolar P_{CO}. Under these conditions, equation 14 becomes

$$D_{CO} = \frac{\dot{V}_{CO}}{P_{A_{CO}}}$$

a) *Steady state technique* (Bohr, 1909). The subject breathes air containing 0.2% carbon monoxide (inhalation of a gas containing 0.2% CO for a fraction of a minute is not dangerous). After a few tens seconds, a stable $P_{A_{CO}}$ value is reached. $\dot{V}_{CO}$ is easily determined by comparing F_{CO} in inspired and expired gas. $P_{A_{CO}}$ can be obtained either by sampling alveolar gas or by applying Bohr's equation, dead space being determined by one of the techniques described on page 103.

b) *Breathholding technique* (M. Krogh, 1914). With this technique, the subject inspires a volume of air to which some CO has been added and holds his breath. During that time, $P_{A_{CO}}$ varies continuously, decreasing during the apnea time. This decrease is an exponential function of time

$$P_{A_{CO_t}} = P_{A_{CO_o}} \cdot e^{-\frac{D_{CO}(P_B - 47)t}{V_A \cdot 60}}$$

where $P_{A_{CO_t}}$ is the alveolar partial pressure of CO at time t, while $P_{A_{CO_o}}$ is the partial pressure at time zero. V_A is the alveolar lung volume in ml STPD during the apnea period. From this equation, D_{CO} can be calculated.

Determination of V_A does not present any problems. $P_{A_{CO_t}}$ is measured in the end-expiratory gas after holding the breath for t seconds. $P_{A_{CO_o}}$ can be determined quite simply.

When the pulmonary diffusing capacity for CO is known, the oxygen diffusing capacity can be obtained by multiplying D_{CO} by 1.23. This factor is based on the relative solubility and molecular weights of carbon monoxide and oxygen. As to the diffusing capacity for CO_2, it is twenty times that of oxygen.

SIGNIFICANCE OF THE PULMONARY DIFFUSING CAPACITY

In spite of its simple definition, the concept of pulmonary diffusing capacity for a gas is very complex. When diffusing capacity for a gas is high, it is usually thought that the gas diffuses easily across the alveolar-capillary *membrane*. This simple interpretation would have been justified if binding of O_2 or CO by blood or liberation of CO_2 occurred instantaneously.

Actually the reactions by which those gases are bound or liberated are not instantaneous (see Forster, 1957 and 1959). When for instance CO is introduced in the alveolar gas, the molecules encounter two resistances before they are bound by hemoglobin: first a resistance across the alveolar-capillary membrane, and then a resistance in the blood itself, between the point at which it enters plasma and that at which it is bound by hemoglobin. There are therefore a diffusing capacity of the membrane, D_M, and a membrane resistance equal to $\frac{1}{D_M}$. On the other hand, there exist a "diffusing" capacity of capillary blood (the term is incorrect since this capacity is limited in part by a chemical reaction), which is $\theta \times V_c$, and an intracapillary "resistance" $\frac{1}{\theta \cdot V_c}$. The sum of these two resistances makes up the total resistance:

$$\underset{\substack{\text{Total}\\\text{resistance}}}{\frac{1}{D}} = \underset{\substack{\text{Membrane}\\\text{resistance}}}{\frac{1}{D_M}} + \underset{\substack{\text{Intracapillary}\\\text{resistance}}}{\frac{1}{\theta \cdot V_c}} \qquad (16)$$

θ stands for the volume of gas, measured in ml, STPD, which can be bound by 1 ml of blood in one minute under 1 mm Hg partial pressure. The value of θ can be determined *in vitro*. V_c indicates the pulmonary capillary blood volume, which can be determined. It is therefore possible to calculate $\theta \times V_c$ and its inverse, the intracapillary "resistance." The membrane resistance can now be calculated by subtracting this intracapillary "resistance" from the total resistance. The resistance of the membrane is proportional to the thickness of the membrane and inversely proportional to its surface area. The membrane resistance and intracapillary "resistance" are thought to be approximately equal.

These considerations are important because they show that a change in pulmonary diffusing capacity cannot be interpreted simply as a change in diffusing capacity of the alveolar-capillary membrane, but may also represent a change in the volume of blood in the pulmonary capillaries or in the properties of this blood in terms of quality, and especially of quantity, of hemoglobin. These recent notions carry an additional implication. In order to determine D_{O_2}, the classical approach, which takes into account only solubility and molecular weights of oxygen and carbon monoxide, consists in multiplying D_{CO} by 1.23. However, since the total diffusing capacity involves a blood factor determined by a chemical reaction (which is quite independent of gas molecular weight or solubility), this method of calculating D_{O_2} can no longer be accepted. The same statement holds for D_{CO_2}.

PULMONARY DIFFUSING CAPACITY VALUES

In an average resting adult, D_{O_2} is about 20 ml STPD/min/mm Hg and D_{CO_2} approximately 400 ml STPD/min/mm Hg.

D_{O_2} is proportional to the surface area of the body. The ratio D_{O_2}/body surface is about 12 ml STPD/min/mm Hg/sq m. The value probably decreases with age. Equation 13, which states that $\dot{V}_{O_2} = D_{O_2} \cdot (P_{A_{O_2}} - P\bar{c}_{O_2})$, allows one to see why D_{O_2} should be related to area. $\dot{V}_{O_2}$ is known to increase in proportion to body surface area, while $P_{A_{O_2}}$ and $P\bar{c}_{O_2}$ are not related to body size (see p. 141). Therefore, D_{O_2} must vary in the same way as $\dot{V}_{O_2}$, and the diffusing capacity per unit surface area must be approximately constant.

During muscular exercise, D_{O_2} increases and may reach 60 ml STPD/min/mm Hg. This increase is more pronounced the heavier the exercise. It has been suggested that D_{O_2} might reach a maximal value which would not be exceeded, even if the intensity of the exercise were increased. This value is called "maximal diffusing capacity," and may decrease with age. The increase in D_{O_2} during exercise can be explained by an increase in the alveolar-capillary membrane surface (increase in D_M) and of the capillary blood volume V_C, due to opening of capillaries which are closed at rest, or to their dilatation.

During very heavy muscular exercise, $\dot{V}_{O_2}$ can be twenty times as high at rest, and the rise in D_{O_2}, which can increase only threefold, is not sufficient to account for this rise. However, an additional change takes place, namely the increase in $P_{A_{O_2}} - P\bar{c}_{O_2}$, an increase which can be attributed to two factors. First of all, $P\bar{v}_{O_2}$ decreases and, secondly, equilibration between $P_{A_{O_2}}$ and $P\bar{c}_{O_2}$ occurs further along the capillary (it is even possible that this equilibrium may not be reached and that end-capillary P_{O_2} may be lower than alveolar).

PULMONARY DIFFUSION OF OXYGEN AND ITS PARTIAL PRESSURE IN ARTERIAL BLOOD

When both $\dot{V}_{O_2}$ and $P_{A_{O_2}}$ remain unchanged, a drop in D_{O_2} causes a drop in $P\bar{c}_{O_2}$ (see equation 13). On the other hand, when the oxygen diffusing capacity of the lungs is high, the partial pressure of oxygen in the capillaries, Pc_{O_2}, reaches equilibrium with the alveolar O_2 pressure, PA_{O_2}, much before the end of the capillary (curve A in Fig. 29). If D_{O_2} is lower, the equilibration takes longer (curves B and C of Fig. 29), but under both conditions the blood leaving the capillary has the oxygen partial pressure that is found in the alveoli. If, however, D_{O_2} is very low, Pc_{O_2} does not reach equilibrium with PA_{O_2}, although the blood remains in the capillaries for almost one second (curve D of Fig. 29) and, in this case, oxygen partial pressure and content are lower than in cases A, B, and C.

In normoxia, at rest and during moderate exercise, gas exchange follows patterns A or B, and the end-capillary O_2 tension equals alveolar tension.

In normoxia, during heavy muscular exercise, in spite of the increase in D_{O_2} and of the drop in $P\bar{v}_{O_2}$, it is probable that end-capillary oxygen tension is below alveolar tension.

In hypoxia, at rest, there is possibly an increase in D_{O_2}. However, it is usually agreed that end-capillary P_{O_2} is not in equilibrium with PA_{O_2}, because of the important decrease in $PA_{O_2} - P\bar{v}_{O_2}$ (case E in Fig. 29). The alveolar-end capillary difference is even more pronounced during muscular exercise in hypoxia.

Quantitative relationships between the various factors involved in alveolar-capillary gas exchange

Application of Fick's equation to carbon dioxide allows it to be stated that the carbon dioxide output, $\dot{V}_{CO_2}$, eliminated by the lungs, is equal to the cardiac output, $\dot{Q}$, multiplied by the venous-arterial CO_2 difference $(C\bar{v}_{CO_2} - Ca_{CO_2})$.

$$\dot{V}_{CO_2} = \dot{Q}(C\bar{v}_{CO_2} - Ca_{CO_2})$$

For oxygen, the relationship is

$$\dot{V}_{O_2} = \dot{Q}(Ca_{O_2} - C\bar{v}_{O_2})$$

where $(Ca_{O_2} - C\bar{v}_{O_2})$ is the arterial-venous oxygen difference. These values for $\dot{V}_{CO_2}$ and $\dot{V}_{CO_2}$ can be substituted for the corresponding values in equations 12 and 11, yielding:

$$PA_{CO_2} = 863 \frac{\dot{Q}}{\dot{V}_A} (C\bar{v}_{CO_2} - Ca_{CO_2}) \qquad (17)$$

and

$$PA_{O_2} = PI_{O_2} - 863 \frac{\dot{Q}}{\dot{V}_A} (Ca_{O_2} - C\bar{v}_{O_2}) \cdot [1 - FI_{O_2}(1 - R)] \qquad (18)$$

These equations can also be applied to part of the lungs provided $\dot{Q}$, $\dot{V}_A$, Ca_{O_2}, and Ca_{CO_2} are replaced by the values referring to the part of the lungs under study.

The interesting feature of these equations resides in the fact that they bring into focus the term $\dfrac{\dot{Q}}{\dot{V}_A}$, that is, the ratio of blood flow to air flow, a ratio called circulation/ventilation or perfusion/ventilation ratio.*

As long as all other factors in the right-hand side of equations 17 and 18 remain fixed, a proportional increase in both $\dot{V}_A$ and $\dot{Q}$ (constant circulation/ventilation ratio) does not change alveolar O_2 and CO_2 pressures. However, if this ratio increases, either because of an increase in blood flow or because of a decrease in ventilatory flow, P_{ACO_2} increases and P_{AO_2} decreases (with a transient drop in respiratory quotient). If the ratio $\dfrac{\dot{Q}}{\dot{V}_A}$ is decreased, variations in P_{O_2} and P_{CO_2} in the opposite direction will occur.

Unevenness of the circulation/ventilation ratio in the lungs (See Rahn, 1949; Riley and Cournand, 1949; Farhi and Rahn, 1956; Bartels, 1956; West and Dollery, 1960.)

A certain degree of inequality of distribution is normally present for inspired air in the lungs (see p. 55). Similarly, blood distribution is not uniform, which is tantamount to saying that some areas are better perfused than others. More specifically, in the erect position, the perfusion of the upper lobes is extremely low (West and Dollery, 1960).

This unevenness of distribution of gas and blood would not have any effect on alveolar gas exchange in the different zones if $\dfrac{\dot{Q}}{\dot{V}_A}$ was the same throughout the lung, that is if the areas that are poorly perfused were proportionately poorly ventilated.

Actually, the ratio $\dfrac{\dot{Q}}{\dot{V}_A}$ is not the same in different areas of the lung, being relatively high in the lower parts of the lung and relatively low in the upper lobes, especially in the erect position. This is the only explanation for the fact that the respiratory quotient of the upper lobes is higher than that of the lower lobes (as shown by lobar bronchospirometry).

In areas where perfusion is low and ventilation is high (relative hyperventilation), P_{AO_2} is high and P_{ACO_2} is low. These areas supply the arterial

---

* In the following discussion we refer to the perfusion-ventilation ratio, $\dot{Q}/\dot{V}_A$, as shown in equations 17 and 18. However, the classical concept (Rahn, 1949; Riley & Cournand, 1949) is that of ventilation-perfusion ratio, $\dot{V}_A/\dot{Q}$.

blood with a component which is rich in O_2 and poor in CO_2. On the other hand, in areas where the circulation/ventilation ratio is high (relative hypoventilation), P_{AO_2} is low and P_{ACO_2} is high. These areas supply blood which is relatively poor in O_2 and rich in CO_2. *The unevenness in alveolar gas composition and in arterialized blood composition in the different parts of the lungs stems from unevenness of the circulation-ventilation ratio.*

What happens, from the standpoint of oxygen and carbon dioxide pressures, when these arterialized blood aliquots are mixed? It is obvious that the mean O_2 and CO_2 *content* is the mean of the contents of the components returning from each area, each of these affecting the mean value in the proportion of its relative contribution (weighted mean). However, the *partial pressure* of oxygen in this mixed blood is not a mean value calculated in the same fashion, because the dissociation curve of O_2 shows a definite curvature between 60 and 150 mm Hg. Figure 30 shows that Pa_{O_2} resulting from a mixture of blood samples B and C is a few millimeters of mercury below what would have been obtained had the relationship HbO_2–P_{O_2} been a straight line. In mixed blood, the P_{O_2} is nearer that of the blood that is the least arterialized, and this is responsible for the difference (a' − a). On the other hand, P_{O_2} resulting from the mixing of the different alveolar gas components (mean alveolar gas) is shifted in the direction of a high P_{O_2}, because of the important contribution of the better ventilated alveoli, and this is responsible for the difference (A − a'). As a consequence, there is a certain oxygen pressure difference between the mixed alveolar gas and the mixed arterial blood (P_{AO_2} − Pa_{O_2}), or (A − a), which is of the order of a few millimeters of mercury in the normal subject breathing air.

In hypoxia, the arterial blood is unsaturated, and between the venous and arterial points, the curvature of the HbO_2–P_{O_2} relationship is decreased. Furthermore, the curve is steeper, so that the P_{O_2} difference between a well-ventilated area and a poorly ventilated one is lower than in normoxia. As a result, the unevenness described above causes a much lower (A − a) pressure difference in hypoxia than in normoxia.

It can be shown that in *hyperoxia,* the unevenness of the circulation/ventilation ratio can produce only a very small difference between alveolar and arterial partial pressure.

In terms of carbon dioxide, the steep slope and near-linearity of the dissociation curve of blood CO_2 reduce the arterial-alveolar CO_2 difference considerably. It is usually accepted that Pa_{CO_2} is only 1 mm Hg higher than P_{ACO_2}, at least in the supine position. It is often stated that the two values are in fact equal, and it is common to take blood P_{CO_2} as mean alveolar P_{CO_2}, when measuring physiological dead space (p. 102) or pulmonary

	B	(B + C)	C
$\dot{Q}$ l/mn	3	6	3
$\dot{V}A$ l/mn, BTPS	2	6	4
$\dot{Q}/\dot{V}A$	1.50	1.00	0.75
Alveolar P_{O_2}	91	108	116
Blood P_{O_2}	91	100	116
C_{O_2} vol %	19.25	19.55	19.85

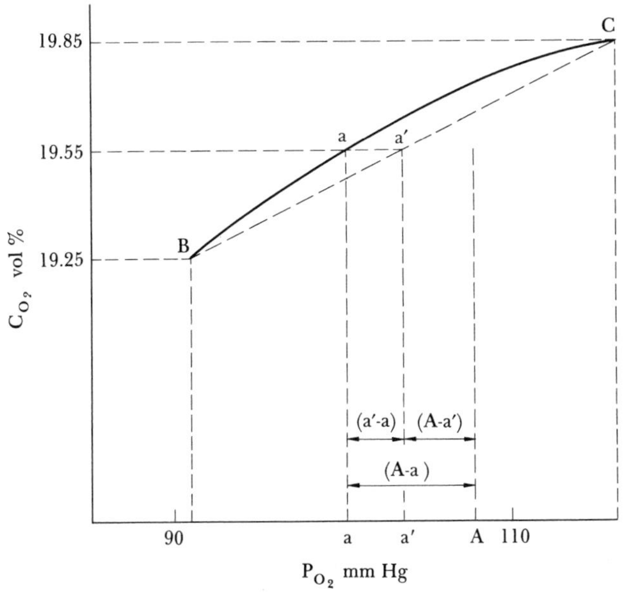

FIGURE 30. Effect of unevenness in circulation-ventilation ratio, $\dot{Q}/\dot{V}A$, on mixed arterial blood P_{O_2} (schematic).

Column B refers to a part of the lungs where the $\dot{Q}/\dot{V}A$ ratio is high, that is a zone which is well perfused but poorly ventilated. Column C deals with another part of the lungs where $\dot{Q}/\dot{V}A$ is low, that is a part poorly perfused and well venti-lated. Actually, each part of the lungs has its own $\dot{Q}/\dot{V}A$ ratio. The example given here is a simplified presentation. The middle column (B + C) corresponds to the mixture of gas and blood from columns B and C. The curve BaC is a segment of the C_{O_2}-P_{O_2} curve from Figure 3 (see p. 32).

Unevenness of $\dot{Q}/\dot{V}A$ ratio causes an alveolar-arterial oxygen difference. In column (B + C) the P_{O_2} of mean alveolar gas is 108 mm Hg, while arterial P_{O_2} is only 100 mm Hg. This difference is due to:

on one hand, the alinearity of the BaC curve. Were this a straight line, point a would be at a', and the alveolar-arterial P_{O_2} difference would be lower. The alinearity of the BaC curve is responsible for the difference (a' − a) out of a total difference (A − a);

on the other hand, the P_{O_2} of mean alveolar gas being shifted toward the high value, because the well-ventilated parts, having a high P_{O_2}, contribute more to the mixed alveolar gas than the poorly ventilated parts, which have a lower P_{O_2}. This is responsible for the difference $(A - a')$ out of the total difference $(A - a)$.

diffusing capacity. When variations in $\dot{Q}/\dot{V}_A$ are pathologically high, Pa_{CO_2} and PA_{CO_2} may differ by several millimeters of mercury and the equality of these two values can no longer be assumed.

Venous admixture to arterial blood ("venous shunt")

Normally, a small amount of venous blood mixes with arterialized blood returning from the lungs. This venous admixture or venous "shunt" originates from three sources: true anastomoses between the arterial and the venous side of the pulmonary circulation, bronchial veins which drain into pulmonary veins, and Thebesian veins which return some blood from the myocardium to the left ventricle.

Assuming that the O_2 content of the blood contributed by the "shunts" is 5 vol% lower than that of the arterialized blood returning from the pulmonary capillaries, and that the volume of venous blood added to arterialized blood represents 2% of the final mixture, venous admixture would lower arterial blood O_2 content by 0.1 vol%.

In hypoxia, where the slope of the O_2 dissociation curve is steep, this decrease in O_2 content causes only a very small drop in P_{O_2} (Fig. 31).

In normoxia, in the region of 100 mm Hg, the dissociation curve is much less steep, so that the small drop in D_{O_2} corresponds to a drop of P_{O_2} of a few millimeters of mercury (Fig. 31). This decrease in P_{O_2} due to venous admixture can be added to the difference $(A - a)$ due to unevenness of the circulation/ventilation ratio.

In hyperoxia, the blood $C_{O_2} - P_{O_2}$ curve is nearly flat since any increase in C_{O_2} under the influence of a rise in P_{O_2} is due only to dissolved oxygen, and O_2 has a low solubility coefficient. Under these conditions, a drop of 0.1 vol% C_{O_2} corresponds to a drop in P_{O_2} of 30 mm Hg. The preceding section has indicated that in hyperoxia the non-uniform ventilation-perfusion relationship could cause only a small alveolar-arterial oxygen difference. It can be stated therefore that the alveolar-arterial P_{O_2} difference in hyperoxia is essentially due to venous admixture, and therefore enables the "shunt" to be calculated. It is obvious that the exact amount by which the P_{O_2} drops depends on the importance of the shunt and on the composition of venous blood.

As for carbon dioxide, the slight rise in CO_2 content due to the admixture

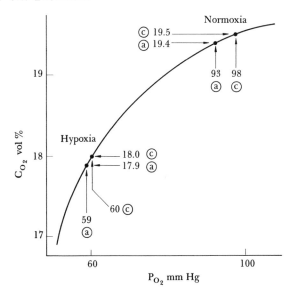

FIGURE 31. Effects of venous "shunt" on arterial oxygen pressure.

The points marked c indicate arterialized blood, coming from the pulmonary capillaries. Points a show arterial blood, resulting from adding to blood c some unsaturated venous blood, coming from the veno-arterial shunts. In the example given in this figure, the addition of venous blood decreases C_{O_2} by 0.1 vol%.

With this drop in C_{O_2} of 0.1 vol% there is a corresponding drop in P_{O_2}. This P_{O_2} decrease varies according to the saturation of the mixed venous blood and to the slope of the $C_{O_2} - P_{O_2}$ curve at c . This P_{O_2} drop can be about 1 mm Hg in hypoxia, 5 mm Hg in normoxia, and 30 mm Hg in hyperoxia.

of venous blood to arterialized blood causes only an insignificant increase in P_{CO_2}, because of the very steep slope of the CO_2 dissociation curve.

Summary of alveolar-capillary gas exchange and of the curves of alveolar-arterial oxygen pressure difference

Three factors may cause a difference between the partial pressure of oxygen in the alveolar gas and in the arterial blood, Pa_{O_2} always being lower than PA_{O_2}. These are:

a) a decrease in the rate of gas diffusion between alveolar gas and capillary blood;

b) unevenness of the circulation/ventilation ratio in different parts of the lungs. This is also called perfusion/ventilation ratio or $\dot{Q}/\dot{V}A$ ratio;

c) venous admixture to the arterialized blood, also called venous "shunt."

This venous blood originates from some bronchial veins, Thebesian veins, and true anastomoses between pulmonary arterial and pulmonary venous systems.

If a part of the lungs is not ventilated, the composition of the blood leaving this part is close to that of mixed venous blood. The resultant drop in P_{O_2} in the mixed arterial blood may be considered as a reflection of either a distribution disturbance (cause b) or venous admixture (cause c).

The relative contribution of these three causes to the $P_{A_{O_2}} - P_{a_{O_2}}$ difference varies with inspired oxygen pressure. Figure 32 pertains to resting normal subjects.

In hypoxia, the "distribution factor" is relatively unimportant, and the venous "shunt" factor is negligible, but, on the other hand, diffusion is slow and therefore the P_{O_2} of the blood leaving the pulmonary capillaries is lower than $P_{A_{O_2}}$ by a few millimeters of mercury.

In normoxia, the $P_{A_{O_2}} - P_{a_{O_2}}$ difference is also of the order of 10 mm Hg, but in this case capillary blood has equilibrated with alveolar gas. The oxygen pressure difference is due to unevenness in perfusion/ventilation ratios and venous "shunts."

In hyperoxia, equilibration of capillary blood is complete and the distribution factor is negligible. However, a venous "shunt" of 1 to 2% of the cardiac output may cause a difference ($P_{A_{O_2}} - P_{a_{O_2}}$) of several tens of millimeters of mercury.

Therefore, regardless of what the partial pressure of O_2 in alveolar gas is, the O_2 pressure in arterial blood is always lower.

As for carbon dioxide, the same factors can also cause a difference ($P_{a_{CO_2}} - P_{A_{CO_2}}$), but it is generally accepted in practice that this is less than 1 mm Hg, and it is often stated that arterial P_{CO_2} is equal to alveolar P_{CO_2}. Nevertheless, in pathological conditions, the difference ($P_{a_{CO_2}} - P_{A_{CO_2}}$) may reach several millimeters of mercury.

It is certain that these concepts, all quite new, will undergo evolution, if not revolution (see symposium on "Gas Exchange in the Lung," International Congress of Physiological Sciences, Leiden, 1962). These notions, showing the complexity of the problems of alveolar-capillary gas exchange and of the composition of arterial blood, are of considerable importance in understanding the arterial hypoxia mechanism found in certain diseases.

Quantitative relationships in respiratory gas exchange — a review

Because it is possible to collect, sample, and analyze inspired and expired gas as well as arterial and mixed venous blood, a highly quantitative analysis of gas exchange is possible and has proved to be of utmost usefulness. Un-

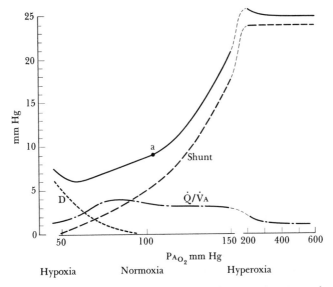

FIGURE 32. Difference between partial pressure of oxygen in mean alveolar gas (PA_{O_2}) and in mixed arterial blood (Pa_{O_2}) as a function of PA_{O_2}. Components of this difference.

The three curves labeled D, $\dot{Q}/\dot{V}A$, and shunt show the alveolar-arterial P_{O_2} differences due respectively to diffusion (D), inequality in circulation-ventilation ratios ($\dot{Q}/\dot{V}A$) and venous admixture (shunts).

The continuous line indicates the *total* difference between alveolar and arterial oxygen pressures. As an example, at point a, the total difference is 9 mm Hg, which means that since PA_{O_2} as read on the abscissa, is 104 mm Hg, $Pa_{O_2} = 104 - 9 = 95$ mm Hg. In this case, the 9 mm difference between PA_{O_2} and Pa_{O_2} is the sum of the corresponding values read on the $\dot{Q}/\dot{V}A$ and shunt lines. (From L. Farhi and H. Rahn, *J. Appl. Physiol.*, 1955, **7**, 699–703; and H. Bartels, *Verhandl. deutsch. Gesellsch. inn. Med.*, 1956, **62**, 25–34.)

fortunately the beginner is often confused by the vast number of equations that can be set, and it may be useful at this stage to review what these operations are, how they are obtained, and how they relate to each other. This is done in Table XI b.

In this table, the first column pertains to CO_2 exchange and the second to O_2 exchange. The top line deals with over-all ventilation, the second with alveolar ventilation, and the third with perfusion. In this manner six basic equations (already discussed) are obtained. It is also possible to interrelate these equations, as can be done by considering simultaneously the O_2 and CO_2 exchange in any line, leading to the concept of gas exchange ratio. By

TABLE XI b

	$\dot{V}_{CO_2}$	$\dot{V}_{O_2}$
Over-all ventilation	CO₂ output equation equation 2 (p. 90) $$\dot{V}_{CO_2} = \dot{V}_E \cdot F_{E_{CO_2}}$$	O₂ uptake equation equation 3 (p. 90) $$\dot{V}_{O_2} = \dot{V}_I \cdot F_{I_{O_2}} - \dot{V}_E \cdot F_{E_{O_2}}$$
Alveolar ventilation	Alveolar ventilation equation for CO₂ equation 12 (p. 105) $$P_{A_{CO_2}} = 863 \frac{\dot{V}_{CO_2}}{\dot{V}_A}$$	Alveolar ventilation for O₂ equation 11 (p. 105) $$P_{A_{O_2}} = P_{I_{O_2}} - 863 \frac{\dot{V}_{O_2}}{\dot{V}_A} [1 - F_{I_{O_2}}(1 - R)]$$
Perfusion	Fick's equation for CO₂ (p. 118) $$\dot{V}_{CO_2} = \dot{Q}(C\bar{v}_{CO_2} - Ca_{CO_2})$$	Fick's equation for O₂ (p. 118) $$\dot{V}_{O_2} = \dot{Q}(Ca_{O_2} - C\bar{v}_{O_2})$$

considering the CO_2 (or O_2) carriage in different systems, the Bohr equation and the perfusion-ventilation relationships can be obtained.

7
Neurogenesis — The Ventilatory System

I. THE RESPIRATORY CENTERS

Definition

Respiratory cycles occur as a result of the periodic contraction and relaxation of the inspiratory — and sometimes the expiratory — muscles. These cycles have a definite periodicity, amplitude, and pattern, all characteristics that vary widely from one subject to the next and are influenced by the external and internal conditions (p. 52).

What parts of the nervous system are responsible for this periodic phenomenon?

Section of the nervous axis between the atlas and the axis below the medulla (or, alternatively, block or interruption of the pathways at this level by anesthesia or cold), even when performed with care to decrease the gravity of this intervention, always results in respiratory paralysis. Therefore the areas of the nervous system required for generation of the ventilatory impulse are in the encephalon. The existence of spinal ventilatory automaticity has been the subject of much discussion. The cord of newborn mammals seems to be endowed with such a property, but it does not seem to exist in the adult animal (see Hermann, 1935).

Le Gallois (1812) discovered that generation of the ventilatory impulse required integrity of the medulla. "Respiration does not depend on the whole brain, but on a rather localized area of the medulla, situated near the occipital foramen and near the origin of the eighth pair of nerves (or vagi)."

Following Le Gallois, a considerable number of publications have been devoted to the study of the localization, organization, and functioning of respiratory centers. A great deal of effort has been directed into finding a well-localized respiratory center. Flourens talked of the vital point or node.

127

At present, it would seem that there is no well-defined unique center, but that several parts of the nervous system constitute a complex anatomical entity, the integrity of which is required to obtain a normal ventilatory activity. It is therefore preferable to speak of "respiratory centers."

The term "respiratory centers" represents certain parts of the reticular formation of the brain stem, the presence of which is necessary for the normal periodic ventilatory movements. The activity level of these centers can be modified and regulated by the activity of fibers of central, cerebellar or somatic origin and by certain properties of the blood perfusing the centers. Not only are the respiratory centers necessary to initiate the ventilatory impulse, but they also fulfill a role in the integration of the input that they receive from neural pathways and from the circulation, an input which supplies the centers with information on the condition and requirements of the body and regulates their activity.

The respiratory centers are connected:

— on one hand with certain motor neurons in the anterior horns of the cervical and thoracic spinal cord by means of fibers which travel in the anterior and lateral tracts, a small number crossing the midline;

— on the other hand to a few motor neurons in the nuclei of the last pairs of cranial nerves.

The neural impulses generated in the respiratory centers are thus transmitted to the motor neurons of the different thoracic respiratory muscles as well as to the motor neurons of the ventilatory muscles of the neck and face (accessory muscles).

Techniques used in studying the respiratory centers

The concepts of the localization and function of the respiratory centers depend to a major extent on the techniques used to obtain information.

The method used by Le Gallois consists of *sectioning* certain parts of the cerebrospinal axis.

Following Flourens, more emphasis has been put on *destroying* or *inhibiting* parts of the nervous system by any of the following: mechanical intervention, electrolysis, heat, cold, local block, or ischemia.

The centers can be *stimulated* either electrically or by injection of minute volumes of solutions of different acidity.

Finally, it is possible to *record* the electrical potentials that occur spontaneously in some parts of the central nervous system and that accompany the ventilatory cycle.

Location of the origin of primary ventilatory efferent activity

The brain and the cerebellum are not responsible for initiating the periodic ventilatory cycle. In all the animals that have been studied, ventilation is not arrested by section of the cerebral and cerebellar peduncles. However, this observation does not imply that brain and cerebellum play no part in the *normal* function of the ventilatory system.

Ventilation is still present in decerebrated animals which have undergone section of the cranial nerves, of the posterior roots of the cervical and dorsal cord, and of the cord itself below the eleventh thoracic segment (Head, 1889; Stella, 1938). The medulla and upper cord possess the intrinsic properties and organization required to produce the respiratory cycle. In other words, there is respiratory automaticity in this preparation.

These are well-established facts, but there is a divergence of opinions as to whether this rhythmic activity comes from the brain stem as a whole or from a localized area within the stem.

1) Lumsden (1923a) and Pitts (1946) state that section of the lower part of the pons of the cat, the part below the section being disconnected from its vagal input, can interrupt the ventilatory rhythmicity and cause a prolonged contraction of the inspiratory muscles, an inspiratory spasm called apneusis. It is accepted that a center, called the pneumotaxic center and situated high in the pons, is capable of inhibiting periodically the inspiratory activity of the medullary centers, at least in this type of preparation, where a decerebrated brain stem is cut from its vagal afferents. On the other hand, section of the brain stem between pons and medulla, with the medulla receiving its normal vagal afferents, does not interrupt periodic ventilatory activity. The isolated medullary respiratory centers are conceived as being able to produce only an inspiratory spasm or apneusis. According to Lumsden and Pitts, maintenance of rhythmic ventilation requires the integrity of the connection between pons and medulla or of the vagal afferents to the isolated medulla.

2) For other authors (see Wyss, 1954a; Hoff and Breckenridge, 1955), the medullary respiratory centers of the dog have an inherent periodic activity of irregular amplitude and frequency, called ataxic respiration. According to this concept, the medulla is the source of elementary ventilatory impulses.

3) These facts may appear mutually exclusive. However, the experimental data were actually obtained under conditions which were not conducive to normal behavior of the areas under study, and on animals from different species, after or under anesthesia, so that the differences in findings or interpretation are not surprising.

The respiratory centers

1) MEDULLARY CENTERS

Several facts indicate that the medulla contains formations which are indispensable for the generation of ventilatory efferent activity.

a) Extensive lesions of the medulla, especially those involving the area of the obex, caused by either trauma, section, injection of caustic substances, or heat, produce respiratory arrest.

b) Injection of small amounts of CO_2-bicarbonate solutions of proper pH into certain areas of the medulla (in particular at the level of the obex) causes hyperventilation.

c) Electrical stimulation of certain areas causes prolonged inspiratory activity, which lasts as long as the stimulus is applied.

d) Electrical stimulation of areas posterior to those mentioned above causes transient arrest of inspiratory activity and contraction of the expiratory muscles.

e) Action potentials, some synchronous with inspiratory activity, others synchronous with expiratory activity, can be recorded from the medulla.

These data, obtained by very different methods, are in general agreement and complement each other. They lead one to believe that in the reticular substance of the medulla there are disseminated formations, distributed in two rather ill-defined groups or centers:

a) *an inspiratory center*, an anterior one, situated behind the oliva;

b) *an expiratory center*, near the posterior face of the medulla, at the level of the obex.

Each of these centers occupies large areas on both sides of the midline. There is no functional discontinuity between the left and right part of these centers, in the sense that stimulation of the lateral formation of the centers has its effects on the respiratory muscles on both sides of the thorax. On the other hand a deep median antero-posterior section of the caudal part of the medulla can cause asynchrony of the ventilatory movements between the two sides of the thorax.

The inspiratory and expiratory centers are also connected, but these connections are inhibitory: activity of the inspiratory center inhibits that of the expiratory center and vice versa. It is accepted that the inspiratory center dominates the expiratory center, because stimulation of the former causes a contraction which lasts as long as stimulation is maintained, while stimulation of the expiratory center causes only temporary contraction of the expiratory muscles and inhibition of the inspiratory muscles, with ventilation resuming in spite of the maintained stimulation of the expiratory center.

The centers are poorly defined within the reticular formation and are mixed with fibers of various origins, and this configuration is probably at the anatomical basis of their integrative function.

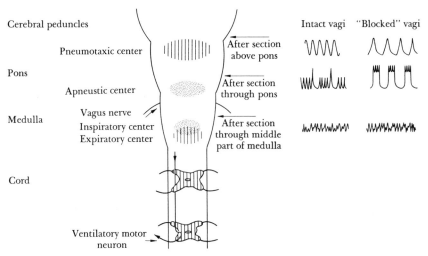

FIGURE 33.   Schema of the brain stem formations which participate in generation of respiratory impulses.

The terms "intact vagi" and "blocked vagi" indicate that conduction in the vagi is normal or interrupted by section or refrigeration. The section on "Respiratory centers" deals only with the case where the vagi are blocked.

2) APNEUSTIC "CENTER"

The apneustic center is located at the level of the area vestibularis. Following section of the brain stem in the lower part of the pons, with vagal afferents cut off, ventilation consists of successive inspiratory spasms or apneusis (or one intense permanent contraction causing death of the animal). This apneusis is usually said to be accompanied by decerebrate rigidity, and it is sometimes stated that the apneustic center is part of the reticular facilitatory system. The same section through the pons in animals in which the vagal afferents have been maintained does not cause apneustic respiration, but rather a regular ventilation of low amplitude, interrupted by near maximal inspirations, inspiratory efforts, or gasps followed by a brief expiratory pause.

3) PNEUMOTAXIC "CENTER"

The pneumotaxic center is located in the upper part of the pons, and is ill-defined. According to Lumsden (1923a), Pitts (1946), and Wang (1957), this center plays an important role in inhibiting the inspiratory activity of the underlying centers. According to this concept, during inspiration, some impulses originating in the medulla are directed to the respiratory muscles' motor neurons, while others are directed to the pneumotaxic center and excite it. When the excitation has reached a sufficient level, this center in turn excites the medullary expiratory center, which then inhibits the inspiratory center. If excitation of the expiratory center is sufficient, the expiratory muscles contract. When the inhibitory input from the pneumotaxic center decreases, the inspiratory center is released from the inhibition originating in the expiratory center and a new respiratory cycle starts. This concept implies obviously that the respiratory centers discharge at the appropriate time constant.

Hoff and Breckenridge (1955) admit the existence of the respiratory center, but do not attribute to it the important role postulated by Lumsden and Pitts. They concede however that, under certain experimental conditions, respiratory periodic activity of the brain stem requires this center. In particular, this pneumotaxic center doubtlessly plays an important role in the thermal polypnea of animals, where the pneumotaxic center, facilitated by impulses originating in the hypothalamic thermoregulatory centers, interrupts the inspiratory activity of the underlying centers early and consequently causes frequent ventilation of low amplitude.

Conclusions

The brain stem, *even when isolated from its cerebral and cerebellar connections and deprived of its somatic afferents*, exhibits a rhythmic ventilatory activity, a ventilatory automaticity. During inspiration, the inspiratory muscles must exert an increased tension since the elastic retractile forces of the thorax increase when the lung volume increases. Therefore the centers must have an inspiratory activity which increases during inspiration. This can be shown by the fact that the frequency of potentials transmitted by the phrenic motor neurons increases during inspiration. This very important property of inspiratory activity leads one to believe that the inspiratory centers are endowed with an auto-excitatory mechanism (see Wyss, 1954a).

After a certain period of inspiratory activity, an exhaustion or an inhibition of the inspiratory activity takes place. Some believe that a pontine center, called a "pneumotaxic center," is required for this inhibition and hence for producing a rhythmic ventilation.

At any rate, the rhythmic activity of the brain stem, which is observed under specific experimental conditions required for physiological analysis of the phenomenon, is not the activity found in a normal organism in which the centers receive a vast amount of information by both neural and humoral pathways.

Insofar as the mechanism of ventilatory efferent impulse generation in the brain stem and the localization of the different respiratory centers are concerned, it should be noted that interpretation of experiments based on section, destruction, or inhibition of different areas, is very delicate. Suppose for instance that the intact brain stem causes a ventilation of type α and that section of the stem at a given level transforms the ventilation into type β. These observations do not indicate that the part of the brain stem above the section is endowed with a center responsible for the difference between type α and type β. However, they show on one hand that integrity of the system is required to produce type α and on the other hand that the isolated elements below the section are capable, under experimental, nonphysiological conditions, of producing type β ventilation. This type β ventilation may actually be due to a circulatory disorder.

The property of the brain stem of generating ventilatory impulses and the role of the different centers have been determined by animal experimentation. There seem to be important differences between the species that have been studied, such as dog, rabbit, cat, or monkey. The analytical experiments described above cannot be performed on man and it is therefore impossible to know exactly how the ventilatory impulse is generated and what is the precise location of the respiratory centers in man. However, in man as in animals, the respiratory centers are to be found in the brain stem. In particular, the important role of medullary structures can be confirmed because in cases of poliomyelitis with respiratory paralysis of central origin, localized lesions in the medulla can be found.

II. VENTILATORY REFLEXES ORIGINATING IN THE LUNG

The preceding section described the problem of the source of the autonomic function of the respiratory centers, that is of the *isolated* respiratory centers, and has shown that the respiratory centers are endowed with autogenous rhythmic activity.

However, under normal conditions, the respiratory centers are not anatomically isolated, since the effector ventilatory apparatus possesses two feedback mechanisms by which it can influence the activity of the centers (Fig. 36):

— the mechanical conditions of the thoraco-pulmonary system influence the centers through proprioceptive neural pathways, which follow the vagi;

— ventilation is one of the factors that determine the partial pressures of O_2 and CO_2 in alveolar gas and arterial blood. These partial pressures in turn influence the activity of the respiratory centers, after a certain delay due to the finite velocity of blood flow. This humoral feedback will be studied later (see p. 151).

Inspiratory inhibitory reflex of Hering-Breuer

1) DEMONSTRATION OF VENTILATORY REFLEX ACTION OF PULMONARY MECHANO-RECEPTORS

a) Hering and Breuer (1868) and Head (1889) have shown that an abrupt interruption of the ventilation of the dog or the rabbit (clamping the airway) produces an immediate change in the activity of the respiratory centers.

Experimentally, the thoracic movements are stopped by blocking the ventilatory circuit of the subject. Thus the spirogram (or the pneumogram) becomes flat and the tracings can no longer supply information on the activity of the respiratory centers. Three methods are available to determine the activity of the respiratory centers when ventilation is blocked:

In the technique of Hering and Breuer, the pressure in the animal's airways is measured with a manometer which reads the pressure at a point between the animal and the point where the respiratory circuit is blocked. A pressure change to a level below atmospheric corresponds to a contraction of the inspiratory muscles, while a pressure above atmospheric indicates relaxation of the respiratory muscles (the pressure is caused by thoracic elasticity). Contraction of the expiratory muscles produces a higher positive pressure. These changes in pressure indicate the activity of the respiratory muscles.

In Head's technique, the myogram of a diaphragmatic slip, isolated from the rest of the diaphragm, but with its normal innervation and perfusion maintained, is recorded.

In Adrian's technique, the action potentials of the phrenic motor neurones, or of the respiratory muscles, are recorded.

b) If the respiratory circuit is clamped either at the end of a normal inspiration or following inspiration of a larger volume (lung inflation or insufflation), the subsequent phase (which would be expiratory if the respiratory circuit had not been blocked) is more prolonged than a normal expiration. The pressure in the airway does not exhibit rhythmic variations with the thorax kept inflated (Fig. 34, A) at least for some time. In other words, the fact that the lungs remain inflated because expiration is opposed extends the duration of the expiratory phase in the respiratory centers, and postpones considerably the appearance of inspiratory activity of the respiratory centers, which would normally have occurred a few seconds later.

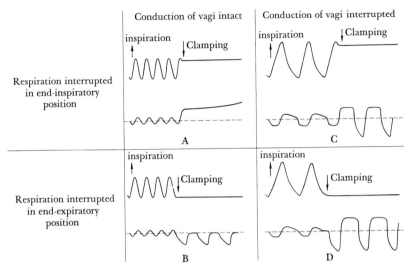

FIGURE 34. Demonstration of the role of pulmonary proprioceptive sensitivity in controlling the activity of the respiratory centers (inspiratory inhibitory reflex of Hering-Breuer).

In each case, the upper diagram is a spirogram, and the lower is a recording of the pressure measured at the level of the tracheal cannula as a function of time. Experiments are performed on an anesthetized rabbit.

A and B: *Intact vagi.*

A: Clamping the airways at the end of an inspiration apparently stops the spirographic tracing. It also shows a sustained unchanging intrapulmonary pressure, which indicates that the rhythmic activity of the respiratory centers has stopped.

B: Clamping at end-expiration decreases the frequency of the rhythmic activity of the respiratory centers.

Figures A and B show that the periodic activity of the respiratory centers depends to a large extent on the movements of the effector ventilatory apparatus (thorax). The rapid appearance of these changes demonstrates that the information pathway from the thorax to the centers is nervous.

C and D: *Cut vagi.*

Note that amplitude of ventilation has increased while frequency has decreased.

Clamping the airway at end-inspiration (C) or end-expiration (D) does not affect the periodic activity of the respiratory centers.

This observation shows that proprioceptive information, originating in the thorax and transmitted to the centers by the vagi, are responsible for the phenomena described in A and B.

On the other hand, if the ventilatory circuit is clamped at the end of a spontaneous expiration, the respiratory centers exhibit an inspiratory activity which lasts longer than normal and the respiratory frequency decreases (Fig. 34, B).

These observations show that *the inspiratory and expiratory activity of the respiratory centers are not independent of the movements of the thorax*, in the sense that blocking these movements immediately modifies the duration of the periodic respiratory phenomenon. There is therefore a mechanism, which must be neural, by which the respiratory centers are informed, practically instantaneously, of the mechanical conditions which prevail in the respiratory system. This is then a reflex phenomenon, known as the Hering-Breuer reflex. The next paragraph will show that this is a reflex inhibiting inspiratory activity.

c) The afferent fibers of the Hering-Breuer reflex are represented by the pulmonary vagal fibers. When both vagi of an animal are cut (or their conduction is interrupted by cooling) the ventilatory pattern changes in two respects: it becomes deeper and slower (Fig. 34, C and D). When the conduction of the vagi is interrupted in this fashion, blocking the airway does not produce the same effect as in the intact animal: when respiration is blocked either at inspiration or expiration, the duration of the respiratory cycle, measured easily with a manometer, is not modified (Fig. 34, C and D). Therefore, in this case, the respiratory centers continue their rhythmic autonomic activity, independently of the thoracic mechanical phenomenon, this being an immobilization of the thorax by clamping the airway.

This leads to the conclusion that the mechanoreceptors, whose stimulation causes a respiratory reflex, are innervated by branches of the vagus. Furthermore, these receptors are localized in the lungs, because destruction of the pulmonary branches of the vagi, without injury to the rest of the vagi, abolishes the Hering-Breuer reflex (Anrep and Samaan, 1933; Hammouda, 1943). This last statement does not represent a foregone conclusion, since section of the vagi interrupts, besides those fibers originating in the lungs, several other fibers which also play a role in the physiology of respiration (baro- and chemoreceptor fibers, laryngeal nerve fibers).

Thoracic immobilization causes the effect described above only transiently. After a short delay, other changes take place in the activity of the respiratory centers. The *secondary* modifications are due to the fact that ventilatory arrest changes considerably the composition of alveolar gas and arterial blood (p. 153). In other words, after a certain delay, a second feedback mechanism, humoral this time, changes the initial responses seen after blocking ventilation, responses which must be a reflex mechanism, because of their immediate appearance.

2) INSPIRATORY INHIBITION BROUGHT ABOUT BY CERTAIN PROPRIOCEPTIVE PULMONARY RECEPTORS

The effects of vagal proprioceptive information of pulmonary origin studied so far consist of inhibition of the respiratory centers (as will be seen below, p. 139, other proprioceptive information of pulmonary origin, having a different effect on the respiratory centers, may also exist). It will also be remembered that in an animal in which the pons is sectioned in its middle portion, with its afferent vagal supply cut off, ventilation is apneustic, that is, consists in inspiratory spasms of varying duration (Fig. 33). During apneusis, stimulation of the central end of the cut vagus immediately abolishes this apneusis and expiration takes place. When vagal stimulation is stopped, the inhibition of the inspiratory centers is maintained for some time, following which apneusis reappears. By intermittent vagal stimulation, it is possible to restore rhythmic ventilatory activity (Lumsden, 1923b; Pitts, 1946).

3) EXCITABILITY OF THE PULMONARY MECHANORECEPTORS

The pulmonary mechanoreceptors sense the degree of lung inflation (pulmonary tension receptors), and are therefore sometimes called stretch receptors. They are located in the walls of the terminal bronchioles and of their ramifications. During inspiration, the pulmonary mechanoreceptors are excited and afferent impulses reach the respiratory centers after synapsing in the solitary nucleus (see Wyss, 1954a). The larger the lung volume, the higher is the number of mechanoreceptors that are excited, and the greater the frequency of the afferent impulses becomes (Fig. 35a). These phenomena were observed by Adrian (1933) who recorded, in the cat and in the rabbit, the potentials propagating along the vagi as a function of changes in lung volume. Electro-physiological studies have established that:

a) the frequency of afferent impulses from pulmonary proprioceptive fibers increases progressively during inspiration, reaches a maximum at the end of inspiration, and decreases progressively during expiration (Fig. 35a, A);

b) the excitation of the mechanoreceptors is essentially related to lung volume (frequency of afferent impulses is proportional to lung volume, Fig. 35a, B); rate of airflow in the airway (it had been thought that there were tracheobronchial receptors which responded to airflow) and intrathoracic pressure do not seem to represent a stimulus for the mechanoreceptors.

c) these mechanoreceptors adapt slowly. That is to say that, if the thorax

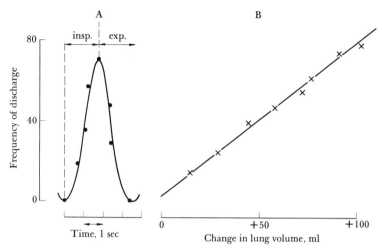

FIGURE 35a. Action potentials originating in pulmonary mechanoreceptors and propagated in afferent vagal fibers (from ADRIAN, 1933).

Curve A shows that the frequency of action potentials in an isolated fiber of pulmonary origin varies during the ventilatory cycle. The frequency is maximal at end-inspiration.

Curve B shows the relationship between frequency of discharge and lung volume.

is maintained at a given lung volume, the frequency of the afferent impulses does not vary much (Adrian, 1933; Davis and others, 1956).

d) the degree of lung distension required to stimulate these receptors (threshold) varies from one receptor to another. At normal end-expiratory volume, certain mechanoreceptors are stimulated, while others are stimulated only at higher lung volumes, that is during inspiration.

Ventilatory reflexes of pulmonary origin other than Hering-Breuer's inhibitory reflex

1) INSPIRATORY REFLEX ELICITED BY DECREASE OF THE THORACIC VOLUME
   (INSPIRATORY EXCITATORY REFLEX OF HERING AND BREUER)

The decrease in thoracic volume to a volume lower than normal end-expiratory volume causes an intense and prolonged contraction of the inspiratory muscles of the animal, well demonstrated by Head with his diaphragmatic slip technique.

This is a reflex phenomenon, the afferent pathways lying in the vagi. Special mechanoreceptors are postulated to be at the origin of this reflex. According to Knowlton and Larrabee (1946), these receptors adapt rapidly.

It is thought that the mechanoreceptors responsible for initiating the excitatory inspiratory reflex have a threshold such that they are stimulated only at a lung volume lower than the relaxation volume (see p. 69). This reflex may play an important role in hyperventilation, to the extent that the latter involves an important decrease of the functional residual capacity below resting value.

2) INSPIRATORY REFLEX CAUSED BY PULMONARY DISTENSION (PARADOXICAL REFLEX OF HEAD)

When conduction in the rabbit's vagi is partially blocked by cold, hyper-inflation of the lungs causes an additional inspiratory activity which tends to increase lung volume even more (Head, 1889; Larrabee and Knowlton, 1946). This is also a reflex mechanism, which disappears after section of the vagi. According to Knowlton and Larrabee (1946), the receptors which initiate this reflex adapt rapidly, and are identical with those taking part in the Hering-Breuer reflex discussed above. These mechanoreceptors may play an important role in hyperventilation involving a large tidal volume.

The existence of a proprioceptive pulmonary system which affects the activity of the respiratory centers has been demonstrated in the dog, the cat, the guinea pig, the rabbit, the monkey, and the mouse (Crosfill and Widdicombe, 1961). It has long been implicitly admitted that the conclusions drawn from these animal experiments are applicable to man. Christiansen and Haldane (1914) have in fact reported some work which strengthens this belief. However, it seems that the Hering-Breuer reflex is much weaker in man than in anesthetized animals. The inspiratory excitatory reflex of Hering-Breuer is weak or absent in anesthetized man. Head's paradoxical reflex has not been observed in man (Widdicombe, 1961).

III. ROLE OF PROPRIOCEPTIVE PULMONARY SENSITIVITY. CONCEPT OF VENTILATORY SYSTEM

During inspiration, the respiratory centers cause the inspiratory muscles to contract and to increase the thoracic volume. As a consequence, the pulmonary mechanoreceptors innervated by vagal fibers are stimulated, and impulses propagate along the afferent vagal fibers to the respiratory centers. This afferent input has an inhibitory effect on the inspiratory centers. During inspiration, this inhibition increases progressively, the number of active mechanoreceptors and the frequency of impulses along the afferent pathways increasing as the lung volume increases. When inhibition reaches a certain level, activity of the inspiratory centers decreases or stops, and expiration occurs. As lung volume decreases, the number of stimulated mechanoreceptors and of impulses along the vagal fibers decreases, and inhibition of the inspiratory centers is lessened. After a certain time, the inspiratory centers can initiate a new respiratory cycle. It should be pointed out that several points concerning the sequence of the mechanisms underlying rhythmic ventilation are far from clear.

The proprioceptive vagal system is not responsible for cyclic ventilation, since this role is filled by the respiratory centers, which possess a well-established rhythmic activity. However, the proprioceptive pulmonary sensitivity plays a part in the mechanism which determines the characteristics, amplitude, and frequency of the basic ventilatory phenomenon. When the vagi are cut, the activity of the respiratory centers is no longer braked by afferent vagal impulses and ventilation becomes deep and slow (Figs. 33 and 34).

Respiratory centers and the mechanical ventilatory system are one functional unit. Additional proof is supplied by the fact that in anesthetized subjects, ventilated artificially, the contraction of the respiratory muscles, which indicates activity of the respiratory centers, can be synchronous with the artificial respiration.

A similar observation can be made in an artificially ventilated animal in which activity of the respiratory centers is monitored by recording action potentials in the phrenic nerve. In this case, the ventilatory activity of the centers increases when the frequency of artificial respiration is increased (Adrian, 1933).

From the standpoint of regulation of ventilation, one cannot speak therefore of respiratory centers, but only of a ventilatory system (Fig. 36) composed of:

a) the respiratory centers;

b) the motor transmission system, connecting the respiratory centers to the ventilatory effector apparatus;

c) the ventilatory effector apparatus;

d) neural proprioceptive pathways leading from the ventilatory apparatus to the respiratory centers.

In order to obtain a normal respiratory pattern, the integrity of the ventilatory system (that is the functional unit respiratory centers — ventilatory apparatus) is required. It is true that at rest, when the ventilatory requirements are minimal, the respiratory centers alone can impose on the thorax a ventilatory pattern giving an appropriate mean alveolar ventilation, that is to say one which will maintain normal alveolar O_2 and CO_2 pressures. If, however, instead of resting ventilation, which constitutes a slow-motion pattern, higher ventilation is required, a ventilatory system in which the proprioceptive pathways have been interrupted is unable to maintain the appropriate ventilation. Scott (1908) and Boyd (1941) have observed that animals whose pulmonary proprioceptivity is interrupted hyperventilate much less when they inhale carbon dioxide. It seems logical to believe that such an animal would be unable to maintain the ventilation required during heavy muscular exercise. The possible role of pulmonary proprioceptivity will be discussed again later (p. 146).

There is a condition in which pulmonary proprioceptivity does not influence the ventilatory pattern. In the dog, during thermal hyperpnea, it is impossible to demonstrate Hering-Breuer reflexes (Hammouda, 1933) and section of the vagi does not modify the ventilatory pattern.

IV. COMPARATIVE PHYSIOLOGY OF MAMMALIAN VENTILATORY FUNCTION.
PROBLEM OF MECHANISM REGULATING VENTILATORY BEHAVIOR

A) Comparative physiology shows that physiological values involving the dimension of time (such as duration of respiratory cycle, of pregnancy, of average life span) are quantitatively related to the weight of the animals. What are the biometric relationships relating gas exchange, total and alveolar ventilation, ventilatory pattern, alveolar and arterial O_2 and CO_2 pressures, and arterial pH to weight in mammals?

There is at present no study covering all these variables from the smaller mammals to the largest, but certain important relationships are known:

1) The basal oxygen consumption, $\dot{V}_{O_2}$ expressed in ml/min, STPD is related to B, the body weight in grams, according to the following equation (simplified form of Brody's equation, see Brody, 1965).

$$\dot{V}_{O_2} = 0.064 \cdot B^{0.734} \tag{19}$$

2) The basal CO_2 production, $\dot{V}_{CO_2}$, under conditions where R = 0.8, is

$$\dot{V}_{CO_2} = 0.051 \cdot B^{0.734} \tag{20}$$

3) Alveolar and arterial O_2 and CO_2 pressures, as well as arterial pH, are approximately the same in mammals of different sizes (see *Handbook of Respiration*, p. 93).

There are no data on alveolar gas and arterial blood on small mammals, and the rest of this discussion assumes that alveolar gas composition is the same in all kinds of mammals, regardless of size.

4) It is also known that CO_2 production $\dot{V}_{CO_2}$, expressed in ml/min, STPD, and alveolar ventilation, in ml/min, BTPS, determine P_{ACO_2} in mm Hg, according to equation 12 on p. 105.

$$P_{ACO_2} = 863 \frac{\dot{V}_{CO_2}}{\dot{V}_A}$$

Assuming P_{ACO_2} to be equal in all species to 40 mm Hg, the relationship between alveolar ventilation and body weight becomes:

$$\dot{V}_A, \text{ml/min, BTPS} = 1.1 \ B^{0.734} \tag{21}$$

5) The relationship between alveolar ventilation, $\dot{V}_A$, tidal volume, V_T, physiological dead space volume, V_D, and respiratory frequency, f, has been shown to be:

$$\dot{V}_A = (V_T - V_D)f$$

and hence

$$(V_T - V_D)f = 1.1 \cdot B^{0.734} \tag{22}$$

in which V_T and V_D are in ml BTPS, f is in breaths per minute, and B in grams.

How do V_T, V_D, and f vary as a function of weight?

a) V_D is a constant fraction of V_T, approximately one third (see Mead, 1960; and *Handbook of Respiration*).

$$V_D = 0.33 \ V_T \tag{23}$$

b) V_T is directly related to body weight (Guyton, 1947) (Fig. 35b).

$$V_T = 0.007 \ B \tag{24}$$

c) Equations 23 and 24 allow the alveolar tidal volume, V_A, to be calculated as a function of body weight.

$$V_A = 0.00469 \ B \tag{25}$$

d) Since $V_A = V_T - V_D$, equation 22 enables one to derive the following expression for frequency of respiration as function of body weight.

$$f = 234 \ B^{-0.266} \tag{26}$$

Therefore, respiratory frequency increases as the weight decreases, and Figure 35 b shows that the mean respiratory frequency of the rat is 80/min, while that of an average man is 12/min.

Equation 26 is derived mathematically from equations 22, 23, and 24, and is essentially that obtained by Guyton (1947) on the basis of direct observations on respiratory frequency in eight species of mammals, from mouse to man.

$$f = 295 \cdot B^{-0.25} \tag{27}$$

e) Equations 24 and 26 allow one to determine the relationship between total ventilation, $\dot{V}_E$, and body weight.

$$\dot{V}_E = 1.64 \; B^{0.734} \tag{28}$$

where $\dot{V}_E$ is in ml/min, BTPS and B is in grams. This equation is shown in Figure 35b.

This theoretical equation is approximately that derived from direct measurements of ventilation in mammals weighing 20 to 70,000 grams (Guyton, 1947).

$$\dot{V}_E = 2.1 \cdot B^{0.74}$$

Both terms of equation 28 can be divided by body weight, in order to obtain minute volume per unit body weight, giving

$$\frac{\dot{V}_E}{B} = 1.64 \cdot B^{-0.266} \tag{29}$$

In this form, equation 28 shows in fact (Fig. 35b) that the ventilation per unit weight is lower the heavier the animal. A mammal weighing 6.5 grams (shrew) breathes in a minute a volume of air approximating its body volume $\left(\frac{\dot{V}_E}{B} = 1 \right)$, while a man weighing 70,000 grams breathes a volume which is only one-tenth his body volume.

6) Equations 23, 24, and 25 satisfy the requirements of equation 21 and therefore our assumption of identical gas composition in animals of all sizes.

There are other mathematical forms of equations 23, 24, and 25 which also satisfy equation 21 and therefore also ensure interspecies constancy of alveolar gas composition. But solutions other than equations 23, 24, and 25 imply biological consequences not realized in nature. Most of these solutions imply that the thoracic volume must be relatively enormous, in reference to body size, in small animals.

7) The data of Crosfill and Widdicombe (1961) indicate that functional residual capacity and tidal volume are linearly related to the weight of the animal and consequently that the mean lung volume (functional residual capacity plus half the tidal volume) is also proportional to body weight. With this knowledge and some simplifying assumptions, it is possible to show because of the form of equations 23, 24, and 25, that the oscillations in alveolar gas composition during the respiratory cycle are the same in all mammals.

In conclusion, the relationship between body weight and resting gas exchange, alveolar ventilation, respiratory frequency, dead space volume, tidal volume (the last three and the shape of the spirogram tracing characterizing

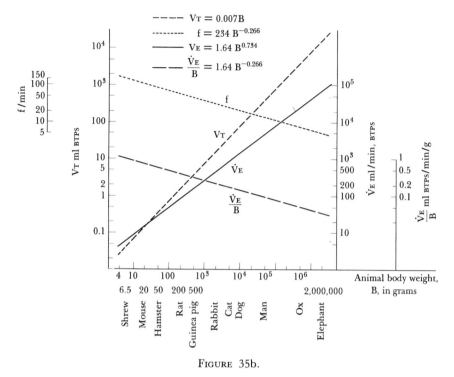

FIGURE 35b.

Tidal volume, V_T, respiratory frequency, f, total ventilation, $\dot{V}_E$, and ventilation per unit weight, $\dfrac{\dot{V}_E}{B}$, in different resting mammals as a function of body weight.

The equations of these straight lines are in part theoretical, but the lines satisfactorily explain recent data, which are as yet inadequate in terms of the range of body weights studied and experimental conditions.

Among the noteworthy features of these equations are the following:

— Tidal volume is directly related to body weight;

— A mouse breathes 20 times as frequently as an elephant;

— Ventilation per unit volume is higher if the animal is smaller. A 6.5 gram shrew breathes a volume equal to its body volume every minute, while a 70 kg (or 155 lb) man breathes only 1/10 of his volume per minute.

the respiratory pattern) are such that the mean alveolar gas composition and the oscillations during the respiratory cycle are the same from the smaller rodents to the largest mammals.

B) What mechanism determines the respiratory pattern, defined by equations 24 and 26?

This problem is a general one and goes beyond respiratory physiology. All biological values, except those having the dimensions of linear velocity (linear velocity of blood, linear velocity of the airflow in the airways, velocity of body movements) are a function of body weight (Lambert and Teissier, 1927). These laws of biometrics may possibly result from the metabolic level and not from the general organization of characteristics of the animals. Thus a small part of an organ, liver for instance, placed in a Warburg apparatus, has a metabolism which is inversely related to the size of the animal from which it was taken (Kayser, Lebreton, Schaeffer, 1925; Krebs, 1950; Kayser, 1951; Martin and Fuhrman, 1955). It has also been shown that the quantity of mitochondria (the seat of cellular oxidations) is higher in small mammals than in large ones (Smith, 1956). Insofar as rhythmicity is concerned, it has been noted that the frequency of spontaneous contraction of the right atrium placed in an artificial medium is inversely related to body weight (Kruta, 1957). It is conceivable that autonomic rhythmicity of the isolated respiratory centers follows the same law, although there is no experimental proof of this.

These considerations show that the problem of the mechanism which determines the respiratory pattern is one aspect of the relationships between metabolic level and animal size (Lambert and Teissier, 1927; Adolph, 1949; Kayser, 1951). The smaller the animals, the higher their metabolism (equations 19 and 20) and the shorter their respiratory and cardiac cycles, as well as their life span. The mechanism determining the respiratory pattern is therefore that of physiological time, which elapses more rapidly in small animals than in large ones. In other words, the number of biological events occurring per unit astronomical time is higher if the animal is smaller. Lambert and Teissier (1927) have based on this a theory of biological similarity, which states that biological phenomena having the dimension of time (for instance duration of the respiratory cycle) are proportional to size (linear dimension) of the animal considered. This theory enables dimension equations to be assigned to all biological values, equations in which time is considered homologous to a linear dimension, and which are therefore simpler than the physicists' dimensional equations. This theory can explain that linear velocities encountered in biology $\left(\text{defined as } \dfrac{\text{length traveled}}{\text{time elapsed}}\right)$ are roughly the same in all animals, since time itself is about proportional to length.

C) Pulmonary proprioceptivity, demonstrated by the Hering-Breuer reflexes, plays an important part in determining the ventilatory pattern, as can be seen from the decrease of respiratory frequency and the increase in tidal volume caused by vagotomy (although this phenomenon has not been demonstrated in man). However, is any physiological benefit derived from the information originating in the pulmonary proprioreceptors? It has been thought that this proprioceptive system leads to a respiratory pattern in which mechanical work is minimal (Otis, Fenn, and Rahn, 1950, see p. 85). However, calculation of the optimal respiratory frequency, that is the frequency at which work is at a minimum, requires a number of assumptions, some of which are somewhat risky. At any rate, the frequency calculated in this fashion is not clearly defined, since doubling or reducing by half this frequency would result in a very small increase in mechanical work. The same criticisms can be applied to the concept according to which the ventilatory pattern is such that the mean force developed by respiratory muscles is minimal (Mead, 1960). In addition, in adult resting men, in a given position, the frequency may vary from 5 to 22 per minute. Thus, important intraspecific variations occur, in addition to the interspecific variations shown by equation 26. The minimal work or minimal mean force theories discussed above do not seem to explain these intraspecific variations, because no relation can be found between the ventilatory pattern and the thoracopulmonary mechanic characteristics in individual subjects.

These concepts of minimal work or of minimal mean force are very interesting because they attach a definite functional significance to pulmonary proprioceptivity. However, at present, it seems preferable to consider the observed ventilatory pattern as an expression of the general properties of the whole ventilatory system. This concept is certainly somewhat too general, but appears to be preferable to the statement of a precise mechanism.

Thus the physiological role of pulmonary proprioceptivity is not clear. It is clear nonetheless that the slow and deep breathing pattern which results from elimination of this proprioceptivity causes important cyclic oscillations of oxygen and carbon dioxide pressures in alveolar gas and therefore of arterial blood. Theoretically, those important oscillations seem to be opposed to the ideal conditions of tissue function, which require a constant interior environment. This may possibly be more than the consequence, representing the teleological purpose of the existence of pulmonary proprioception.

At any rate, any attempt to explain the role played by pulmonary proprioception must take into account the three following points:

a) The role of this proprioceptivity must be integrated in the mechanism which accounts for the biometric law that expresses the relationship between respiratory frequency and body weight (equation 26).

b) The part played by pulmonary proprioceptivity must, in all probability, be extended beyond the ventilatory pattern. It is usually forgotten that the role of the thorax is not only to ensure a cyclic movement of gas. The remarkable anatomical structure of a liquid pump within an air pump (the heart is inside the thorax) clearly indicates that the thoracic respiratory movements have also a hemodynamic role. For instance, the inspiratory movements which are accompanied by a decrease in intrathoracic pressure (and at times an increase in intra-abdominal pressure) play an important part in venous return. This anatomical and physiological interrelation of the respiratory system on one hand, and of the heart and thoracic blood vessels on the other, is essential for understanding the mechanism by which circulatory function and ventilatory function are linked.

c) It has been stated that the respiratory pattern following vagotomy, although considerably modified, nevertheless assures normal alveolar ventilation and mean alveolar gas composition. In the dog, life is possible after pulmonary denervation, but this is life in a laboratory animal house, where the physical efforts required of the animal, and therefore the necessary increases in ventilation, are minimal. What possibilities does the animal, deprived of proprioception, have in terms of respiratory adaptation to muscular exercise? Can he achieve the same ventilatory levels as an intact animal? Does he have the same aptitude as the latter in terms of the muscular exercise of normal life?

8

Regulation of Ventilation

I. GENERAL ASPECTS OF VENTILATORY REGULATION AND OF VENTILATORY STIMULI

Definition of regulation of ventilation

As discussed above (p. 22), the ventilatory system is but one part of a larger complex, the gas exchange system, which can adjust its behavior in response to changes either in energy expenditure, or in the oxygen pressure in the environment (altitude). When one of these two factors varies, activity of the ventilatory system must also vary, or otherwise tissue gas exchange could not be maintained at an adequate level. Study of the regulation of ventilation consists in studying the mechanisms which make ventilatory system activity respond to internal and external conditions.

Normal ventilatory behavior does not express the intrinsic activity of the respiratory centers but that of the ventilatory system, which is composed of the respiratory centers and the ventilatory mechanical apparatus, interconnected by afferent and efferent pathways (Fig. 36). This means that a study of the regulation of ventilation is the study of regulation of the ventilatory system and not that of the respiratory centers. Evaluation of the activity of the respiratory centers by measuring ventilation would imply that the mechanical ventilatory apparatus can be used to measure the activity of the respiratory centers. This reasoning is not acceptable because of lack of knowledge of the calibration of the mechanical ventilatory apparatus, that is the relationship between the thoracic ventilatory response and the activity of the respiratory centers (and therefore intensity of the stimuli which act upon them). All that can be said is that an observed change in ventilation due to a known factor (provided however that this factor has no direct effect on the mechanical ventilatory system) is due to a change in respiratory centers activity, under the influence of this factor. In short, a ventilatory change resulting from a ventilatory stimulus allows one to

148

measure neither the intensity of this stimulus nor the variation in central activity. Nevertheless, the observed ventilatory change measures quantitatively the control exerted by this factor on the ventilatory system, and allows it to be stated to what extent ventilation depends on this factor.

Study of the activity of the respiratory centers would require measurement, not of pulmonary ventilation but of respiratory centers activity — a rather difficult task. As a matter of fact, we lack an index of respiratory centers activity. In the animal, we can study action potentials in the motor neurons of the ventilatory muscles, a method that cannot be applied to man. Measurement of the energy expenditure of the respiratory muscles, or of the mechanical work performed by these muscles allows an approximate evaluation to be made for the activity of the respiratory muscles. This method enables respiratory centers activity to be assessed more accurately than the method which equates ventilation and respiratory centers activity, but it assumes a known and constant relationship between activity of the respiratory centers and forces developed by the ventilatory muscles. In addition, measurement of either energy expenditure or mechanical work is far from easy.

Consequently, we shall study regulation of ventilation as that of the ventilatory system as a whole, that is as one functional unit.

Definition of ventilatory stimuli

A ventilatory stimulus is a regulatory factor, the physiological variations of which act directly or indirectly on the respiratory centers, supplying them with information on the respiratory requirements of the body.

A factor that changes ventilation is not necessarily a stimulus, since some factors can directly affect the mechanical ventilatory apparatus, and thereby change ventilation. We know, for instance, that during asthmatic attacks there is an intense broncho-constriction which leads to hypoventilation. Administration of epinephrine can relax the spasm and increase ventilation. This observation does not indicate that epinephrine is a ventilatory stimulus, if this term is reserved for factors acting on the ventilatory system through the respiratory centers. Factors affecting ventilation by a mechanism similar to that seen in this example are called ventilatory "modifying" factors.

Definition of a respiratory stimulus implies the concept that only physiological variations of a regulatory factor must be considered. It is not because a factor is necessary to the respiratory centers function that it can be considered a respiratory stimulus. For example, a certain composition of the fluid which bathes and maintains the respiratory centers is, of course, necessary to ensure functional integrity and excitability of the respiratory centers. In addition, any important variation of a physical or chemical factor at the level of the respiratory centers can modify their activity, exactly as it can modify the activity of any neuron: this does not make this factor a respiratory stimulus. Only *physiological* variations of a physical or chemical agent to which the respiratory centers are sensitive can be considered as normal factors in the regulation of ventilation, and as adequate stimuli to the respiratory centers.

Furthermore, the concept of ventilatory stimuli implies that a stimulus carries certain information about the conditions of the body, since the purpose of the various respiratory stimuli is to maintain a ventilatory behavior which satisfies the gas exchange system requirements of the body.

In studying regulation, the terms of stimulus threshold and of sensitivity of the ventilatory system to a stimulus are often used, and it is proper to define them:

A stimulus *threshold* is the value above which or below which this stimulus acts on the respiratory centers.

On the other hand, the *sensitivity* of the ventilatory system to a stimulus is the ratio between changes in ventilation and the causal change in level of the stimulus.

Classification of ventilatory stimuli

There are two groups of ventilatory stimuli, of different origin:

a) *Humoral stimuli:* these are modifications in the physical or chemical properties of the *circulating blood*, acting on the respiratory centers:

— directly through the blood. It is said that the ventilatory action of these stimuli is central (or centrogenic) (pathway 3a, Fig. 36).

— or indirectly, through afferent nerves originating in receptors in contact with blood vessels, receptors which are sensitive to certain variations in blood, either physical (baroreceptors) or chemical (chemoreceptors) (pathway 3b, Fig. 36). The action on the ventilation is then mediated by a reflex mechanism, and the action of these stimuli is reflexogenic. Although a neural afferent links the vascular receptor to the respiratory centers, the stimuli which act in this fashion are truly humoral stimuli, that is, factors inherent in circulating blood.

b) *Neural (or neurogenic) stimuli* which originate in the brain or in cutaneous, mucosal, or deep peripheral receptors, stimulated by local conditions. These stimuli are therefore not due to properties of the circulating blood. In the first case, there is an intercentral activation mechanism (path-

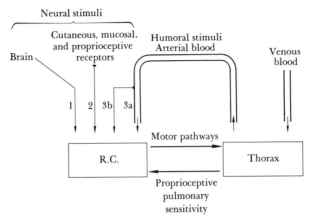

FIGURE 36.   Schematic representation of the ventilatory system and of the different
categories of ventilatory stimuli.

The complex formed by the respiratory centers (R.C.), the motor pathways to
the ventilatory muscles, the thorax, and the thoracic proprioceptive sensitivity pathways, represents a single functional unit — the ventilatory system.

The respiratory centers receive information on the body requirements through
stimuli that can be classified under two headings: neural stimuli and humoral
stimuli.

Neural Stimuli (pathways 1 and 2)	Intercentral (pathway 1)	cortical or subcortical origin
	Reflex (pathway 2)	cutaneous receptors mucosal receptors proprioceptors (somatic mechanoreceptors) muscular chemoreceptors?
Humoral Stimuli (pathway 3)	Chemical	CO_2 (pathways 3a and 3b) H^+ O_2 (pathway 3b) epinephrine-norepinephrine other chemical factors?
	Physical	blood temperature? blood pressure (pathway 3b)

way 1, Fig. 36), while in the second case, the respiratory centers are brought
into play reflexly (pathway 2, Fig. 36).

Demonstration and evaluation of the quantitative role of the stimuli
and of their possible interaction pose difficult methodological and technical
problems. For instance, humoral stimuli are represented by certain proper-

ties of arterial blood. Although it is possible to estimate indirectly certain properties of the arterial blood (for instance, on the basis of alveolar gas composition), the best technique consists in studying arterial blood directly, and this technique is not used as widely as venous puncture.

The methodological difficulties are numerous. One of them, which is not specific to respiratory physiology, is that, in analytical physiology, any factor that changes body equilibrium causes several secondary reactions which may mask the isolated effect of the factor under study. Some examples of these difficulties and of the way in which they can be overcome will be seen later.

II. ANALYTICAL STUDY OF VENTILATORY STIMULI

CO_2 stimulus

Haldane and Priestley (1905) have shown that carbon dioxide plays an important role in the regulation of ventilation. Any cause which tends to increase or decrease alveolar carbon dioxide pressure, Pa_{CO_2}, from its normal resting value, causes a ventilatory reaction which limits the variation of Pa_{CO_2}. This fundamental discovery was made possible by a valid technique for sampling alveolar gas (p. 101). Although certain of the initial conclusions of Haldane and Priestley have been modified, their contribution to our knowledge and to the development of the study of regulation of ventilation remains paramount.

1) HYPOCAPNIA, CAUSE OF HYPOVENTILATION

a) If the subject takes a *single deep voluntary inspiration similar to a sigh* (Fig. 37, B), Pa_{CO_2} drops by several millimeters of mercury. After this voluntary hyperventilation which affects only one respiratory cycle, the subject breathes spontaneously, without exerting any voluntary control. The respiratory cycle which follows the sigh is identical to those preceding it, but after a short time (approximately ten seconds) ventilation decreases. If, on the other hand, during the hyperventilation cycle the subject, instead of inspiring air, inspires a mixture containing CO_2, so that no hypocapnia occurs, no subsequent hypoventilation is noted. These observations can be interpreted as follows: hyperventilation leads to alveolar, and hence arterial, hypocapnia; this hypocapnic blood reaches the systemic circulation, and after a period corresponding to the circulation time, reaches arterial chemoreceptors and the respiratory centers and causes a decrease in their activity, resulting in hypoventilation. This transient hypocapnia is physiological, and is observed following a spontaneous sigh.

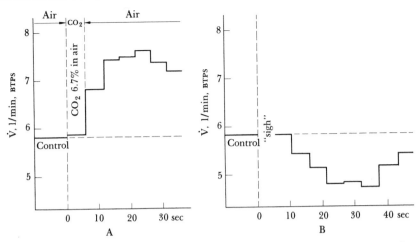

FIGURE 37.   (From DEJOURS and others, *J. Physiol.*, Paris, 1958, **50**, 239–243.)

Ordinate: Ventilation. The horizontal lines indicate the ventilation in each of the successive respiratory cycles.

Abscissa: Time. The length of the horizontal lines corresponds to the duration of the cycles.

Control: Ventilation level before the "CO_2" and voluntary "sigh" tests.

A. During the cycle labeled CO_2, the subject inhales a mixture containing 6.7% CO_2 and $P_{A_{CO_2}}$ increases by a few millimeters of mercury. During the following cycles, the subject inspires air again. Note that the hypercapnia produced during the first cycle leads to a secondary hyperventilation after a certain lapse of time.

B. During the cycle marked voluntary "sigh," the subject inspires deeply, then breathes again spontaneously. The hyperventilation which corresponds to the "sigh" cycle causes a hypocapnia of 10 mm Hg. Note that after a few seconds, hypoventilation occurs. If during the sigh the inspired gas contains some CO_2, so that no hypocapnia occurs, there is no hypoventilation.

b) *Prolonged voluntary hyperventilation* (Figs. 38 and 41) causes considerable elimination of carbon dioxide and alveolar and arterial hypocapnia and alkalosis. After the end of this voluntary hyperpnea, there is a prolonged hypopnea (and, on rare occasions, total apnea) during which $P_{A_{CO_2}}$ returns gradually to its normal value, that is, the value found during the spontaneous ventilation which preceded the hyperventilation maneuver. During the hypoventilation period which follows hyperventilation, the body eliminates less carbon dioxide than it produces and therefore replenishes its CO_2 stores (p. 27). This experiment shows that hypocapnia resulting from hyperventilation causes a decrease in ventilation. This hypoventilation allows the CO_2 stores to be replenished and $P_{A_{CO_2}}$ to regain its normal value. As long as $P_{A_{CO_2}}$ is below the normal $P_{A_{CO_2}}$, hypoventilation will persist.

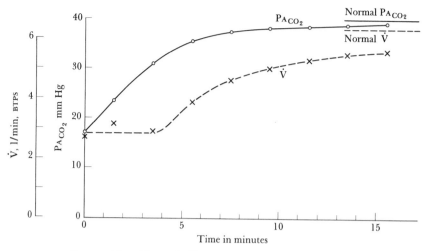

FIGURE 38.   (From *J. Physiol.*, Paris, 1954, **46,** 329–334.)

Recovery of partial pressure of CO_2 in the alveoli, $P_{A_{CO_2}}$ and of ventilation $\dot{V}$ after 10 minutes of hyperventilation at 25 l/min.

Note that during the first few seconds of recovery, $P_{A_{CO_2}}$ and $\dot{V}$ are 17.5 mm Hg and 2.7 l/min respectively. $P_{A_{CO_2}}$ returns to its normal resting value progressively and at a rate which decreases gradually. Note also that $\dot{V}$ starts to increase only after $P_{A_{CO_2}}$ has reached approximately 30 mm Hg. This may be related to a $P_{A_{CO_2}}$ threshold of the respiratory centers. As long as $P_{A_{CO_2}}$ has not recovered its normal resting value, hypoventilation will persist.

2) HYPERCAPNIA, CAUSE OF HYPERVENTILATION

a) If a subject inspires a *mixture of oxygen, nitrogen, and a few volumes percent of CO_2* (Fig. 37, A), $P_{A_{CO_2}}$ increases by a few millimeters of mercury. After this single inspiration of gas containing CO_2, the subject inspires room air again. After a short interval, ventilation increases. When the CO_2 content of inspired gas is lower, hypercapnia is less pronounced and the following hyperventilation less elevated. These observations can be interpreted as follows: during inspiration of the CO_2-enriched gas, alveolar and arterial hypercapnia occur. A few seconds later, this hypercapnic blood reaches the arterial chemoreceptors and the respiratory centers and causes hyperventilation.

b) If a subject inspires, for several minutes, a gas mixture rich in CO_2 (Figs. 39, 40, and 41), ventilation increases progressively and reaches a new level, which is nearly stable. Hyperventilation lasts as long as inspiration of the hypercapnic mixture is maintained, and decreases progressively during the first few minutes following replacement of the gas mixture by air.

The hyperventilation is more marked if the inspired mixture contains more CO_2 (Fig. 39). Hyperventilation is distinct, that is, easily measureable, when F_{ICO_2} is of the order of 2%, and can reach 90 l/min, BTPS when F_{ICO_2}

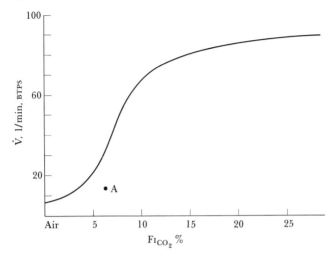

FIGURE 39.   (From LAMBERTSEN, in *Pharmacology in Modern Medicine*, 1957, pp. 815–835, McGraw-Hill.)

Total ventilation, $\dot{V}$, as a function of the CO_2 fraction in the inspired gas, F_{ICO_2}. Ventilation is measured after breathing a CO_2-enriched gas mixture for a few minutes. When this mixture contains more than 5% CO_2, ventilation is unpleasant and usually psychological disturbances occur. At very high F_{ICO_2}, there may be loss of consciousness. Generally, the respiratory centers of anesthetized subjects are rather insensitive to inhalation of hypercapnic mixtures, which is manifested by a relatively moderate hyperventilation and a relatively more pronounced hypercapnia (point A).

is above 10%. When F_{ICO_2} is high, hyperventilation is distressing and is accompanied by disturbances in consciousness. In prolonged experiments the subject may lose consciousness (more rapidly if F_{ICO_2} is very high). This intoxication by CO_2 is sometimes known in psychiatry under the name of "CO_2 narcosis." Thus, hypercapnic gas mixtures stimulate ventilation and it has been suggested such mixtures be used in certain cases of respiratory depression, in particular during general anesthesia. However, in anesthetized subjects, inhalation of a hypercapnic mixture is not without danger because, in such subjects, carbon dioxide frequently depresses the respiratory centers even if the mixture contains only a few volumes percent of carbon dioxide. This shows that great care must be taken when administering hypercapnic mixtures to anesthetized subjects in order to overcome depression of ventilation.

The increase in ventilation resulting from inhalation of hypercapnic mixtures consists essentially of an increase in tidal volume, with little change in frequency, at least as long as hyperventilation does not reach 20 to 30 liters per minute. As discussed above (p. 105), this type of hyperventilation is particularly well adapted to increase alveolar ventilation.

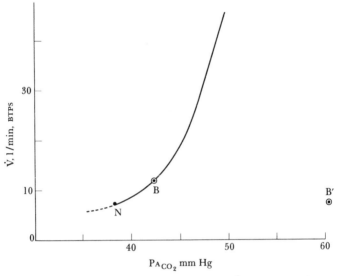

FIGURE 40. Relationship between total ventilation, $\dot{V}_E$, and alveolar carbon dioxide pressure, PA_{CO_2}, observed in subjects breathing for a few minutes mixtures containing various fractions of CO_2.

This relationship varies from one subject to the next, and is generally alinear for minor degrees of hypocapnia. If there was no hyperventilation, inhalation of a mixture containing 3% CO_2 would lead to considerable hypercapnia (point B'). Because of hyperventilation, hypercapnia remains moderate (point B).

Point N corresponds to air breathing. The broken line, to the left at the bottom, shows the $\dot{V}-PA_{CO_2}$ relationship during hypocapnia following voluntary hyperventilation (see Fig. 38).

Inhalation of mixtures containing carbon dioxide causes alveolar and arterial hypercapnia, which stimulates ventilation. Figure 40 shows the relationship between hyperventilation and alveolar hypercapnia. This relationship varies considerably between subjects, and is generally curvilinear at low hypercapnic levels. If CO_2 inhalation did not produce hyperventilation, considerable alveolar and arterial hypercapnia and respiratory acidosis would occur and rapidly lead to disturbances of consciousness. For example, inhalation of a mixture containing 3% CO_2 would yield, in the absence of hyperventilation, a value of $P_{A_{CO_2}}$ of approximately 60 mm Hg (Fig. 40, point B'). Because of hyperventilation, hypercapnia remains moderate (43 mm Hg, point B) and can be tolerated for a very long time. The increase in $P_{A_{CO_2}}$ under the influence of an inspiratory mixture enriched with CO_2 can be considered the cause of hyperventilation. For instance, at point B, a hypercapnia of about 4 mm Hg increases ventilation by about 5 l/min.

It is difficult to demonstrate clearly the occurrence of hyperventilation if the inspired mixture contains less than 2% CO_2. However, there is no doubt that inspiration of a mixture containing only 1% CO_2 (approximately 7 mm Hg) causes alveolar hyperventilation (and therefore overall hyperventilation, since there is no change in respiratory frequency), because no change in $P_{A_{CO_2}}$ can be observed. If ventilation had not changed, an increase in $P_{A_{CO_2}}$ of about 7 mm Hg would have been observed in this case.

3) ROLE OF THE CO_2 STIMULUS

These facts show that variations in $P_{A_{CO_2}}$ affect ventilatory behavior considerably. Experiments in which physiological variations in $P_{A_{CO_2}}$ are studied show the role $P_{A_{CO_2}}$ plays normally in ventilatory control (pp. 177 and 181). The short periods of hypercapnia and hypocapnia, which they show, correspond to the physiological variations, that is the variations occurring during temporary ventilatory arrest, speech and swallowing on one hand and following a sigh on the other.

The experiments involving *prolonged and considerable* hypocapnia and hypercapnia, due to voluntary hyperventilation or inspiration of a hypercapnic gas mixture, complement the previous experiments, but do not show that physiological variations in $P_{A_{CO_2}}$ play a role in ventilatory control, because these prolonged variations in $P_{A_{CO_2}}$ are much larger than the physiological variations encountered normally. Ventilatory CO_2 sensitivity can be defined as the ratio of variation of ventilation to variation in $P_{A_{CO_2}}$. In normocapnia, this sensitivity corresponds to the slope of the curve on Figure 40, at N. This is not easy to measure, because the relationship between $\dot{V}$ and $P_{A_{CO_2}}$ is not always linear, and if $\dot{V}$ and the concomitant hypercapnia are measured during inspiration of a hypercapnic mixture (as for instance, point B), the slope of NB differs obviously from the tangent at N, which describes the normal sensitivity.

It is also difficult to determine quantitatively the role played by the CO_2 stimulus in normal control of ventilation, that is to assess what part of this ventilation depends on this stimulus. For this purpose, one should determine the relationship of $\dot{V}$ to $P_{A_{CO_2}}$ in the hypocapnic region (broken line of

Fig. 40). Unfortunately this curve can be determined only after a prolonged hyperventilation, which is not in the least physiological.

In addition, H^+ ion will also be shown to be a ventilatory stimulus (p. 160). Any hypercapnia produced by inhaling a mixture containing CO_2 and any hypocapnia due to hyperventilation produce respiratory acidosis and respiratory alkalosis respectively. This is in itself a factor affecting the respiratory centers, and the effects shown in the previous experiments are due to more than a variation in CO_2. This question will be studied subsequently.

4) MODE OF ACTION OF CO_2 STIMULUS

a) *Humoral stimuli* can act on the respiratory center by two mechanisms:

— a direct central or centrogenic mechanism, by which the humoral stimulus acts directly on the respiratory centers;

— an indirect, reflex, or reflexogenic mechanism, by which the humoral stimulus does not act directly on the centers but on arterial receptors. Stimulation of the latter, which is connected to the respiratory centers by afferent pathways, causes a ventilatory reflex. A receptor which is sensitive to chemical variations of blood is called a chemoreceptor.

The works of Heymans, Bouckaert and Regniers (1933), Bjurstedt (1946), Schmidt (1956), and Heymans and Neil (1958) give historical, anatomical, histological, and physiological data on arterial chemoreceptors. In the dog and the cat, the following have been described:

1) the two carotid chemoreceptors, or carotid bodies, located at the angle formed by the bifurcation of the primary carotid arteries. The fibers coming from those receptors are in the glossopharyngeal nerves;

2) some aortic chemoreceptors or aortic bodies, located at the level of the aortic arch. The fibers travel in the vagi.

The chemoreceptors are very well perfused. The blood flow per unit weight is probably the highest in the body, 2000 ml/min/100 gm weight. Under normal conditions, the arterial-venous O_2 and CO_2 difference is minimal and the mean P_{O_2} in these organs can be assumed to be very near arterial P_{O_2} (Daly, Lambertsen, Schweitzer, 1954, in the dog).

Stimulation of the chemoreceptors causes an increase in ventilation. Lobeline and cyanides stimulate the chemoreceptors selectively. Oxygen, carbon dioxide, and H^+ ion can stimulate the chemoreceptors. The higher P_{CO_2} and H^+ are, the more the chemoreceptors will be stimulated. On the other hand, the chemoreceptors' stimulation increases when P_{O_2} drops.

b) *Demonstration of action of CO_2 stimulus on arterial chemoreceptors.*

1) It is possible to study the frequency of potentials along the afferent chemoreceptor fibers, when the chemoreceptors are perfused with blood or

solutions in which P_{CO_2} can be changed. These potentials appear when P_{CO_2} of the perfusing blood is 30 mm Hg, and their frequency increases with an increase in P_{CO_2} (Fig. 43) (Euler, Liljestrand and Zotterman, 1939; Bartels and Witzleb, 1956; Eyzaguirre and Lewin, 1961).

2) In a special preparation where the carotid sinus or the aortic arch are perfused with a liquid having a relatively high P_{CO_2}, while the blood perfusing the brain has a normal composition, hyperventilation is observed. Experiments on this type led Heymans to the discovery of chemoreceptors in the dog.

3) If the chemoreceptor fibers of a hyperoxic normocapnic animal are blocked by cold (Gesell, 1940; Hesser, 1949), a decrease in ventilation is observed.

c) *Demonstration of direct action of CO_2 stimulus on the respiratory centers.*

Acute or chronic extirpation of the chemoreceptors does not prevent hyperventilation if the animal inspires a hypercapnic mixture (Gemmill, 1933). However, as yet experimental conditions have not allowed a quantitative comparative study to be made of the ventilatory effects in the intact animal and in the animal with denervated chemoreceptors, in particular, the establishment of the relationship between $\dot{V}$ and PA_{CO_2} in both. At any rate, it is certain that the CO_2 stimulus can act directly on the respiratory centers. It has also been shown that injection of hypercapnic solutions in the medullary centers causes hyperventilation.

It is customary to study variations of ventilation due to CO_2 stimulus as a function of arterial P_{CO_2}. In fact the activity of the respiratory centers does not seem to depend directly on arterial P_{CO_2}, but rather on P_{CO_2} within the respiratory centers (Douglas and Haldane, 1909; Hesser, 1949). Tissular P_{CO_2} is very near the venous P_{CO_2} of these centers and Lambertsen (1953) has found a very close correlation between ventilation and cerebral venous blood P_{CO_2}.

d) *In summary*, it is proven that the CO_2 stimulus can act on the respiratory centers, directly and indirectly through the carotid and aortic chemoreceptors. In other words, its action can be both centrogenic and reflexogenic. The problem is then to define the respective importance of these two mechanisms, and the conditions in which they play a part.

According to Comroe and Schmidt (1956), in normocapnia, the reflexogenic response to the CO_2 stimulus plays only a small role, the mechanism of this stimulus being essentially centrogenic. However, in case of severe hypercapnia (associated with acidosis and hypoxia) the respiratory centers respond poorly to direct action of the CO_2 stimulus, and the ventilatory effect of this stimulus is mainly reflexogenic.

On the other hand, several authors (see Heymans and Neil, 1958) believe that under normal conditions, the CO_2 stimulus acts through both central and reflex mechanisms. With the knowledge now available, it is difficult to delineate precisely the respective roles of the two mechanisms.

H^+ stimulus

1) DEMONSTRATION OF EFFECTS OF VARIATIONS IN BLOOD pH ON RESPIRATION

a) Rapid intravenous injection of an acid solution causes hyperventilation (Walter, 1877).

b) Rapid intravenous injection of an alkaline solution, such as a very dilute NaOH solution causes hypoventilation or apnea (Hougardy, 1904).

However, these two observations do not show that variations in pH as such act on ventilation, since addition of an acid breaks down part of the blood bicarbonate and increases free carbon dioxide and P_{CO_2}, while the opposite occurs when an alkali is added to blood. Consequently, the changes in ventilation observed in those rapid injection experiments may be explained by a change in P_{CO_2}.

c) Hyperventilation is observed in prolonged metabolic acidosis (Fig. 41 and curve A of Fig. 42), such as diabetic acidosis, or experimental acidosis due to daily ingestion of ammonium chloride. Since metabolic CO_2 production is unchanged, hyperventilation causes hypocapnia. This metabolic acidosis is characterized by a decrease in HCO_3^- ion and in P_{CO_2}, the drop in HCO_3^- being more marked than that of P_{CO_2}. It is probable that hyperventilation due to the decrease in pH results in a drop in $P_{A_{CO_2}}$ which partly compensates the acidosis. Without hyperventilation, and therefore without hypocapnia, acidosis would be much more pronounced. The Henderson-Hasselbalch equation (p. 49) allows these relationships to be visualized.

d) Ingestion of large doses of bicarbonate causes a metabolic alkalosis, characterized by an increase in pH and in concentration of bicarbonate ions, and by an increase in P_{CO_2} (Fig. 41), which is not however sufficient to re-establish the HCO_3^- to P_{CO_2} ratio and the pH which correspond to a normal acid-base balance (Davies, 1920).

In summary, metabolic acidosis causes hyperventilation in spite of the existence of hypocapnia which normally decreases ventilation. On the other hand, metabolic alkalosis leads to a decrease in ventilation, although hypercapnia, which usually increases ventilation, is present. This leads to the conclusion that an increase in H^+ ion concentration (variation of pH toward the lower values) stimulates ventilatory activity while, on the other hand, a decrease in H^+ (increase in pH) decreases ventilatory activity.

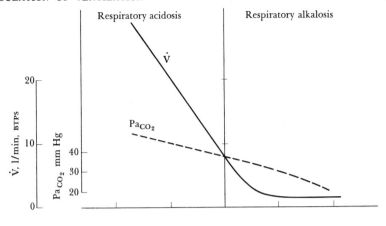

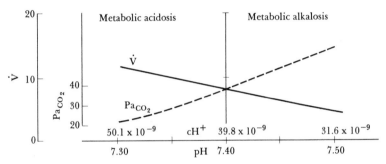

FIGURE 41.   Schematic representation of the various disturbances
in acid-base balance.

Abscissae: pH values and corresponding $[H^+]$ values (pH $= -\log[H^+]$).
Ordinates: Continuous line: total ventilation, $\dot{V}$.

Broken lines: Partial pressure of CO_2 in arterial blood. Normal values are
assumed to be: $\dot{V} = 8$ l/min, pH $= 7.40$ and $Pa_{CO_2} = 38$ mm Hg.

Respiratory acidosis results from inhalation of CO_2-enriched mixtures: hypercapnia
and marked hyperventilation results. There are two respiratory stimuli: acidosis
and hypercapnia.

Metabolic acidosis, such as that produced by fasting or diabetic acidosis. There is
hypocapnia and moderate hyperventilation. Acidosis causes hyperventilation, which
is moderated by the resulting hypocapnia.

Respiratory alkalosis, such as that which follows voluntary hyperventilation: there
is hypocapnia and marked hypoventilation. Hypoventilation is considerable because
both CO_2 and H^+ stimuli are decreased or absent.

Metabolic alkalosis, such as the one that follows ingestion of bicarbonate. There is
hypercapnia and moderate hypoventilation. Alkalosis causes hypoventilation, which
is moderated by the hypercapnia it causes.

This diagram shows that both $[H^+]$ and P_{CO_2} can regulate ventilation.

2) IMPORTANCE OF RESPIRATORY REACTIONS TO VARIATIONS IN pH OR IN CO_2

In the different experimental and pathological conditions listed above, simultaneous variations in P_{CO_2} and in pH take place. These simultaneous variations are due to two causes:

— biochemical: relationship between pH, P_{CO_2}, and HCO_3^- is expressed by the Henderson-Hasselbalch equation (p. 49);

— physiological: this is the ventilatory reaction itself. For example, the hyperventilation of metabolic acidosis causes alveolar and arterial hypocapnia.

In the case of respiratory acidosis (inhalation of CO_2), hypercapnia and a drop in pH occur simultaneously. On the contrary, in metabolic acidosis a drop in pH and hypocapnia are encountered. In both types of acidosis, hyperventilation is present.

These observations led to the belief once that carbon dioxide as such was not a stimulus and that its effect on ventilation was tied to the drop in pH which it caused. Hyperventilation was attributed in both cases to acidosis, regardless of its cause (Winterstein, 1911). However, the same variation of pH in the acid direction causes a much higher degree of hyperventilation when it is accompanied by hypercapnia (respiratory acidosis, curve B on Fig. 42) than when it is accompanied by hypocapnia (metabolic acidosis, curve A on Fig. 42). This observation shows that the hyperventilation that occurs in acidosis cannot be attributed solely to the blood changes in the acid direction and that the importance of the ventilatory change depends also on arterial P_{CO_2}. One must therefore conclude that both H^+ and CO_2 are stimuli. Because of the biochemical relationships and the physiological effect of these factors:

— in the case where a CO_2-enriched mixture is inspired, hypercapnia and acidosis occurring simultaneously cause an important hyperventilation. The ventilatory reaction is the resultant of these two stimuli (Fig. 42, B);

— in the case of metabolic acidosis, the excitatory action on ventilation is moderated in part by hypocapnia, and the resultant of these two antagonistic actions is a rather weak hyperventilation (Fig. 42, A).

One can therefore attempt to estimate how much ventilation depends on the CO_2 stimulus and how much it depends on the H^+ stimulus, that is, to estimate the partial stimulus values of carbon dioxide and of H^+ ion. In theory, this information can be obtained by studying the ventilatory responses which occur during metabolic or respiratory acidosis (see Gray, 1950), but these efforts have yielded only figures which are open to criticism because of the paucity of data dealing simultaneously with ventilation, arterial P_{CO_2}, and pH. In addition, some of these data pertain to acute changes (for instance, figures obtained a few minutes after starting to breathe

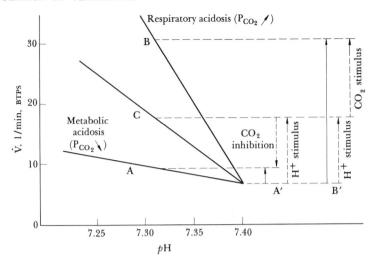

FIGURE 42. Ventilatory reactions as a function of changes
in arterial blood pH (schematic).

Curve A: Ventilatory reactions in metabolic acidosis (diabetic acidosis, ingestion
of NH$_4$Cl, etc.). In this case, there are acidosis and *hypocapnia* (see Fig. 41).

Curve B: Ventilatory reactions in respiratory acidosis (inhalation of a gas containing CO$_2$). In this case, there are acidosis and *hypercapnia* (see Fig. 41).

For the same degree of acidosis, the ventilatory effects are much more marked
in respiratory acidosis than in metabolic acidosis.

Curve C: Ventilatory reactions in experimental acidosis, where hypocapnia is
avoided, that is where normal P$_{CO_2}$ is maintained by inhalation of a mixture containing the proper amount of CO$_2$ (alveolar iso-P$_{CO_2}$ technique). If the subject
breathed air, that is if hypocapnia was not avoided, this experimental acidosis would
lead to curve A.

The schema labeled A' and B' show the respective role of CO$_2$ stimulus and H$^+$
stimulus in the hyperventilation of both types of acidosis at a pH of 7.31.

In A' (metabolic acidosis), the H$^+$ stimulus is opposed by a decrease in the CO$_2$
stimulus (shown as an arrow pointing downward, called CO$_2$ inhibition). The
ventilatory effect is the algebraic sum of these two factors, and is represented by the
continuous arrow.

In B' (respiratory acidosis), the total ventilatory effect is the result of the simultaneous action of an H$^+$ stimulus and a CO$_2$ stimulus.

a hypercapnic mixture) and others to conditions where the changes have
been maintained for quite some time, as in metabolic acidosis.

The respective roles of P$_{CO_2}$ and pH have been assessed recently by another method. This consists in a continuous intravenous infusion of an acid
solution (which produces hyperventilation and hypocapnia), while hypo-

capnia is circumvented by replacing inspired air with a mixture containing CO_2. This experiment, performed on the anesthetized dog by Domizi (1959), allows one to estimate the change in ventilation due only to changes in H^+ (curve C of Fig. 42). A similar method has been used in man by Loeschcke (1960), Katsaros (1960), and Lambertsen (1961), yielding data which confirm that both CO_2 and H^+ ion are important ventilatory stimuli.

3) MODE OF ACTION OF THE H^+ STIMULUS

Carotid and aortic chemoreceptors are stimulated by a decrease in pH, but the experimental conditions under which this effect has been demonstrated do not enable one to determine the sensitivity of the chemoreceptors to the H^+ ion, nor to state that H^+ normally affects ventilation only through reflexogenic mechanisms. It is possible to state that in a completely denervated animal injection of acid increases ventilation markedly (Banus, 1944). At present, however, the mechanism by which H^+ variations modify ventilation remains obscure.

The theory that H^+ is the sole stimulus to which the respiratory centers are sensitive has attracted considerable attention, but it is now well established that blood pH is not the only stimulus capable of affecting the respiratory centers. Winterstein (1921) and Gesell (1923) have hypothesized that respiratory center activity is determined by the pH within the respiratory centers. A recent concept proposes that the variations in pH which affect the respiratory centers are in fact those taking place in the cerebrospinal fluid (Winterstein, 1955; Loeschcke, 1958; Leusen, 1961).

CONCLUSIONS

Both carbon dioxide and H^+ ion are ventilatory stimuli. The two are related biochemically through the Henderson-Hasselbalch equation and physiologically in the sense that the physiological reactions caused by the variations in one affects the value of the other. When variations in P_{CO_2} take place (CO_2 inhalation, voluntary hyperventilation) there are necessarily variations in pH, and part of the ventilatory response comes from variations in H^+ ion. In metabolic acidosis or alkalosis, ventilatory changes alter the partial pressure of CO_2 in the arterial blood, which now acts in the opposite direction and moderates the ventilatory reaction as well as the variations in acid-base balance. It is possible to determine what part of the ventilatory reaction, occurring in respiratory acidosis or alkalosis or in metabolic acidosis, is due to the CO_2 ventilatory stimulus and what part is due to H^+ stimulus.

O_2 stimulus

The O_2 stimulus is a factor in the regulation of ventilation and is represented by a certain partial pressure of O_2 in the arterial blood, Pa_{O_2}, which stimulates the aortic and carotid chemoreceptors and, through their action, increases the activity of the respiratory centers. When Pa_{O_2} decreases, the stimulation of the chemoreceptors increases. Ventilatory control of the O_2 stimulus is therefore reflexogenic (pathway 3b in Fig. 36).

1) DEMONSTRATION OF THE EXISTENCE OF THE O_2 STIMULUS

a) When the circulation of aortic or carotid chemoreceptors is isolated, perfusion of the aortic arch or of the carotid sinus with blood having a low P_{O_2} causes hyperventilation. This ventilatory effect does not occur after aortic or carotid sinus denervation (see Heymans, 1933; Heymans and Neil, 1958).

b) Prolonged hypoxia in an animal in which the chemoreceptors have

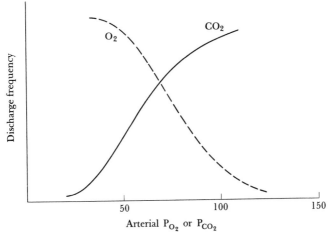

FIGURE 43. Discharge frequency of chemoreceptor fibers originating in the carotid sinus, as a function of either partial pressure of CO_2 (at high O_2 pressure) or partial pressure of O_2 (at low CO_2 pressure) in the blood perfusing the chemoreceptors in cat (schematic).

Normally both the O_2 and CO_2 partial pressures (for instance, $Pa_{O_2} = 95$ and $Pa_{CO_2} = 38$ mm Hg) stimulate the receptors. In addition these stimuli interact, that is the response to stimuli applied simultaneously is higher than the sum of the individual responses to oxygen and carbon dioxide (see von Euler, Liljestrand, and Zotterman, 1939; Witzleb and others, 1955; Bartels and Witzleb, 1956; Hornbein, Griffo and Roos, 1961; Eyzaguirre and Lewin, 1961; Dejours, 1962).

been destroyed or denervated does not produce hyperventilation. On the contrary, in this case a decrease in ventilation is observed, and this leads one to believe that the direct effect of hypoxia on the respiratory centers is inhibitory (Watt, Dumke, and Comroe, 1943).

c) If the chemoreceptor fibers of a hypoxic animal are blocked by cold, the hypoxic hyperventilation stops immediately and reappears when the nerves are allowed to rewarm (see Bjurstedt, 1946).

d) At P_{O_2} values above 120, no action potentials can be recorded in the chemoreceptor fibers of the cat. At lower P_{O_2} values, it is possible to record potentials, the frequency of which increases when P_{O_2} decreases (Fig. 43) (Euler, 1939; Witzleb, 1955; Heymans and Neil, 1958). Data obtained in man by the O_2 tests (see p. 168) are in accord with the electrophysiological observations in the cat.

2) THE OXYGEN STIMULUS IS RELATED TO PARTIAL PRESSURE OF OXYGEN IN BLOOD AND NOT TO OXYGEN CONTENT

a) The hyperventilation which occurs at altitude is due to hypoxia (see p. 198). However, although the partial pressure of oxygen and arterial oxygen saturation are lower than at sea level, the blood oxygen content is higher at altitude than at sea level because of the increase in hemoglobin concentration (p. 195). Therefore, this altitude hyperventilation can be due only to the decrease not in O_2 content, but in O_2 pressure of the arterial blood (Fitzgerald, 1913).

b) According to Asmussen and Chiodi (1941), hypoxia due to carbon monoxide intoxication (anemic hypoxia, type VI, p. 208), even when very marked, does not cause hyperventilation, while the marked hypoxia caused by a decrease of oxygen in pressure inspired air and in alveolar gas (type I, p. 201) causes hyperventilation.

c) In an isolated carotid sinus preparation, perfusion with blood in which the oxygen content, C_{O_2}, has been lowered, causes hyperventilation only if this decrease in C_{O_2} is accompanied by a decrease in P_{O_2}. If the decrease in C_{O_2} is due to the presence of a large amount of HbCO, without decrease in P_{O_2}, the ventilation does not increase (Comroe and Schmidt, 1938).

d) Duke, Green, and Neil (1952) have confirmed, on the basis of action potentials recorded from chemoreceptor fibers, that only the decrease in P_{O_2} and not that in C_{O_2}, stimulates chemoreceptors.

3) DEMONSTRATION OF O_2 STIMULUS IN MAN

One may be led to believe that if an O_2 stimulus is normally present, suppression of this stimulus by oxygen breathing should cause a decrease in ventilation. In fact, interpretation of the changes in ventilation which occur during *prolonged* oxygen breathing is rather difficult, because this maneuver does indeed abolish all O_2 stimuli, but also causes considerable changes in other factors (such as P_{CO_2} of arterial blood and of respiratory centers, general and cerebral circulation, possibly rate of anaerobic metabolism, etc.) which act, or may act, on the respiratory centers. Under these conditions changes in ventilation due to prolonged inhalation of oxygen (or inhalation of a

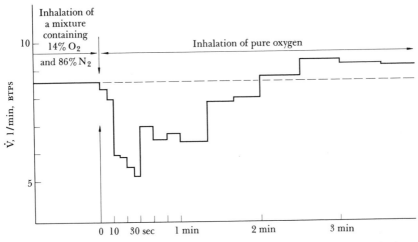

FIGURE 44.   Effects of oxygen inhalation on ventilation. (From DEJOURS and others, *C. R. Acad. Sci.*, 1957, **245**, 1946–1948.)

The subject has been breathing a hypoxic mixture containing 14% oxygen for a few minutes. Starting at time 0, the subject inhales pure oxygen. Ventilation is measured for each cycle during the first 30 seconds and then for groups of several cycles.

A few seconds after oxygen breathing starts, ventilation decreases markedly. This decrease is due to abolition of the O_2 stimuli, which was present when a hypoxic mixture was inhaled, by the oxygen inhalation. The O_2 stimulus acts indirectly on ventilation, by a reflex mechanism originating in the aortic and carotid chemoreceptors. The O_2 effects of ventilation are said to be chemoreflexogenic.

When inhalation of pure oxygen is maintained, ventilation increases and even exceeds the ventilation when breathing the hypoxic gas mixture. The mechanism controlling ventilation during prolonged oxygen breathing is complex. In this case, not only the O_2 stimuli, but other factors in regulation of ventilation, are modified. In particular, the respiratory centers become hypercapnic (Lambertsen, 1953). The secondary modifications due to hyperoxygenation mask the ventilatory effects due to abolition of the O_2 stimulus. These effects are visible only during the initial phase of O_2 inhalation, before the secondary effects have had time to appear.

hypoxic gas mixture) must be attributed to several factors, some of which are related to oxygenation changes in the body, and cannot be interpreted simply in terms of O_2 stimuli.

It is possible to avoid these difficulties in the interpretation of the data. When inhalation of pure oxygen is suddenly started, an immediate increase in alveolar gas P_{O_2} and in arterial blood, Pa_{O_2}, occurs. After a few seconds delay, this hyperoxygenated arterial blood reaches the chemoreceptors, and the increase in Pa_{O_2} decreases or abolishes chemoreceptors' stimulation (if present) and causes a decrease in ventilation. This method avoids the secondary effects of prolonged inhalation of pure oxygen, which appear rather rapidly and render interpretation difficult. Figure 44 gives an example of the use of this method.

The decrease in ventilation observed a few seconds after oxygen inhalation can be more or less marked. It is of the order of 10% in a normoxic subject, in whom Pa_{O_2} is approximately 95 mm Hg, and can reach 50% when an important hypoxia exists (Pa_{O_2} of about 50 mm Hg). On the other hand, if the subject is made hyperoxic by inspiration of an O_2-enriched mixture, which brings Pa_{O_2} to a value higher than 150 mm Hg, the O_2 test does not affect ventilation (Dejours and others, 1958 b).

In man as in cat, the value of Pa_{O_2} which represents the threshold for the O_2 stimulus is between 100 and 150 mm Hg. Any lower value stimulates the chemoreceptors, and through them, the respiratory centers. The stimulation is stronger when Pa_{O_2} is lower. Although the extent by which ventilation is decreased during the O_2 test does not show exactly what part of the ventilation is due to O_2 stimulus, it is reasonable to assume that the ventilatory decrease is related to the intensity of the pre-existing stimulus.

This O_2 test technique is the only one that can be easily applied to man. The data it supplies are in perfect agreement with those obtained by animal experimentation. This extension of the physiological analysis demonstrates the reflexogenic mechanism of action of the O_2 stimulus.

CONCLUSIONS

When the partial pressure of oxygen in arterial blood is below approximately 120 mm Hg, the chemoreceptors are stimulated. This stimulation is more pronounced when P_{O_2} decreases. The O_2 stimulus is related to partial pressure and not to O_2 content of arterial blood. The mechanisms of action of the O_2 stimulus are entirely reflex. Hypoxia of the respiratory centers, deprived of stimuli originating in the chemoreceptors, decreases the centers' activity.

Epinephrine and norepinephrine stimulus (Stimulus E–NE)

1) In man, injection of epinephrine or norepinephrine causes hyperventilation (point A in Fig. 45a) (see Barcroft, 1957).

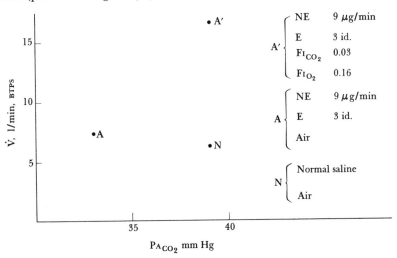

FIGURE 45a.   Effects of epinephrine and norepinephrine on ventilation in man.

On the ordinate: Ventilation, $\dot{V}$.

On the abscissa: Partial pressure of CO_2 in alveolar gas, Pa_{CO_2}.

Point N: The subject breathes air.

Point A: The subject breathes air and receives for several hours an infusion of 3 μg/min epinephrine and 9 μg/min norepinephrine. This perfusion causes a slight hyperventilation, accompanied by alveolar hypocapnia and hyperoxia.

Point A': The subject receives the same infusion, but instead of breathing air, he inspires a low O_2 mixture (16% O_2) containing a few volumes percent of CO_2, so that Pa_{CO_2} and Pa_{O_2} are maintained very near the normal levels. The ventilatory effect (which is no longer partly balanced by alveolar and arterial P_{O_2} and P_{CO_2} changes) is much more marked than in A.

(From Y. LABROUSSE and J. RAYNAUD, *J. Physiol.*, Paris, 1959, **51**, 469.)

If the subject breathes air, this hyperventilation leads in turn to alveolar hyperoxia and hypocapnia and to respiratory alkalosis. The hyperventilation that is observed is very limited because it is reduced by the concomitant decrease in O_2, CO_2, and H^+ stimuli. However, if during infusion of epinephrine or norepinephrine, hyperoxia and hypocapnia are prevented by having the subject inhale a gas mixture which is low in O_2 and rich in CO_2, the observed ventilatory effect is much more pronounced (point A' of

Fig. 45a). This effect indicates approximately the extent to which an increase in catecholamines controls ventilation.

2) The mechanism of action of the stimulus E–NE is not absolutely clear. Epinephrine has been thought to stimulate directly the reticular formation and the respiratory centers. However, intracarotid or intravertebral injection of epinephrine or norepinephrine in man does not produce hyperventilation. It is possible that a substance derived from epinephrine is the real stimulus, and as a matter of fact, the ventilatory action of epinephrine and norepinephrine continues for several minutes after the infusion is discontinued, although epinephrine and norepinephrine as such disappear from blood in less than a minute.

3) In heavy muscular exercise the concentration of epinephrine and norepinephrine in blood is very high. It is probable that under these physiological conditions epinephrine and norepinephrine represent an important ventilatory stimulus.

"Blood pressure" stimulus

The blood pressure in certain arteries can exert some control of ventilatory activity through baroreceptors, which possess nerve fibers ending near the respiratory centers. This mechanism of action of blood pressure on ventilation falls within the framework of reflexogenic control, since it is dependent on a physical property of circulating blood (pathway 3b, p. 151).

Baroreceptors can be found in most vascular areas, but much attention has been concentrated on the circulatory effects resulting from stimulation of barosensitive areas. This and the fact that experimental conditions often render interpretation of the observations difficult, explain that our knowledge about the role of the baroreceptors in the control of ventilation is rather limited.

1) BAROSENSITIVE AREAS OF THE SYSTEMIC ARTERIAL CIRCULATION

Increase in arterial blood pressure causes hypoventilation or apnea, by affecting aortic and carotid sinus baroreceptors (the afferent fibers of which constitute the aortic depressor nerves of Cyon and the carotid depressor nerves of Hering). On the contrary, a decrease in arterial pressure at the level of the arterial baroreceptors produces hyperventilation. At normal pressures the baroreceptors are stimulated and may have an inhibitory action on the ventilation. In general, this information has been gained through experiments involving either cross-circulation between two dogs, isolated sinuses, electrical stimulation, section of aortic and carotid nerves, or electrophysiological experiments involving recording of action potentials along the baroreceptor fibers (see Heymans, Bouckaert, and Regniers, 1933; Schmidt, 1956; Heymans and Neil, 1958).

Prior to the discovery of the barosensitive areas of the general circulation, it had been thought that variations in pressure acted directly on the respiratory centers. This is in fact how the apnea observed a few seconds after injection of a *very high* single dose of epinephrine was explained. Actually this is due to stimulation of arterial baroreceptors, because when the latter are sectioned massive injection of epinephrine no longer causes apnea. It should be noted that this effect of a single massive dose of epinephrine has nothing in common with infusion of epinephrine in physiological doses, which, as has been seen, causes an increase in ventilation.

2) BARORECEPTOR AREAS OF INTRATHORACIC VESSELS OTHER THAN THE AORTA AND ITS BRANCHES

The existence of mechanoreceptors in the walls of the veins and left and right atria has been established by electrophysiological methods which reveal, in the fibers originating from these receptors, action potentials which appear in volleys synchronous with the cardiac cycle. It is generally accepted that the increase in blood pressure stimulates these receptors and causes, by reflex mechanism, an increase in activity of the respiratory centers. In this respect, the ventilatory effects of stimulation of these mechanoreceptors are opposite to those observed during stimulation of aortic and carotid baroreceptors. However, it is proper to emphasize that the action of the mechanoreceptors described in this paragraph is still poorly elucidated (see bibliography in *J. Physiol.* (Paris), 1959, **51**, 226–229).

CONCLUSIONS

Only the action of carotid and aortic baroreceptors on ventilation is well known. The increase in systemic arterial pressure stimulates the baroreceptors and, by a reflex mechanism, decreases the activity of the respiratory center. A decrease in arterial pressure decreases the stimulation of the baroreceptors and causes hyperventilation. This is at least what happens in animal experiments. Anatomical and histological formations similar to those of the experimental animals are found in man, and some experimental observations confirm that their physiology is similar. The part played by the baroreceptors in the control of ventilation is still not clear. It is not even known in what direction the activity of the respiratory centers is finally influenced, as they receive at the same time information on the pressure in the different vascular compartments, with the impulses originating in the carotid or aortic receptors tending to inhibit ventilation, while those coming from caval, atrial, or pulmonary vascular sources tend, at least in theory, to stimulate ventilation. It should also be remembered that the ventilatory effects of stimulation of the baroreceptors have been observed during non-pulsatile pressure variations. However, it is known that circulatory responses to baroreceptor stimulation, for a given mean pressure, are more marked when pressure is pulsatile than when it is continuous.

Ventilatory control factors of cerebral origin

These are the most apparent factors: it is possible to hyperventilate or to hold the breath voluntarily. The functional relationships between cerebral and ventilatory activities must be considered together with neuroanatomical and neurophysiological data. In particular, electrical stimulation of certain cerebral areas causes ventilatory reaction (see Rossi and Zanchetti, 1957; Colle and Massion, 1958).

These control factors of cerebral origin permit an explanation of a certain number of ventilatory phenomena. Emotional upsets are accompanied by ventilatory manifestations, generally hyperventilation. The simple act of paying attention to one's ventilation may change its pattern. The ventilatory phenomenon of speech shows the essential role played by cerebral activity in controlling the activity of the ventilatory system. There are certainly some conditioned reflexes with ventilatory manifestations, not yet adequately studied.

During very heavy exercise of short duration, such as weight lifting or running at maximal speed (sprint), the thorax is fixed, usually in an inspiratory position. This thorax fixation characterizes straining. In dynamic exercise without effort such as walking, ventilatory frequency is often related to the frequency of body movements.

Extrathoracic proprioceptive stimulus

Stimulation of certain mechanoreceptors causes a reflex increase in ventilation (pathway 2, p. 151). This stimulus is neurogenic by definition, since it is not related to the properties of circulating blood. The existence of such mechanoreceptors in the limbs has been proven, and it is reasonable to believe that they exist in all parts of the body.

1) MECHANICAL STIMULATION OF PROPRIOCEPTIVE RECEPTORS

a) Passive movements of the limbs (as would occur for instance if the knees of a supine subject were bent at a frequency of 60/min) cause hyperventilation, which starts within seconds after initiation of the movements and stops when the movements are discontinued. This phenomenon has been described by Harrison (1932).

The above phenomenon can be easily observed in man and in dog. The hyperventilation which accompanies passive limb movement persists after circulation to these limbs is arrested, but disappears in the animal after section of either the nerves subserving the mobilized area, or of the spinal cord. In man, the phenomenon is maintained under light general anesthesia, but disappears following spinal block.

b) Another method of stimulating the mechanoreceptors consists in tapping repeatedly the tendons, as for example the patellar or the Achilles tendons at the rate of 60/min. The reflex muscular contractions that occur are accompanied by hyperventilation. This phenomenon disappears under general anesthesia when this is deep enough to abolish tendinous reflexes.

c) The ventilatory response to passive movements is more marked when the frequency of movements is higher.

d) If passive mobilization is maintained for several minutes, hyperventilation persists, but is less than that encountered during the early part of mobilization. This phenomenon is easily explained by the fact that passive movements do not increase gas exchange. As a result, hyperventilation causes hypocapnia, and therefore a decrease in CO_2 stimulus, and the observed hyperventilation is the resultant of a proprioceptive stimulus caused by passive mobilization and a carbon dioxide stimulus which is weaker than during the early phase of mobilization.

2) ELECTRICAL STIMULATION OF AFFERENT FIBERS OF MUSCULAR ORIGIN

Simultaneous stimulation of a few seconds' duration of fibers of Group I (which innervate the muscle spindles and Golgi tendon organs) and of Group II (which innervate the spindles) causes, after a period of approximately one second, an increase in ventilation, which subsides two to three seconds after stimulation is discontinued. This increase is less marked when stimulation is limited to type I fibers. Therefore, it is certain that stimulation of the muscle spindles causes a reflex hyperventilation. It is not possible to state if stimulation of type I fibers originating in the tendons is responsible in part for the observed ventilatory response. Similarly, it is not yet known whether stimulation of other proprioceptive receptors, particularly those located in the joints, can also cause reflex hyperventilation (Bessou, Dejours, Laporte, 1959).

CONCLUSION

Stimulation of limb mechanoreceptors, by passive mobilization or repetitive percussion of the tendons, causes a reflex hyperventilation (and also circulatory effects). Neurophysiological techniques show that stimulation of fibers which innervate the muscle spindles causes a ventilatory reaction. It is not known whether there are other proprioceptors which, when stimulated, cause reflex hyperventilation. The ventilatory effect varies with the intensity of proprioceptive stimulation.

Nervous stimuli of various origins

Intense stimulation of sense organs or receptors in the skin or mucosae produces a ventilatory reaction. In particular, excitation of pain receptors causes either hyperventilation and hypocapnia, or apnea, especially if pain is sudden and severe. These ventilatory reactions to stimulation of any receptor must be considered as a manifestation associated with pain, or simply discomfort. Their meaning is therefore entirely different from that attributed to the ventilatory reactions which follow stimulation of the receptors previously studied, for instance, arterial chemoreceptors.

Ventilatory reactions to intense cutaneous stimulation are used in practice as a means of reanimating subjects in respiratory syncope. It is also usual to stimulate vigorously the skin of the newborn if the establishment of normal ventilation is delayed.

Ventilatory reactions to stimulation of the receptors located in the nasal mucosa or in the tracheobronchial tree call for particular attention, since these are well-defined phenomena, the sneeze and cough reflexes. Stimulation of the nasal mucosa, innervated by branches of the trigeminal nerve, causes *sneeze*, a deep inspiration followed by a rapid expiration through the mouth and the nose passages, which tends to displace the initiating agent.

The phenomena which characterize *cough* start with a deep inspiration, followed by closure of the glottis. A consequent intense contraction of the respiratory muscles raises the pressure of the gas in the lungs by several centimeters of mercury. The glottis opens suddenly and gas is expelled violently. During this explosive expiration the tracheobronchial airways become narrower, so that the linear velocity of expired gas may reach 200 to 300 meters per second (Ross, 1955). This is particularly well suited for the purpose of dislodging and expelling foreign material. Cough is, like sneeze, a reflex phenomenon. It is initiated in the mucosal receptors of the respiratory airways, which are innervated by the vagus. The most sensitive cough-producing areas are the larynx and the tracheal bifurcation. Cough is a fundamental phenomenon because of its part in protecting the tracheobronchial airways and is often brought into play. Abolition of cough reflex carries a substantial risk of clogging the airways, and therefore of ventilatory disturbance and infection. This explains the danger of local anesthesia of the airways which abolishes the mucosal initiation of the cough reflex, of general anesthesia which disturbs the central phenomena of this reflex, and finally of respiratory paralysis, which impairs the sequence of the mechanical phenomena involved in cough.

Other stimuli

1. THE "CENTRAL TEMPERATURE" STIMULUS PROBLEM

In the *animal*, a dog for instance, placed in a hot environment, it is possible to observe a thermal tachypnea, with low tidal volume and high frequency, sometimes ten times as high as the frequency occurring under normal temperature conditions. This kind of ventilatory reaction is the best possible example showing the role of dead space in its relationship to alveolar ventilation (see p. 105). In the thermal hyperpnea of the unanesthetized dog, total ventilation is increased, sometimes considerably, while alveolar ventilation is increased only slightly and is still proportionate to gas exchange, so that arterial O_2 and CO_2 pressures and pH remain normal (Albers, 1961). The thermal tachypnea observed in the animal is due at least in part to the effects of elevation of central temperature on the hypothalamic (thermoregulation) centers. It is conceivable that, by the intermediary of connections between these centers and the pneumotaxic center, the activity of the latter is increased, resulting in early inhibition of inspiratory activity and tachypnea (see p. 132). In decerebrate animals, central hyperthermia does not cause this characteristic tachypnea.

In *man*, this thermal tachypnea phenomenon does not take place. In cases where moderate hyperthermia is caused by reducing heat loss (hot, humid environment) a slight increase in metabolism and a proportional increase in ventilation, without tachypnea, can be observed. When ambient conditions are very uncomfortable and are such that heat loss is rendered extremely difficult (very hot bath), central hyperthermia can be considerable, and is accompanied by hyperventilation with increased alveolar ventilation and hypocapnia. This kind of ventilatory reaction is entirely different from the thermal hyperpnea observed in the dog. A central thermal stimulus may be responsible for the ventilatory reactions which have just been described, but it seems more reasonable to believe that these reactions are due either to the intense and generalized cutaneous stimulation, which is required to produce a marked central hyperthermia, or to subjective discomfort related to the ambient conditions which impede heat loss.

2. THE TISSUE CHEMORECEPTOR STIMULUS PROBLEM

It has been thought that tissue receptors may be stimulated by certain local physico-chemical conditions, the excitation being transmitted to the respiratory centers by afferent fibers. This hypothesis has been advanced in order to explain the mechanism of ventilatory regulation during muscular exercise. Physico-chemical changes do indeed take place in the muscles and the extent of these changes is without doubt related to the degree of exercise. Tissue chemoreceptors affecting ventilation could supply the respiratory centers with accurate information on the body requirements.

All the experiments which have attempted to demonstrate the existence of such tissue chemoreceptors have yielded only negative results. In the animal, these experiments have consisted in trying to detect ventilatory reactions following injection of various substances in the arteries leading to the limbs or following ischemia of the limbs obtained by tourniquets. In some cases, the observed physico-chemical changes are not accompanied by any changes in ventilatory behavior. In cases where ventilatory reactions occur, they may reasonably be attributed to stimulation of pain receptors, because such reactions are observed only in conjunction with very important physico-chemical changes, unrelated to the changes which occur normally. Ischemia of the lower limbs in man causes ventilatory reactions only if the test is unpleasant or painful.

Thus, proof of the existence of a muscular chemoreceptor system, capable of modifying ventilatory activity, is lacking at present. It is possible, however, that physico-chemical changes in muscle tissue during exercise may modify the magnitude of the ventilatory stimulus originating in the muscle proprioceptors.

3. UNKNOWN VENTILATORY STIMULI

It has been postulated on different occasions that hyperventilation observed during exposure to altitude or during muscular exercise is due to unknown humoral factors.

At present, such factors need not be postulated. Their existence would have to be invoked only if the effect of the different known stimuli, taking into account their possible interaction, was inadequate to explain the ventilatory pattern which obtains under different physiological conditions.

III. PROBLEMS PERTAINING TO THE REGULATION OF VENTILATION

There are several respiratory stimuli: What are their respective roles? Under what circumstances are they brought into action? How do they combine to achieve a certain ventilation?

It had been thought for a long time that respiratory center activity was maintained by humoral stimuli, O_2, CO_2, or H^+. At present, on the basis of the work of Comroe (1944) and Gray (1950), it is accepted that in addition to these, other humoral or nervous stimuli, studied individually in the preceding sections, are also present. Nevertheless, with our present knowledge, it is impossible to give an adequate overall explanation for any ventilatory behavior (resting, awake, or asleep; muscular exercise; low and high altitude).

Regulation of ventilation at rest

The mechanism of regulation of ventilation at rest, the simplest of all cases, is still far from being completely clear. It is known that at rest, there is:

1) an O_2 stimulus. In normoxia, this stimulus can account for 10 to 15% of the observed ventilation. In hypoxia, its role in the control of ventilation is much more important (see pp. 165 and 197).

2) CO_2 and H^+ stimuli (see pp. 152 and 160) to which the respiratory centers are very sensitive. However, knowledge of the ventilatory sensitivity to this stimulus does not indicate how much ventilation is normally due to such a stimulus. Such information can be obtained only by determining the decrease in ventilation that would result from abolition of the CO_2 and H^+ stimuli. When this method is applied to the study of the stimuli, it is of little value because it requires production of severe hypocapnia with marked respiratory alkalosis, in fact a pathological condition. It is certain that resting ventilation does not depend only on CO_2 and H^+ stimuli, since an O_2 stimulus can be demonstrated under normal conditions. In addition, in abnormal conditions where profound hypocapnia and alkalosis are found — as would occur following voluntary hyperventilation — and in the absence of any O_2 stimulus, ventilation usually persists, although it is markedly decreased (see p. 153). The classical statement that hypocapnia with alkalosis causes apnea has led to the conclusion that resting ventilation depended only on CO_2 and H^+ stimuli. However, hypocapnia does not generally lead to apnea in normal man. Even when apnea does occur, this indicates only that hypocapnia and alkalosis are indeed responsible for apnea, but not that P_{CO_2} and H^+ under normal conditions are responsible for all the ventilation which is observed.

It is important to emphasize that the CO_2 stimulus is not however indispensable for ventilatory activity or for activation of ventilation by other stimuli. In acute hypoxia, a clear-cut hyperventilation, due to O_2 stimulus, can be observed although P_{CO_2} and H^+ are very low, and under these conditions, ventilation is independent of those two factors (Nielsen and Smith, 1951). In addition, in hypopnea due to hypocapnia and alkalosis (Fig. 38), application of an extrathoracic proprioceptive stimulus (passive movements, p. 172) increases ventilation exactly as it does under normal conditions.

3) At rest, there are probably ventilatory stimuli in addition to O_2, CO_2, and H^+. It has been shown that ventilation only decreases when O_2, CO_2, and H^+ stimuli are abolished, and at present, the origin of this residual ventilation is not known. We also lack information on the exact role played by circulating epinephrine, by ventilatory stimuli of baroreceptor origin, by various somatic stimuli which are known to be capable of creating hyperventilation, or by the intrinsic activity of the respiratory centers.

In this connection, it should be noted that ventilation during *sleep* is significantly different from what it is at rest. Sleep causes hypoventilation, and hence alveolar hypercapnia and hypoxia (Robin *et al.*, 1958b). The mechanism involved in this hypoxia of sleep is not clear, but it does not seem to depend on a decrease in CO_2 sensitivity of the respiratory centers (Reed and Kellogg, 1958, 1960). It is possible to explain a decrease in ventilation without change in CO_2 sensitivity if a certain part of the ventilation is assumed to be due to the intrinsic activity of the respiratory centers, and that the activity level of these centers can change with the degree of wakefulness.

Regulation of ventilation during muscular exercise (See Dejours, 1959.)

1) During muscular exercise, most of the humoral and neurogenic ventilatory stimuli are brought into play. Their activation and importance vary considerably in types of exercise differing in the power developed, the localization of motor activity, the dynamic or static nature of the exercise, and the environmental conditions. The various combinations of the characteristics of exercise can in fact determine different physiological conditions, having in common only muscular contraction. The mechanism of ventilatory regulation, although based in every case on the action of certain humoral or neurogenic factors, is not uniform.

2) In light dynamic muscular exercise, for example walking, it is easy to distinguish between the part played by neurogenic stimuli on one hand and the part played by humoral stimuli on the other. At the beginning of exercise, ventilation increases suddenly, at the very first second. Following this, ventilation climbs gradually and after a few minutes reaches a steady state. Termination of the exercise results in an abrupt drop in ventilation, followed by a gradual decrease, and after a number of minutes, the ventilatory behavior prevailing before exercise is re-established. This is shown in Figure 45b.

It is obvious that the near instantaneous increase and drop are due to neurogenic stimuli. The slower variations observed during the initial unsteady state and recovery are probably related to the progressive appearance and disappearance of humoral stimuli.

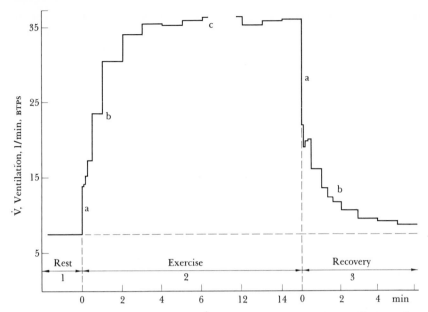

FIGURE 45b.   Changes in ventilation, $\dot{V}$, in different phases of muscular exercise.
(From *J. Physiol.*, Paris, 1956, **48,** 484–488.)

At the onset of exercise and recovery, ventilation is measured for every breath, at other times averaged over a few breaths.

1) At rest.
2) During moderate exercise (walking on a treadmill at 3.1 miles per hour, on a 10% slope. The oxygen uptake is 1400 ml/min, STPD):
    a) Sudden rise in ventilation during the first second of exercise.
    b) Onset of exercise (lasting 6 minutes in this example) during which ventilation increases progressively.
    c) Steady state.
3) During recovery:
    a) Sudden decrease in ventilation.
    b) Recovery period, which can last up to an hour if the preceding exercise is intense.

The oxygen consumption and the carbon dioxide production also increase immediately when exercise is started, and after a few minutes a steady state is reached. This steady state is achieved earlier for oxygen uptake than for CO_2 output, and ventilation is the last function to stabilize.

3) In summary, during light dynamic exercise, the following plan for the interaction of both types of stimuli can be proposed:
    a) At the beginning of exercise of this nature, neurogenic stimuli related to motor activity cause an instantaneous increase in ventilation. During this

initial period, only the neurogenic stimuli of exercise are present and the first two or three respiratory cycles have essentially the same characteristics.

b) After approximately fifteen seconds, humoral stimuli appear and cause a secondary increase in ventilation. The intensity of the humoral stimuli increases progressively and ventilation increases slowly, while the neurogenic stimuli are maintained.

c) After a few minutes the intensity of humoral stimuli reaches a constant value, and a ventilatory steady state obtains. The degree of hyperventilation achieved at this time depends on the simultaneous action of the neurogenic stimuli due to motor activity and of the humoral stimuli.

d) At the end of exercise, the neurogenic stimuli due to motor activity disappear and an instantaneous decrease in ventilation occurs.

e) From then on, only humoral stimuli are present. These are responsible for the hyperpnea which persists in the early part of recovery. The humoral stimuli maintain essentially the same level for 20 to 30 seconds, probably due to the circulatory time lag and because composition of mixed venous blood changes only slowly at first. After this, the humoral stimuli decrease progressively, and ventilation decreases accordingly over a period of time which depends on the intensity of the exercise.

4) *Neural stimuli* may be either proprioceptive or cerebral in origin. During dynamic exercise, there is a proprioceptive ventilatory stimulus resulting from excitation of limb mechanoreceptors by movement. In automatic forms of muscular exercise, like walking, the existence of a cerebral stimulus, which can be visualized as an irradiation of the impulses originating in the motor zones to the respiratory centers, is not certain, although the simple relationship which is observed between step frequency and breathing frequency makes such a stimulus plausible. On the other hand, fixation of the thorax, observed during an intense static exercise and which is characteristic of straining, as well as the hyperventilation which may precede exercise, are of cerebral origin.

The *humoral stimuli* are represented by the CO_2 and H^+ stimuli, an O_2 stimulus (which exists even at low altitude), and, during severe exercise, an epinephrine stimulus. The role played by baroreceptors in ventilatory control during exercise is not yet clear. Central hyperthermia, at least when it is moderate, is not a stimulus. Other humoral stimuli may exist, but they certainly do not play an important part.

5) If the factors that regulate ventilation during exercise were all humoral, the ventilatory increase would not be instantaneous, because of the circulatory lag. This emphasizes the role of the neurogenic stimuli, which produce hyperventilation from the first second of exercise. Had those stimuli been absent, after 10 to 20 seconds a dyspneic hyperventilation would occur,

and this might compel the subject to moderate his power output. However, the instantaneous occurrence of hyperventilation at the beginning of exercise would be of little value if it was not accompanied by a concomitant increase in cardiac output and therefore of oxygen and carbon dioxide transport between tissues and lungs. In fact, at the beginning of mild dynamic exercise, cardiac output and ventilatory output both increase simultaneously.

6) What is the mechanism which makes a subject choose a specific ventilatory pattern, characterized by a certain frequency and a certain tidal volume in preference to any other? This question can be asked of all ventilatory patterns, whether at rest or during exercise, at sea level or at high altitude. There is no simple answer to this question (p. 141), but it can be said that choice of the ventilatory pattern is dictated by the properties of the ventilatory system, that is the functional unit consisting of the respiratory centers, the motor pathways to the respiratory muscles, the ventilatory apparatus, and the pulmonary proprioceptive system. According to this concept, pulmonary proprioceptive sensitivity plays no part in the determining of the magnitude of ventilatory minute volume, but is important in terms of ventilatory movements, a blanket term covering such characteristics as frequency, amplitude, expiratory position, and shape of the volume-time curve.

Special characteristics of the O_2, CO_2, and H^+ stimuli

Among the respiratory stimuli, three are endowed with a noteworthy characteristic. The partial pressures of oxygen and carbon dioxide in alveolar gas, and therefore in arterial blood, are quantitatively related to ventilation itself. Furthermore, the H^+ ion concentration in a given blood physicochemical system is determined by the values of P_{O_2} and P_{CO_2}. The ventilatory behavior is such that it tends to limit the variations in P_{O_2}, P_{CO_2}, and H^+.

This leads to formulation of the following law: "In any given condition of the body, any cause which may modify the P_{O_2}, P_{CO_2}, and pH values, produces ventilatory reactions which limit or prevent the modification of these three values."

A few examples of this general law have already been considered. Inhalation of carbon dioxide (p. 154), which would lead to marked hypercapnia and acidosis in the absence of ventilatory reaction, does in fact produce a hyperventilation which considerably reduces hypercapnia and acidosis. The hyperventilation which occurs in metabolic acidosis (p. 160) causes hypocapnia which limits the acid variation in pH. This last example also shows that the different stimuli may be in conflict. Thus the hyperventilation, which moderates plasmatic acidosis, does so only by lowering P_{CO_2}, a variable regulated by ventilation. This hypocapnia prevents a more pronounced hyperventilation.

It should be noted that these reactions cause important variations in P_{O_2}, to which the body does not appear to be very sensitive, but this should not lead to the hasty conclusion that there is no O_2 stimulus. The latter does exist, but, in normoxia, its intensity varies little, even when the changes in P_{O_2} are quite important. This is equivalent to saying that at low altitude, the ventilatory sensitivity to the O_2 stimulus is low. At high altitudes, things are different: on one hand the O_2 stimulus is intense, and on the other hand the ventilatory sensitivity to this stimulus is higher. Regulation of ventilation at high altitude will be considered separately (p. 197).

Since these three stimuli (O_2, CO_2, and H^+) depend on ventilation, it would seem natural to think that, among them, they control ventilation. This concept cannot be accepted because these stimuli, even at rest, do not account for the activity level in the respiratory centers nor for the ventilation observed (see p. 177). During exercise, on the basis of the sensitivity of the respiratory centers to O_2, CO_2, and H^+ stimuli, a marked increase in these stimuli would be required to explain the hyperventilation, and such an increase does not occur.

In reality, the mean activity level of the respiratory centers is determined by an aggregate of neurogenic and humoral stimuli (among them O_2, CO_2, and H^+) which keep the centers informed of the respiratory requirements of the body, and establish a certain regulatory level of the centers, from which results a certain ventilatory activity, the amplitude and frequency of which determine the required alveolar ventilation. These characteristics depend, at least in part, on the properties of the system constituted by respiratory centers and thorax.

However, the respiratory centers must be kept informed of the adequacy of the ventilatory behavior thus determined, and know whether this behavior ensures appropriate alveolar ventilation and gas exchange. This information is supplied by arterial blood P_{O_2}, P_{CO_2}, and pH which indicate if alveolar ventilation is adequate, that is proportional to the volumes of oxygen and carbon dioxide exchanged with the atmosphere. The regulation is such that P_{O_2}, P_{CO_2}, and pH vary little from the normal values which determine constancy of the internal environment. Insufficient ventilation causes hypoxia, hypercapnia, and a pH decrease, all of which tend to increase ventilation, while excessive alveolar ventilation leads to the opposite variations and corrections. It seems therefore that the main contribution of the O_2, CO_2, and H^+ ventilatory stimuli is not to determine the overall ventilatory flow, for if this had been their role, considerable variations in composition of the interior environment would be required. In reality the overall ventilatory level is determined by the simultaneous action of the neurogenic and humoral stimuli, the latter including, among others, the O_2, CO_2, and H^+ stimuli. However, since the arterial P_{O_2}, P_{CO_2} (and pH) values are directly dependent on alveolar ventilation, the main role of these stimuli must be to control the exact ventilatory behavior which maintains an adequate composition of the internal environment.

Oscillations in ventilatory system function — periodic respiration

An important characteristic of arterial blood P_{O_2}, P_{CO_2}, and pH values, which depend on alveolar ventilation, is that several seconds elapse between the time these values are determined in the lungs and the time at which these values can influence chemoreceptors and respiratory centers. When there is an interval between the time when a regulated variable assumes a given value and the time this can act on the regulatory mechanism, this system can oscillate.

1) Normally, oscillations in ventilation and arterial blood P_{O_2}, P_{CO_2}, and pH are small. Most probably one of the reasons for this is that even an abrupt change in alveolar ventilation causes only a relatively slight change in arterial blood P_{CO_2} and respiratory center P_{CO_2}. The variations in P_{CO_2} are minimized by several factors:

a) The lungs contain a certain volume of air which, when abruptly exposed to an increased flow of fresh air, acts as a diluent for this fresh air. Similarly, when alveolar ventilation is abruptly decreased, the carbon dioxide eliminated by blood is diluted in the whole alveolar gas mass, and the $P_{A_{CO_2}}$ increase is less marked the larger the lung volume.

b) The lung tissues and blood which exchange carbon dioxide with alveolar gas have a high CO_2 combining power, that is they can bind a high volume of CO_2 with only limited changes in P_{CO_2}. For instance, if the end-expiratory lung volume (functional residual capacity) is 2500 ml, the addition of 25 ml of CO_2 does not increase the alveolar CO_2 fraction by 1%, but only by 0.7%, because carbon dioxide has been taken up, not only by the lung gases, but also by the lung tissues and blood. This virtual volume into which carbon dioxide is distributed is called "equivalent lung volume," and, in the preceding example, can be calculated to be 3500 ml.

c) When a sudden change takes place in alveolar P_{CO_2} and therefore in arterialized blood P_{CO_2}, the variation in P_{CO_2} of the arterial blood which reaches chemoreceptors and respiratory centers a few seconds later is decreased and spread out because the blood flow in the vessels has a parabolic profile.

d) Finally, in the respiratory centers themselves, there is an additional damping in P_{CO_2} changes because the respiratory centers, like all tissues, have a high carbon dioxide buffering capacity (Douglas and Haldane, 1909).

Insofar as oxygen is concerned, the equivalent lung volume is much smaller than that for carbon dioxide. In addition, the arterial chemoreceptors, minute organs perfused by an enormous blood flow cannot adequately damp the variations in P_{O_2} of the arterial blood they receive. As a consequence, variations in alveolar P_{O_2} cause relatively marked variations of P_{O_2} in the chemoreceptors.

The absence of important oscillations in the functional behavior of the ventilatory system under normal conditions can therefore be explained by the fact that variations of P_{CO_2} in the lungs are considerably damped in the chemoreceptors and in the respiratory centers.

2) Under certain conditions, the ventilatory system may show oscillations.

a) If the circulation time from lungs to respiratory centers is increased, the respiration is often periodic. Guyton (1956) has observed that the ventilatory pattern of the dog shows oscillations and becomes of the Cheyne-Stokes type, if a tube long enough to increase circulation time is interposed along the carotid artery.

b) In hypoxia, a periodic pattern of ventilation is not unfrequent, and can be explained as follows: assuming that at a certain time a decrease in alveolar P_{O_2} takes place (swallow, speech, etc.), after a few seconds, the hypoxic blood reaches the chemoreceptors, excites them and causes an increase in ventilation. This hyperventilation causes hyperoxia which, after an additional lapse of time, is followed by an increase in P_{O_2} in the blood perfusing the chemoreceptors, and therefore a decrease in O_2 stimulus and a decrease in ventilation. In this fashion, periodic variations in ventilation can follow each other.

c) Another cause of oscillations in ventilatory pattern resides in periodic changes in respiratory center excitability. This is probably the cause of the very irregular periodic respiration which takes place when falling asleep (Haab, 1957). On the other hand, during deep sleep no ventilatory oscillations are observed, at least at low altitude.

Conclusions

From all these considerations, it appears that regulation of ventilation is such that the partial pressures of carbon dioxide and oxygen in alveolar gas and arterial blood as well as arterial pH are maintained approximately constant. However, the end purpose in the organism is not to limit the variations of P_{O_2}, P_{CO_2}, and pH in arterial blood, but rather to stabilize the conditions in which the tissues live, which are, in terms of respiration, P_{O_2}, P_{CO_2}, and pH. Regulation of ventilation and of alveolar gas composition represents therefore only some of the body mechanisms which ensure adequate conditions for tissue gas exchange.

When the body is subjected to permanent changes in function, the characteristics of the internal environment change. For example, a factor which changes pH permanently not only causes ventilatory reactions, but also causes the factors which regulate acid-base balance to change. This is what happens during acclimatization to high altitudes (p. 194). Elimination of bases by the kidney and decrease in HCO_3^- ion in plasma tend to reduce the alkalosis which characterizes the early part of residence at high altitude. Furthermore, at altitude the body possesses an additional mechanism, besides hyperventilation, to counteract hypoxia. As discussed below (p. 194) the increase in hemoglobin concentration, found at altitude, although it has no effect on arterial blood P_{O_2}, limits tissue hypoxia.

Along this line, the circulatory reactions which are observed each time the conditions or the magnitude of gas exchange vary (altitude, exercise) are obviously paramount. Blood circulation ensures transport of respiratory gases between lungs and tissues, and during exercise, for example, ventilatory adaptation would be useless without an adequate parallel adaptation of the circulatory flow. For this reason, decompensated cardiac patients cannot exercise. Similarly, a subject whose circulatory adaptation is adequate but who cannot adjust his ventilation, is also incapable of exercising. The two systems are functionally coupled and close quantitative relationships exist between blood flow, ventilatory flow, and metabolic level. This shows definitely that study of ventilation — which ensures oxygen and carbon dioxide exchange between the alveolar gas and the atmosphere — cannot be separated from the study of gas exchange between alveolar gas and tissues, that is the study of gas transport by blood. The ventilatory and circulatory systems are closely interwoven, from the anatomical and functional point of view as well as in terms of regulatory mechanisms. Regulation always proceeds in parallel in these two systems, and limitation of the study to one or the other regulatory mechanism is highly artificial.

What is therefore important, from the point of view of respiratory physiology, is the value of the O_2 and CO_2 pressures and H^+ ion concentration in the tissues. If the law to which we referred above (p. 181) is correct from the pulmonary respiratory standpoint, in terms of the whole body the law should be stated as "Any cause which is susceptible of modifying the values of P_{O_2}, P_{CO_2}, and H^+ in the blood perfusing the body tissues causes reactions in ventilation, circulation, and sometimes blood composition, which correct or moderate the variations of these three factors."

9
Respiration at High Altitude

I. DEFINITION AND TYPES OF ALTITUDE HYPOXIA

"The decrease in barometric pressure acts on living beings only by decreasing the oxygen tension in the air they breathe," said Paul Bert in his book on barometric pressure (*La Pression Barométrique*) in 1878. This general law, as stated by Paul Bert, is not altered by the fact that disturbances can occur during explosive decompression (since these are of traumatic origin) or by the fact that certain conditions which usually go hand in hand with altitude, such as ambient temperature, insulation, diet, can also cause physiological reactions. All these additional climatic and dietetic factors are not specific to altitude, and can be encountered at sea level.

It is difficult to state at what altitude the body will be in hypoxia, in relation to sea level oxygenation conditions. However, since no physiological reaction is encountered as long as the altitude does not exceed 1000 meters (3300 ft, P_B = 626 mm Hg and $P_{I_{O_2}}$ is 122 mm Hg), high altitude can arbitrarily be defined as any elevation above 1000 meters. In this book, the term altitude, when not expressly designated as high altitude, indicates an altitude above 1000 meters (3300 feet).

The term "altitude hypoxia" by itself does not imply abnormal or pathological conditions. Life at high altitude is normal, and men have lived under these conditions for untold generations, with physical activity, longevity, and birth rate identical to those of populations living at low altitude. Approximately 15 million people live at an altitude higher than 3000 meters (10,000 ft), and permanent population centers can even be found at altitudes higher than 5000 meters (16,000 ft). In the Andes, at an altitude of 4500 meters (15,000 ft), favorite hobbies are soccer for the native population and tennis for recently arrived residents.

186

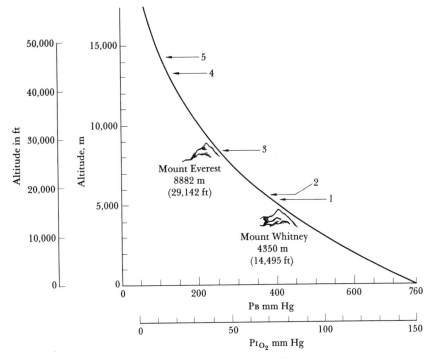

Figure 46. Relationship between altitude and barometric pressure.

On the abscissae, the partial pressure of inspired oxygen, $P_{I_{O_2}}$, saturated with water vapor at 37 °C, is given for the various barometric pressures P_B. At an ambient pressure of 47 mm Hg (19,100 meters or 63,000 ft), water boils. Therefore, if a body at 37 °C was placed in pure oxygen at a pressure of 47 mm Hg, no oxygen would enter the airways, from which water vapor would escape continuously. Subcutaneous emphysema, filled with water vapor, would occur immediately. Since water vapor always exerts a pressure of 47 mm Hg in the lungs, at a pressure of 141 mm Hg (altitude of 12,170 meters or 40,000 ft), one third of the lung gases would be water vapor. At 760 mm Hg, $\frac{47}{760}$ or roughly 6.2% of the air in the lungs is water vapor.

Arrow 1 indicates the altitude (and barometric pressure) at which most acutely exposed subjects lose consciousness or are on the verge of doing so. This altitude corresponds to inhalation of 10% oxygen at sea level. Although such an acute hypoxia is not dangerous for subjects when such laboratory experiments are performed under supervision, it represents a deadly danger for airplane pilots.

Arrow 2 indicates the level at which the highest human permanent habitat is situated.

Arrow 3 corresponds to the maximal altitude that subjects breathing air — but previously acclimatized to a lower altitude — can tolerate without danger for a few hours.

Arrow 4 shows the maximal altitude that can be reached, without immediate death hazard, by a pilot breathing *pure* oxygen in a non-pressurized plane. In this case, the inspired oxygen pressure must be read on the upper abscissae axis (0 to 760).

Arrow 5 shows the maximal altitude that a pilot can reach breathing oxygen at positive pressure (+20 mm Hg). Higher altitudes can be reached only in pressurized cabins, or full-suits.

The altitudes shown by arrows 1, 4, and 5 can be tolerated without major psychological disturbances only by subjects who are particularly resistant to hypoxia, and on the condition that the exposure be limited to a few minutes. The altitude "ceilings" vary considerably between subjects.

Several types of altitude hypoxia must be distinguished:

a) *Acute hypoxia:* this refers to subjects who have been at altitude for a few minutes or a few hours, subjects who are not yet acclimatized to altitude. However, from the moment they reach altitude, there is a revolutionary change in physiological functions, which marks the onset of altitude acclimatization.

b) *Chronic hypoxia*, found in subjects living permanently at high altitude. These subjects are acclimatized to altitude.

c) In fact, the duration of residence at altitude that is required for *complete acclimatization* is not well defined. In order to achieve complete acclimatization, several years are probably required, but subjects who have lived for a few days at altitude are already partially acclimatized, as can be judged from their near-normal physical and intellectual performance, which is comparable to that of subjects who have resided at altitude for much longer times. Thus a person new to high altitude goes first through a phase of acute hypoxia, then a phase of acclimatization to high altitude which, after a poorly defined period, produces an acclimatized state, also known as permanent or chronic hypoxia. In this chapter we shall consider only the effects of altitude exposure on the *resting* body.

II. ACUTE HYPOXIA

a) Rapid ascent, on foot, by plane, or by cable car, leads to such a condition. In the laboratory, there are two means for studying subjects in hypoxia:

— in a decompression chamber, where the subject is exposed to a decrease in ambient pressure;

— because of its simplicity, inhalation of a low oxygen mixture has often been used. For instance, at sea level, in a gas mixture containing 14% oxygen and 86% nitrogen, the oxygen partial pressure is 100 mm Hg. This oxygen pressure is approximately that of air at an altitude of 3000 meters (10,000 ft) (see Table XII). Inhalation of a hypoxic mixture creates an "equivalent" altitude.

The physiological reactions to hypoxia, whether due to decrease in barometric pressure, at a constant F_{IO_2} of 0.21, or to a decrease in F_{IO_2}, at a constant P_B of 760 mm Hg, are always the same. However, Fenn, Rahn, and Otis (1946) have shown that in fact it is not possible to have exactly the same alveolar gas composition during acute hypoxia at true altitude and during equivalent altitude hypoxia, except when the respiratory quotient is unity. Equation 6 (p. 98) shows an explanation of this. In this equation, the term F_{IO_2} remains the same (0.21) at any true altitude, but is decreased in experiments with equivalent altitude. Although Fenn's comments are justified, the quantitive difference in composition of alveolar gas between true and equivalent altitude is such that Paul Bert's law is not affected.

TABLE XII

	F_{IO_2}	P_{IO_2}	F_{AO_2}	P_{AO_2}	F_{ACO_2}	P_{ACO_2}
$P_B = 760$	0.210	150	0.155	111	0.055	39
$P_B = 760$	0.140	100	0.085	61	0.055	39
$P_B = 523$	0.210	100	0.128	61	0.082	39

The fraction and partial pressure of oxygen and carbon dioxide in inspired air and alveolar gas are given by F_I and P_I and by F_A and P_A respectively. Remember that partial pressure of a gas x, at a fractional concentration F_x in dry gas is given by $P_x = F_x(P_B - 47)$, where P_B is the barometric pressure.

First line: at sea level, breathing air, $F_{IO_2} = 0.21$.

Second line: at sea level, breathing a low oxygen mixture, $F_{IO_2} = 0.14$ (equivalent altitude).

Third line: at an altitude of 3,000 meters (10,000 ft), breathing air, $F_{IO_2} = 0.21$.

The alveolar pressure values given for the three conditions are calculated for a respiratory quotient equal to one. Both equivalent hypoxia and true hypoxia have *just been established* and have not yet caused ventilatory reactions.

The second line of the table shows that at sea level ($P_B = 760$ mm Hg) the oxygen pressure of a hypoxic gas mixture ($F_{IO_2} = 0.14$) is 100 mm Hg, and is equivalent to that of air ($F_{IO_2} = 0.21$) at an altitude of 3,000 meters or 10,000 ft ($P_B = 523$ mm Hg).

This table also shows that at true altitude (third line) the fraction of carbon dioxide in alveolar gas is higher than at sea level, while its partial pressure has not changed, because P_B has decreased.

b) In acute hypoxia, at altitudes of less than 3000 meters (10,000 ft), there is neither overall nor alveolar hyperventilation, and alveolar hypercapnia does not occur, in spite of a marked decrease in P_{AO_2} (at 3000 meters,

$P_{A_{O_2}}$ is approximately 60 mm Hg, as opposed to 100 mm Hg at sea level); this appears at point N of Figure 47.

On the contrary, above 3000 meters (10,000 ft), as $P_{A_{O_2}}$ decreases to values below 60 mm Hg, overall and alveolar hyperventilation appear immediately (Fig. 47). Since the gas exchange values are not changed by altitude, a well-known fact, the alveolar hyperventilation causes alveolar hypocapnia (see equation 12, p. 105 and Fig. 27) (Boycott and Haldane, 1908). The observed hyperventilation is due mainly to an increase in tidal volume, the respiratory frequency remaining essentially the same.

c) Circulatory reactions take place. The cardiac output is increased. In severe hypoxia it can probably double. The heart rate increases by a few tenths of its value (Van Liere, 1942).

d) The O_2 saturation of arterial blood, Sa_{O_2}, decreases at altitude. The desaturation is more marked as hypoxia increases. The O_2 content of the arterial blood, Ca_{O_2}, also decreases. The blood O_2 capacity is not changed by acute hypoxia in man, at least during the first minutes of acute hypoxia (Fig. 48).

The partial pressure of oxygen in the venous blood and in the tissues is significantly lower than the value at low altitude (Figs. 49 and 53). However, the decrease in venous and tissue P_{O_2} is not as severe as the drop in arterial P_{O_2}. This is due to two causes (one biochemical and one functional):

— for a given arterial-venous O_2 content difference, the P_{O_2} difference is less in hypoxia than in normoxia. This phenomenon is due to the shape of the $C_{O_2} - P_{O_2}$ curve (Fig. 3). For instance, a difference of 5.6 vol% in C_{O_2} is found in hypoxia when $Pa_{O_2} = 30$ mm Hg and $P\bar{v}_{O_2} = 18$ mm Hg, while in normoxia the corresponding values are 95 and 37 mm Hg;

— the increase in cardiac output in acute hypoxia decreases the $(C\bar{v}_{O_2} - Ca_{O_2})$ difference, and as a result, if the cardiac output doubles, $P\bar{v}_{O_2}$ in the preceding example will increase from 18 to 23 mm Hg.

Arterial blood pH is increased in acute hypoxia (Haldane, 1919; Haggard and Henderson, 1920) (Figs. 50 and 51). This alkalosis is due to two causes:

— hypocapnia, when it occurs (above 3000 meters), causes respiratory alkalosis;

— arterial blood O_2 unsaturation, because reduced hemoglobin is less acid than oxyhemoglobin (Rahn and Otis, 1949).

e) During the first hours at altitude, the subject is usually euphoric and may admit feeling some dyspnea if he performs some exercise. In reality, the subject shows intellectual disturbances, of which he is often not conscious; the thought process is slow, and there are mistakes in the most elementary mental operations. This is why aviation regulations are very clear on this subject and require oxygen inhalation or cabin pressurization, even at altitudes which may seem ridiculously low.

After a few hours spent at altitude, the initial euphoria is followed by a certain confusion. The subject complains of a certain number of physical and psychological disturbances: poor general feeling, slowness of thought process, dyspnea occurring at very mild exertion, headache, insomnia, sometimes nausea and vomiting. All these disturbances constitute what is called altitude sickness, and are in general more marked when the hypoxia is more severe. In certain subjects, they may be very mild, while in others they may be dramatic, although usually devoid of danger. However, when the altitude is high (above 6000 meters) and is reached very quickly, the above disturbances can occur very rapidly and can even be fatal.

III. ACCLIMATIZATION TO PROLONGED HYPOXIA. THE ACCLIMATIZED STATE

When altitude exposure is maintained beyond a few hours, physical and mental performance improve, and gradually return to what they were at sea level. (However, in certain cases, especially at very high altitude, the altitude sickness disturbances do not disappear.) The acclimatization period lasts several days, and some physiological changes require several weeks.

a) Ventilation (Figs. 47 and 51) increases. This increase is rapid for the first few days, then gradually slower, and ventilation is usually stable after approximately one week at altitude. This hyperventilation always occurs. It has been shown that acute hypoxia at altitudes below 3000 meters (10,000 ft) ($P_{AO_2} > 60$ mm Hg) causes no appreciable hyperventilation (curve NA of Fig. 47), but after 24 hours at altitude, this hyperventilation is always present. In the case of hypoxia occurring at altitudes higher than 3000 meters (10,000 ft) ($P_{AO_2} < 60$ mm Hg), the initial hyperventilation, which is the rule, increases progressively and, as in the previous case, reaches a steady state after a few days at altitude. The final hyperventilation (curve A of Fig. 47) is more marked as hypoxia becomes more severe.

b) The ventilatory increase is accompanied by changes in alveolar gas composition. In the course of a few days, oxygen pressure increases and carbon dioxide pressure decreases, as values for alveolar P_{CO_2} and P_{O_2} go from NA to curve A on Figure 47 (Fitzgerald, 1914; Rahn and Otis, 1949). This change in alveolar gas composition is one of the most important body reactions which take place during altitude acclimatization. For instance, in Figure 47, the alveolar oxygen pressure, P_{AO_2}, of a subject brought rapidly to an altitude of 3000 meters (10,000 ft) is 58 mm Hg (point N). After a few days, because of hyperventilation, P_{AO_2} has increased to 66 mm Hg (point N'),

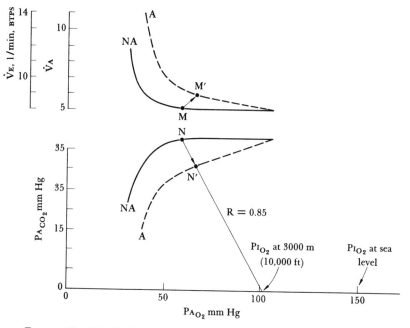

FIGURE 47.   Ventilation and composition of alveolar gas at altitude.
(From RAHN and OTIS, 1949.)

Upper section: Alveolar ventilation, $\dot{V}_A$, and minute volume, $\dot{V}_E$, as a function of alveolar oxygen pressure, $P_{A_{O_2}}$. The $\dot{V}_E$ scale is obtained by adding to $\dot{V}_A$ the dead space ventilation, assumed to be constant at 3 l/min.

Lower section: Alveolar partial pressure of carbon dioxide, $P_{A_{CO_2}}$, as a function of $P_{A_{O_2}}$.

The continuous curves marked NA correspond to the non-acclimatized subjects (acute hypoxia), the broken curves A to the acclimatized subjects (chronic hypoxia).

Note that in non-acclimatized subjects, hyperventilation, and therefore hypercapnia are found only at altitudes which reduce $P_{A_{O_2}}$ to values lower than approximately 60 mm Hg. (If the respiratory quotient is 0.85 and $P_{A_{CO_2}}$ is 38 mm Hg, this corresponds to an inspired O_2 pressure of 101 mm Hg.) For example, in acute hypoxia, ventilation is at M and alveolar gas at N.

After a few hours at altitude, an increase in ventilation and a change in alveolar gas composition occur. These changes are rapid at first and their rate decreases gradually. In the example given in the figure, these changes would lead, in a few days, to a final hyperventilation at point M′ (final in the sense that no further change occurs over a few weeks) which increases alveolar P_{O_2} and decreases alveolar P_{CO_2} (point N′). This increase in P_{O_2} due to hyperventilation is certainly one of the main features of altitude acclimatization.

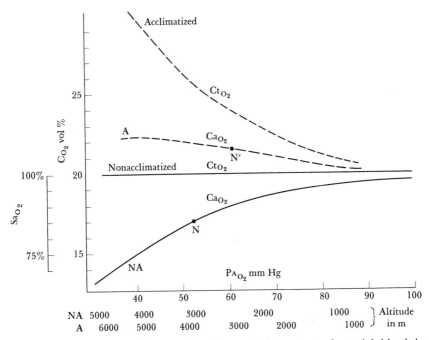

Figure 48. Total blood O_2 capacity, Ct_{O_2}, and O_2 content of arterial blood in altitude-acclimatized and in non-acclimatized subjects, as function of arterial blood O_2 pressure, Pa_{O_2}. (Data from the *Handbook of Respiration*, 1958.)

The continuous lines pertain to non-acclimatized subjects (acute hypoxia), while the broken lines pertain to altitude-acclimatized subjects (chronic hypoxia of several months duration).

In addition, the continuous Ca_{O_2} curve also represents the arterial O_2 saturation, and is valid for both acute hypoxia and chronic hypoxia (the same Sa_{O_2} scale for both cases assumes that the shape of the $C_{O_2} - P_{O_2}$ relationship is identical for both).

In altitude-acclimatized subjects, the O_2 capacity is increased, because the hemoglobin concentration is increased. In spite of the fact that arterial blood is not saturated, the arterial blood of the acclimatized subject contains more oxygen than the saturated arterial blood of a subject living at sea level.

The alveolar oxygen pressure which corresponds to the different Pa_{O_2} values can be obtained by adding to the latter the alveolar-arterial oxygen difference, a few millimeters of mercury. With this, and using the data from Figures 46 and 47, it is possible to assign to each Pa_{O_2} an approximate altitude, at which this Pa_{O_2} would be found either in non-acclimatized (NA scale) or acclimatized (A scale) subjects. Thus a saturation of 85% is found during acute exposure to an altitude of 3000 meters (10,000 ft) or chronic exposure to 4000 meters (13,500 ft). In addition, in the non-acclimatized subject at 10,000 ft, the arterial oxygen content corresponding to 85%

saturation is 17 vol% (point N), while in the acclimatized subject at the same altitude, the saturation is 90% and the O_2 content 21.5 vol% (point N). This increase in content during acclimatization is due to two causes: on one hand the Pa_{O_2} increase due to relative hyperventilation (see Fig. 47) and on the other, the increase in hemoglobin concentration.

a value which would occur during acute hypoxia obtained by exposing the subject to an altitude of 2400 meters (8000 ft). The ventilatory acclimatization process, by modifying the alveolar gas composition, is equivalent to a descent to a lower altitude.

c) Cardiac output and heart rate are increased in acute hypoxia. During acclimatization, cardiac output and heart rate decrease progressively and return to values very near those observed at sea level. Therefore, in terms of cardiac output, the changes during acclimatization are the reverse of those taking place in the ventilatory flow (Asmussen and Consolazio, 1941).

d) In blood, in addition to the changes in P_{O_2} and P_{CO_2} which accompany the progressive changes in alveolar gas composition, there is an increase in red blood cells and hemoglobin concentration, very rapid during the first days, then slower for several months or maybe years (Hurtado, 1945 and 1948). The mechanism which increases hemoglobin concentration is complex (Stickney and Van Liere, 1953). The changes in red blood cell count and in hemoglobin concentration are related to the severity of hypoxia (Fig. 48). Because of this hyperhemoglobinemia and although the blood remains unsaturated (albeit less unsaturated than during acute hypoxia, because the alveolar hyperventilation due to acclimatization has caused an increase in alveolar P_{O_2}), arterial blood contains more oxygen at altitude than at sea level (Fig. 48). This observation is one of the reasons why it is accepted that the effects of hypoxia on the body are related to the partial pressure of oxygen, and not to the O_2 content of arterial blood (see p. 166).

During acclimatization (although the return of the cardiac output to a value near that prevailing at sea level increases the arterial-venous oxygen difference), partial pressure of O_2 in mixed venous blood and in the tissues increases, relative to the values in acute hypoxia. This is due to two causes: hyperventilation, which decreases alveolar hypoxia, and the increase in hemoglobin (see legend of Fig. 49).

We have seen that, during acute hypoxia, arterial blood pH increases. During acclimatization, this alkalosis is progressively compensated, mainly by elimination of bicarbonate in the urine. It is usually accepted that after a few days, or weeks, arterial pH returns to a value near that prevailing at sea level (Haldane, 1919; Haggard and Henderson, 1920) (Figs. 50 and 51).

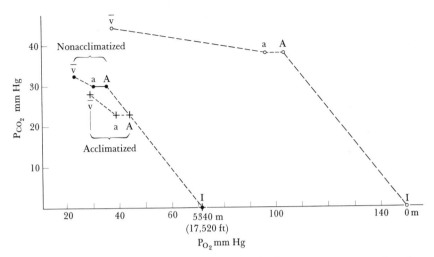

FIGURE 49. Inspired, alveolar, arterial, and mixed venous oxygen and carbon dioxide at sea level and at altitude (acclimatized and non-acclimatized subjects).

Point I at 150 mm Hg on the abscissae shows inspired air at sea level. Point I at 71.5 mm Hg shows inspired air at an altitude of 5340 meters (14,500 ft, P_B = 388 mm Hg).

Points A, a, and $\bar{v}$ represent pressures of carbon dioxide and oxygen in alveolar gas, arterial blood, and mixed venous blood respectively. The broken lines connect values pertaining to the same conditions: sea level (normoxia), acute exposure to an altitude of 5340 meters or 14,500 feet (recent hypoxia, non-acclimatized), prolonged exposure and acclimatization to that altitude (permanent or chronic hypoxia).

The nomogram of Dill, Edwards, and Consolazio (1937) has been used in order to calculate arterial and venous P_{O_2} and P_{CO_2} of the normoxic and the non-acclimatized subject. The nomogram of Dill, Talbott, and Consolazio (1937) has been used to compute a and $\bar{v}$ values in the subject residing at 5340 meters (14,500 ft). It is assumed that during acute hypoxia the cardiac output is double that measured at sea level, which decreases the $(Ca_{O_2} - C\bar{v}_{O_2})$ and $(C\bar{v}_{CO_2} - Ca_{CO_2})$ differences to one-half the sea level values. The cardiac output of the acclimatized subject is assumed to be the same as that of the normoxic subject.

This diagram shows that the partial pressure of oxygen in the mixed venous blood (and in the tissues) of the acclimatized subject is higher than that of the non-acclimatized subject. This increase in $P\bar{v}_{O_2}$ is the result of several phenomena:

a) Alveolar hyperventilation (point A for the acclimatized subject shows hypocapnia and hyperoxia in relation to point A of the acclimatized subjects).

b) Increase in the O_2 capacity (see Fig. 48) and decrease of the $(Pa_{O_2} - P\bar{v}_{O_2})$ difference for the same $(Ca_{O_2} - C\bar{v}_{O_2})$ difference. If no changes occurred in the physico-chemical properties of blood, in particular if no increase in hemoglobin concentration had taken place, $P\bar{v}_{O_2}$ would have been 23 instead of 29 mm Hg.

c) Cardiac output is near normoxic values, while in acute hypoxia, cardiac output is increased. This last phenomenon by itself would have decreased $P\bar{v}_{O_2}$, but because of the changes stated in a) and b), $P\bar{v}_{O_2}$ is higher in the acclimatized subject than in the non-acclimatized subject.

The oxygen capacity, content, and saturation of the arterial blood of the three examples given here can be read in Fig. 48.

e) Adaptation to altitude involves the whole gas exchange system, since in addition to the ventilatory, circulatory, and hematological reactions, tissue reactions also occur: hypervascularization of the tissues (increase in number of capillaries), increase in myoglobin concentration and mito-chondrial density, and finally some enzymatic changes which enhance oxidation-reduction reactions (see Pace, 1959; B. Reynafarje, 1959).

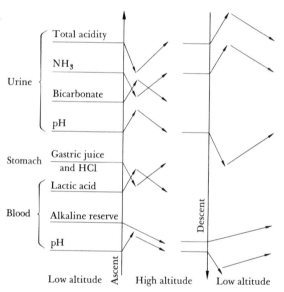

FIGURE 50. Schematic representation (from Grandjean, 1948) of the changes in pH and in related values in urine, gastric juice, and blood during acute exposure to altitude and during acclimatization as well as during descent to sea level and de-acclimatization.

In summary, when altitude acclimatization has been achieved, the body, considered as a gas exchange system, is markedly changed in comparison to what it was at sea level. The higher the altitude, the more important are the observed changes.

Ventilation is increased, and as a result the P_{O_2} difference between ambient air and alveolar gas is decreased.

Hemoglobin concentration and the oxygen binding capacity of blood are increased, and this causes an increase in arterial blood oxygen content in relation to sea level conditions, in spite of the considerable decrease in arterial oxygen saturation and pressure.

Arterial pH is most probably quite near that found at sea level, because the initial alkalosis due to hypocapnia and to the relative decrease in HbO_2 is compensated by a marked decrease in bicarbonate concentration.

All these facts seem well established, but some of them, especially those dealing with hyperventilation and alveolar gas composition, have been established mainly by studying subjects acclimatized for only a few weeks, and it is not certain that the physiological reactions which have been described are quantitatively the same as those of subjects living at altitude for several years. It should be noted that some subjects, residing at altitude for long periods and presenting all the signs of excellent acclimatization can develop some disturbances, at times probably related to a very marked increase in red cell concentration, which constitute the strange condition known as mountain sickness (see Van Liere, 1942).

When a subject acclimatized to altitude returns to sea level, he loses the respiratory features of altitude acclimatization. This de-acclimatization is slow and lasts several weeks. In particular, hemoglobin concentration returns to normoxic values only after a lapse of two months. This de-acclimatization can be said to be an acclimatization to oxygenation conditions which prevail at sea level, by definition normoxic conditions.

IV. MECHANISM OF REGULATION OF RESPIRATION AT ALTITUDE

Acute hypoxia (non-acclimatized subject)

In acute hypoxia, at an altitude below 3000 meters (10,000 ft) ($P_{A_{O_2}} > 60$ mm Hg), no hyperventilation occurs. At altitudes above 3000 meters (10,000 ft) ($P_{A_{O_2}} < 60$ mm Hg) a certain hyperventilation can be found. We have seen (p. 168) that in acute hypoxia, the O_2 stimulus is much higher than in normoxia, which raises the question of why, in acute hypoxia, hyperventilation is absent or only minor. The answer is probably to be found in the fact that if there is an increase in the O_2 stimulus, there is also a decrease in the CO_2 and H^+ stimuli, due to two causes: blood O_2 unsaturation (HbO_2 is less acid than Hb), alveolar hypocapnia, and respiratory alkalosis.

This generally accepted concept is represented in Figure 51, which shows that at the very beginning of residence at altitude, the O_2 stimulus is increased and the CO_2 and H^+ (and possibly other) stimuli are decreased, in relation to their values in normoxia. If hypoxia is only moderate, the combination of the two groups of stimuli leaves ventilation unchanged. On the other hand, if hypoxia is marked, the O_2 stimulus is sufficiently intense to cause hyperventilation.

Chronic hypoxia (altitude acclimatized subject)

Although an O_2 stimulus exists in acute hypoxia, it is not certain *a priori* that it is the same during acclimatization to altitude. Even if altitude-induced hyperventilation is really due to body hypoxia, it is not definite that this hyperventilation is maintained by a ventilatory O_2 stimulus, that is, a ventilatory regulatory factor which acts directly by stimulating arterial chemoreceptors (see p. 165). This question has received two radically different answers:

1) Some accept the idea that the O_2 stimulus is important only in acute hypoxia and that during acclimatization, the progressive compensation of the initial alkalosis (through urinary base elimination and decrease in plasma bicarbonate) restores the CO_2 and H^+ ventilatory stimuli, which would then replace the O_2 stimulus. In order to explain hyperventilation, an increased sensitivity of the respiratory centers to the CO_2 and H^+ stimuli is suggested. This still leaves unexplained the reason for the disappearance of the O_2 stimulus.

2) The other view considers that the O_2 ventilatory stimulus is present as long as the subject remains at altitude and that the intensity of the stimulus is related to the degree of hypoxia. The hyperventilation which develops progressively during the acclimatization period must be attributed to the compensation of alkalosis and some degree of restoration of the CO_2 and H^+ stimuli. While in the first theory, the CO_2 and H^+ stimuli must account for nearly the total hyperventilation of the altitude acclimatized subject, in the second theory, the CO_2 and H^+ stimuli are only partial stimuli, the O_2 stimulus still playing the essential part. The main argument in favor of this second theory is that the O_2 test method, described on p. 168 (see Fig. 44) and applied to the acclimatized subject, shows during chronic hypoxia a ventilatory decrease as significant or even greater than that in acute hypoxia, at the same oxygen alveolar pressure. Figure 51 shows schematically these two theories.

The role of the CO_2 and H^+ stimuli at altitude, in the acclimatized subject, is still only imperfectly known. It probably represents one of the

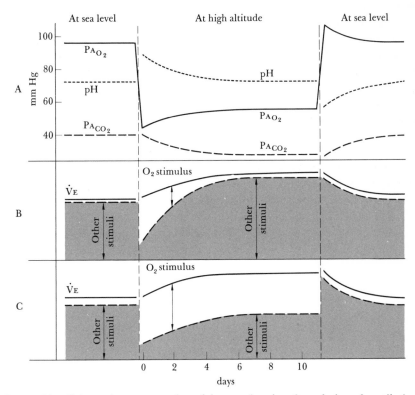

FIGURE 51.   Schematic representation of the two theories of regulation of ventilation at altitude (from *Rev. franc. études clin. et biol.*, 1959, **4,** 115–127).

In A, changes in alveolar O_2 and CO_2 pressures as well as arterial pH which occur in a subject, living first at sea level, taken to moderate altitude, who then returns to sea level. Note that pH is increased on the first day of altitude exposure, and returns to its sea level value in a few days, during which hyperventilation takes place and leads to hypocapnia and to a decrease in hypoxia (in comparison to the initial exposure).

In B and C, changes in ventilation during acclimatization, in the acclimatized state and during de-acclimatization.

B shows schematically the theory according to which the CO_2 stimulus is of importance only at the beginning of the acclimatization phase and then is replaced by other stimuli, mainly the CO_2 stimulus.

C shows schematically the theory according to which O_2 plays a very important role throughout the exposure to altitude. In this theory, the role of other stimuli is not yet clear, but it seems reasonable to believe that one of them is the CO_2–H^+ stimulus, which has however a less important part than in the preceding theory.

factors covered by the label "other stimuli" in Figure 51. At any rate, the marked decrease in P_{CO_2}, while H^+ regains a value near that observed at sea level, allows us to think that the process of adaptation to altitude aims at achieving the following chain of events. Hyperventilation decreases alveolar hypoxia, and must cause hypocapnia. Hypoxia and hypocapnia would produce plasma alkalosis if blood bicarbonate concentration was not decreased. This compensation takes place in a few days and is effected by base elimination in the urine. Once the new ventilatory equilibrium is achieved, ventilation is regulated as if at sea level, in such a manner that $P_{A_{CO_2}}$ and $P_{A_{O_2}}$ vary only slightly around their new value. By this adaptive mechanism, the body reduces hypoxia and maintains arterial pH at a value near that prevailing at low altitude, at the cost of changes in CO_2 partial pressure, which decreases considerably in relation to its value at sea level.

I O

Applied Physiology

I. HYPOXIA. CYANOSIS. HYPERCAPNIA AND ASPHYXIA

Classification of hypoxias

A hypoxic state can be defined as one in which the cells lack oxygen, or more precisely, in which the oxidizable substrates of the cell "lack" oxygen. A hypoxic state is defined in reference to a normoxic state, in which oxygenation conditions of the body are those prevailing at low altitude, that is an altitude not exceeding a few hundred feet.

Hypoxia is caused by an abnormal resistance to the flow of oxygen molecules through the gas exchange system resulting from an abnormality in one of the series of chain links between ambient air and the oxidizable substrates in the cells (see p. 21, Fig. 1 and Table XIII).

The classification proposed here is based on the different physiological and physiopathological mechanisms which cause the hypoxic condition. Other classifications are based on whether the cause of hypoxia is pathological or not, on its biological action, or on the speed at which it may develop.

It is obvious that if a disturbance in oxygen transport is found at one point of the gas exchange system, all elements of the system between this point and the cells will be hypoxic, while the part of the body interposed between this point and ambient air is oxygenated normally.

TYPE I. HYPOXIA DUE TO DECREASE OF PARTIAL PRESSURE OF OXYGEN IN THE INSPIRED AIR, OR ALTITUDE HYPOXIA

This type of hypoxia is caused by *high altitude*. The whole gas exchange system is hypoxic.

201

Table XIII

CLASSIFICATION OF HYPOXIAS ACCORDING TO THEIR PHYSIOLOGICAL OR PHYSIO-
PATHOLOGICAL MECHANISMS.

Ambient air	V E N T I L A T I O N	Type I	Hypoxia due to altitude (decrease in $P_{I_{O_2}}$)
Alveolar gas		Type II	Hypoxia due to alveolar hypoventilation
		Type III	Hypoxia due to marked unevenness in circulation/ventilation
Alveolar- - - - - - - - - - - - Capillary wall	Diffusion	Type IV	Hypoxia due to alveolar-capillary block (decrease in oxygen diffusing capacity)
	C I R C U L A T I O N	Type V	Hypoxia due to venous admixture
Blood		Type VI	Hypoxia due to decrease in concentration of functional hemoglobin
		Type VII	Hypoxia due to ischemia (generalized or localized circulatory insufficiency)
Capillary - - - - - - - - - - Wall	Diffusion		
Interstitial fluid	Diffusion	Type VIII	Hypoxia due to edema (decrease in O_2 diffusion from blood to cells)
Cell - - - - - - - - - - Wall	Diffusion	Type IX	Histotoxic hypoxia (poisoning of oxidative enzymatic systems)
Cell		Type X	Hypoxia due to overutilization

The left column shows the different links in the gas transport system (see Fig. 1, p. 21, and Fig. 2, p. 23).

In Barcroft's classification, the first five types of hypoxia are grouped under the heading "anoxic anoxia" because all these hypoxias share the common characteristic of a decrease in arterial blood P_{O_2} and S_{O_2}.

Hypoxias of type III, IV, and V have in common an abnormally high alveolar-arterial P_{O_2} difference. They result from a pathological exaggeration of the three possible physiological causes of $(A - a)P_{O_2}$ difference (see p. 123).

Altitude hypoxia which is compatible with permanent residence is not a pathological condition. In this case, the subject has adapted to a certain altitude and to a certain oxygen pressure in the inspired air, and it is possible to consider that these specific oxygenation conditions, to which the body is perfectly adapted, represent the normoxic conditions for this subject. From this standpoint, when a subject who is adapted to altitude descends to sea level, he is in hyperoxia. However, as soon as he has adapted to the new oxygenation conditions, he will be normoxic again.

Altitude hypoxia is studied separately (p. 186).

TYPE II. HYPOXIA DUE TO A DECREASE IN PARTIAL PRESSURE OF OXYGEN IN THE ALVEOLAR GAS, RELATED TO OVERALL ALVEOLAR HYPOVENTILATION, OR ALVEOLAR HYPOVENTILATION HYPOXIA

Alveolar hypoventilation hypoxia may be due either to respiratory muscle paralysis or to an abnormality of the effector ventilatory system.

a) PARALYSIS OF THE RESPIRATORY MUSCLES:

Neurological syndromes affecting the respiratory centers or intoxication of the respiratory centers: morphine, various anesthetics.

Lesions of the motor pathways of the spinal cord.

Lesions of the motor neurons, such as would occur in poliomyelitis.

Lesions of the muscles, in myasthenia or by drugs (curarization, for instance).

b) ABNORMALITIES OF THE VENTILATORY APPARATUS:

Thorax rigidity, residing either in the chest walls (various bone diseases, obesity) or in the lung (pulmonary fibrosis).

Decrease of lung volume, due either to compression of the lungs by liquid or gas in the pleural cavity or to a decrease in the volume of ventilated lung, such as in some cases of bilateral tuberculosis.

Increase of airway resistance to gas flow. This would occur in paralysis of the larynx, croup, tumors, or edema of the airways.

In this type of hypoxia, oxygen pressure, content, and saturation in the arterial blood (Pa_{O_2}, Ca_{O_2}, and Sa_{O_2} respectively) and in venous blood (Pv_{O_2}, Cv_{O_2}, and Sv_{O_2}) are decreased. Alveolar hypoventilation causes not only hypoxia but also hypercapnia, and leads to what is defined as an asphyxic state.

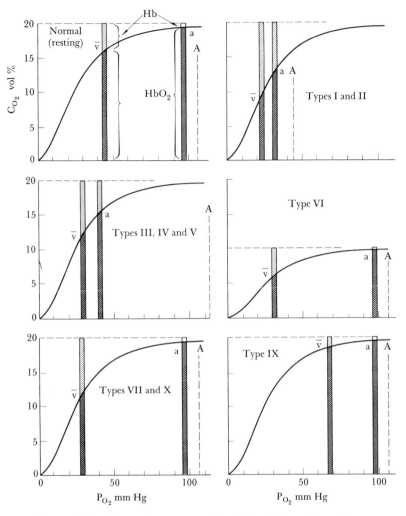

FIGURE 52.   Schematic representation of the effects of hypoxia
on the C_{O_2}–P_{O_2} curve.

Type I: hypoxia due to altitude. Type II: hypoxia due to alveolar hypoventilation.

Type III, IV, and V: hypoxia due to an increased alveolar-arterial difference
in partial pressure of oxygen.

Type VI: hypoxia due to a decrease in concentration of functional hemoglobin.
The case shown in the figure pertains to anemic hypoxia. In hypoxia due to carbon
monoxide poisoning, the C_{O_2}–P_{O_2} relationship is altered (see Fig. 6, p. 37) so that

for the same concentration of functional hemoglobin, capillary hypoxia is even more marked.

Type VII: hypoxia due to ischemia. Type X: hypoxia due to overventilation.

Type IX: histotoxic hypoxia. The venous blood is abnormally rich in O_2, because the poisoned tissues use only to a small extent the oxygen from arterial blood.

In these drawings, the Bohr effect and the possibility of an increase in hemoglobin concentration or of circulatory reactions have been neglected.

The position of the broken vertical line A corresponds to alveolar P_{O_2}.

The vertical bar a corresponds to arterial P_{O_2}.

The vertical bar $\bar{v}$ corresponds to mixed venous blood P_{O_2}.

The distance from line A to line a corresponds to the $(A - a)P_{O_2}$ difference.

In the three following types, hypoxia is due to a pathological exaggeration of the physiological difference between alveolar and arterial oxygen pressures $[(A - a)O_2$ difference]. As discussed previously, this difference can be attributed to three causes, and when one of them is abnormal, hypoxia may occur. Thus types III, IV, and V could be grouped in a single category, labeled "hypoxia due to pathological exaggeration of the $(A - a)O_2$ difference."

TYPE III. HYPOXIA DUE TO MARKED UNEVENNESS
OF CIRCULATION/VENTILATION RATIOS

Unevenness of the circulation/ventilation ratios of the different areas of the lung is most probably a physiological phenomenon (p. 119). It causes a difference of a few millimeters of mercury between alveolar and arterial oxygen pressures in the normoxic subject. When unevenness is very marked, arterial hypoxia may occur. It is possible that hypoxia due only to this cause never occurs, but this mechanism may play a role in certain diseases, for example, pulmonary emphysema.

In areas where ventilation is low in relation to perfusion (areas poorly ventilated and well perfused), alveolar gas is both hypoxic and hypercapnic, and arterial blood is significantly unsaturated and hypercapnic. On the other hand, in areas which are well ventilated and poorly perfused, alveolar gas is hyperoxic and hypocapnic. In these areas, the increase in P_{O_2} increases only slightly the oxygen *content* of the efferent arterialized blood, while both pressure and content of CO_2 are low. This last phenomenon compensates for pressure and content hypercapnia of the poorly ventilated and adequately perfused areas, and as a consequence the arterial blood is hypoxic but is only slightly, if at all, hypercapnic (p. 120).

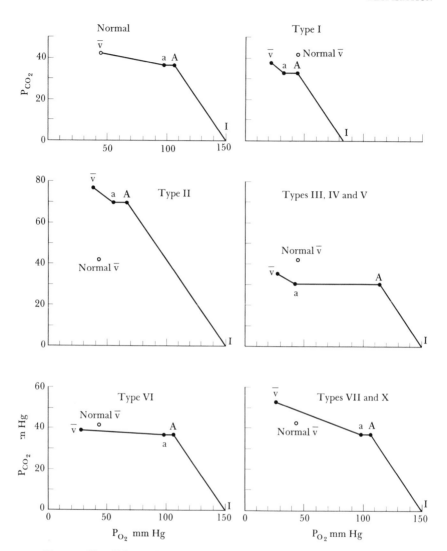

FIGURE 53.   Schematic representation of the different types of hypoxia
on the P_{O_2}–P_{CO_2} diagram.

Points I, A, a, and $\bar{v}$ represent inspired, alveolar, arterial, and mixed venous P_{O_2} and P_{CO_2}. On each of the diagrams, the "normal $\bar{v}$" point corresponds to the mixed venous blood of the normal resting subject. The diagrams do not take into account the changes (often imperfectly known or completely unknown) that can take place in the circulation, as well as the changes in hemoglobin and in other factors in acid-base balance, which can occur during the different types of hypoxia. During exercise, hypoxia increases.

Hypoxia of type IX is not shown. In this histotoxic hypoxia point $\bar{v}$ is very near point a because oxygen is utilized by the tissues only in small amounts.

These diagrams may be completed by plotting the isopleths for O_2 content and for CO_2 content (see Fig. 9, p. 41).

TYPE IV. HYPOXIA DUE TO A DECREASE IN OXYGEN DIFFUSING CAPACITY OF THE LUNG (ALVEOLAR-CAPILLARY BLOCK HYPOXIA)

Decrease in area and thickening of the alveolar wall are usually associated, for instance in pulmonary granulomatoses (sarcoidosis, berylliosis), pulmonary fibrosis, and miliary tuberculosis. In this type of hypoxia, arterial blood P_{CO_2} is not increased because carbon dioxide diffuses much more rapidly than oxygen. Hyperventilation is often present and arterial P_{CO_2} is low.

TYPE V. HYPOXIA RESULTING FROM AN ABNORMALLY HIGH VENOUS ADMIXTURE TO ARTERIALIZED BLOOD RETURNING FROM THE LUNGS, OR SHUNT HYPOXIA

Normally, a small amount of venous blood finds its way into arterialized blood (see p. 122). This amount may increase markedly in the following pathological conditions: presence of non-ventilated lung areas, atelectatic or not, in which blood does not undergo gas exchange and maintains venous composition, various types of pulmonary anastomoses, pulmonary hemangiomas, and congenital cardiopathies with right-to-left shunt (blue babies). The carbon dioxide pressure changes only slightly because there is usually a slight hyperventilation which compensates easily for the P_{CO_2} elevation which would occur because of the admixture of venous blood (Husson and Otis, 1957; Otis, 1959).

The hypoxias of the first five types all have in common a decrease in arterial P_{O_2} and O_2 saturation. This is why in Barcroft's classification, they are grouped under the heading of "anoxic anoxia." In these five types, the arterial oxygen *content* is variable. In acute hypoxia, this content is lower than normal, but if hypoxia has been maintained for some time, the O_2 content can be higher than in normoxia, because these types of hypoxias are usually accompanied by an increase in hemoglobin concentration (see p. 194 and Fig. 48).

In the two following types, VI and VII, arterial P_{O_2} is normal, but O_2 transport is abnormal because of a hemoglobin anomaly or general circulatory insufficiency.

TYPE VI. HYPOXIA DUE TO A DECREASE IN CONCENTRATION OF FUNCTIONAL
HEMOGLOBIN, OR HEMOGLOBIN HYPOXIA

Functional hemoglobin has been previously defined as hemoglobin that can
bind and liberate large quantities of oxygen.

a) All the blood hemoglobin is normal, but its concentration is low.
This is the case of anemias, acute or chronic, of any cause.

b) Hemoglobin concentration is adequate, but part of this hemoglobin
has lost its power to bind oxygen: carboxyhemoglobin, methemoglobin
(aniline poisoning for instance) (see p. 36).

In this type of hypoxia, ambient air, pulmonary ventilation, oxygen
diffusing capacity, and arterial partial pressure of oxygen are all normal.
The saturation of *functional* hemoglobin is normal, but the O_2 content, Ca_{O_2},
is low.

TYPE VII. HYPOXIA DUE TO INSUFFICIENT AMOUNT OF OXYGEN SUPPLIED TO
THE TISSUES BECAUSE OF INSUFFICIENT BLOOD FLOW, OR ISCHEMIC HYPOXIA

The blood flow insufficiency may be general, as in cardiac insufficiency, or
localized, following vascular occlusion (by embolism, thrombosis, or compression), or due to vasomotor disturbances. This type of hypoxia also includes muscular hypoxia caused by the arrest of the circulation during severe
isometric contraction.

These hypoxias are also called circulatory hypoxias, stagnant hypoxias,
or hypokinetic hypoxias. In this type of hypoxia, alveolar ventilation, pulmonary diffusion, arterial pressures of oxygen and carbon dioxide in arterial
blood are normal (or at least are not modified). However, the venous blood
which returns from the tissues is very poor in oxygen and very rich in CO_2.
In the tissues, O_2 pressure is abnormally low and CO_2 pressure abnormally
high. The tissues are both hypoxic and hypercapnic, that is asphyxic.

TYPE VIII. HYPOXIA DUE TO EDEMA AND CONSEQUENT DECREASE IN OXYGEN
DIFFUSION FROM PERIPHERAL CAPILLARY TO CELLS, OR EDEMA HYPOXIA

An increase in the volume of interstitial fluid between capillary blood and
cells decreases the oxygen pressure at the cellular level, because, in order
to move a given number of oxygen molecules, the required difference in
oxygen pressure between capillaries and cells is higher than normal.

TYPE IX. HYPOXIA DUE TO POISONING OF ENZYMATIC SYSTEMS TAKING PART
IN CELLULAR OXYDO-REDUCTION, OR HISTOTOXIC HYPOXIA (Peters and Van
Slyke, 1931)

The enzymatic systems are not able to bind the oxydizable substrates to
atomic oxygen, as is the case, for instance, in intoxication by cyanides, which

inactivate cytochrome, or in oxygen poisoning, initially described by Paul Bert (1878). In this type of hypoxia, venous blood is abnormally rich in O_2 since the poisoned tissues cannot adequately utilize the oxygen supplied by arterial blood.

TYPE X. HYPOXIA BY HYPERPRODUCTION OF OXYDIZABLE SUBSTRATES, OR "OVER-UTILIZATION HYPOXIA"

This type occurs in very severe muscular exercise. The mechanism is not clear because this hypoxia can be due either to 1) a physiological limitation in muscle circulation, which is inadequate in respect to the enormous requirements of the muscles (this would then be a circulatory hypoxia of type VI), 2) limitations in oxygen diffusion to the cells, or 3) oxygen utilization in the muscular fiber itself.

In practice, it is very frequent to find a hypoxia which does not fall exactly into any one of the above types, but is complex in nature. For example, it is rare that the hypoxia of the decompensated cardiac patient, at least in advanced stages of the disease, be only of the circulatory type (VII). Quite often, disturbances in alveolar ventilation and oxygen diffusion (cardiac lung) make this a hypoxia of mixed origin. In addition, it is also obvious that a resting subject, that is one in which the functional level is minimal, may present neither clinical manifestations nor biological signs of hypoxia, although during exercise, even very mild, the increased oxygen requirements of the tissues bring about a hypoxic state.

Although all hypoxias are, by definition, characterized by a lack of oxygen or by an anomaly of cellular oxygen utilization, each type of hypoxia is endowed with clinical and biological characteristics. In this respect, it is obviously wrong to believe that all hypoxias are accompanied by hyperventilation, dyspnea, and cyanosis.

Cyanosis

Cyanosis is characterized by a purplish color of the skin and mucosae. It is due to the presence of an abnormally high amount of non-oxygenated hemoglobin, a purplish pigment, in the capillaries of the skin and mucosae.

1) According to Lundsgaard and Van Slyke (1923) cyanosis appears when capillary blood contains more than 5 grams % of non-oxygenated hemoglobin. This high concentration can be found only in severe hypoxia. For this purpose, let us assume that mean capillary blood composition corresponds to a mixture of arterial and venous blood in equal amounts. If the

total oxygen capacity of blood is 20 vol%, corresponding to a hemoglobin concentration of 15 grams %, cyanosis will occur when mean capillary blood contains at least 5 grams % of non-oxygenated hemoglobin, that is a maximum of 10 grams % oxygenated hemoglobin. Such a condition would occur for instance if oxyhemoglobin values in arterial and venous blood were 12 and 8 grams % respectively (arterio-venous oxygen difference = $4 \times 1.36 = 5.4$ vol%). In this example, arterial oxygen saturation is $\frac{12}{15}$ or 80%, corresponding to an oxygen pressure of 48 mm Hg. Such a hypoxia would occur at sea level if the subject breathed a gas mixture containing 12% oxygen. Generally, hypoxias of types I to V, when they are permanent, are accompanied by an increased hemoglobin concentration. This increases the amount of non-oxygenated hemoglobin and enhances the appearance of cyanosis.

2) Although hypoxias of types I to V, when sufficiently marked, can cause cyanosis, hypoxias of group VI never do. Suppose for example that blood of an anemic patient contains 7.5 grams % hemoglobin, and furthermore that arterial blood is only 80% saturated and therefore contains only 6 grams % hemoglobin (this is clearly a case of mixed hypoxia), if the arterio-venous difference taken in the preceding example applies here, venous blood would contain 2 grams % of non-oxygenated hemoglobin. In this case, hypoxia does not cause cyanosis. Hypoxias of types VIII and IX, caused by factors outside the circulatory system, cannot produce cyanosis.

3) The color of the skin does not depend only on the contents of oxygen in arterial and venous blood, but also on the amount of blood in the capillaries, the color of the plasma, the quality of the blood pigments, and skin color and thickness. From all that has been said, it is apparent that cyanosis appears only in certain hypoxias and is always an index of marked capillary hypoxia. At any rate, it is often difficult to state whether cyanosis is present or not.

Hypercapnia and asphyxia

Only hypoxias accompanied by marked hypercapnia are called asphyxia. They can be encountered under three circumstances:

1) The subject breathes a confined atmosphere, one that is poor in O_2 and rich in CO_2.

2) Hypoxias of type II, due to alveolar hypoventilation are asphyxias, because alveolar hypoventilation implies both alveolar hypoxia and alveolar hypercapnia (p. 106 and Fig. 27).

Isolated hypercapnia can be produced by two causes:

a) Carbon dioxide inhalation.

b) Marked hyperoxia. This hyperoxic hypercapnia (for instance, due to inhalation of pure oxygen) is not astonishing, since hemoglobin plays an important part in carbon dioxide transport. If the amount of oxyhemoglobin is relatively high, blood can bind carbon dioxide only through an increase in carbon dioxide pressure (Haldane effect, see p. 39). This effect of variation of arterial oxygen content on tissue CO_2 pressure is called the Gesell effect (Gesell, 1923).

As an example, if a subject breathes pure oxygen, the volume of oxygen carried by arterial blood is approximately 3 vol% higher than that transported in normoxia. This is because the arterial blood is now completely saturated, and especially because of the increase in dissolved O_2 (p. 31). Under these conditions, venous blood will be more saturated than in normoxia, and in this case it will contain 17.5 vol% instead of 14.5 vol%. If the total O_2 capacity is 20 vol%, the amount of non-oxygenated hemoglobin in 100 ml of venous blood will be 1.85 grams % in hyperoxia as against 4.05 grams % in normoxia. Because of this decrease in non-oxygenated hemoglobin, carbon dioxide can be bound by blood only through an increase in P_{CO_2} (in this case, a few millimeters of mercury) of the venous blood in relation to the pressure at which the same amount of CO_2 is transported in normoxic conditions.

These considerations lead to very important conclusions in terms of *oxygen therapy*. It is necessary to start by stating that in asphyxias which accompany ventilatory or circulatory insufficiency, a greater danger may result from hypercapnia and acidosis than from hypoxia, and that only treatment of the ventilatory or circulatory disturbances will correct both hypoxia and hypercapnia. Administration of oxygen in asphyxia is dangerous because hyperoxygenation increases hypercapnia and tissue acidosis.

Furthermore, in some subjects, oxygen inhalation may cause a decrease in ventilation or even apnea, an additional cause of hypercapnia, sometimes with catastrophic results. For example, it is frequent to note that subjects deeply anesthetized and breathing spontaneously exhibit respiratory center depression, especially if the subject had been given morphine or barbiturates. Respiratory center depression is evidenced by hypoventilation, hypercapnia, and hypoxia. In this case, regulation of respiration is not based on CO_2 and H^+ stimuli, but is maintained only by a strong O_2 stimulus (respiratory centers maintain their excitability to the O_2 chemoreceptor stimuli). Abolition of the latter by inhalation of a hyperoxic gas mixture produces apnea (Marshall and Rosenfeld, 1936). A similar situation can be observed in emphysematous subjects with ventilatory hypoventilation and increase in $(A - a)P_O$ difference. Inhalation of oxygen abolishes abruptly the O_2

stimulus, and the subject hypoventilates even more or becomes apneic, and as a result, hypercapnia increases. Since hyperoxia causes cyanosis to disappear, one may feel satisfied, at least temporarily, with the results obtained by oxygen therapy. This mistake can be fatal, because the increment in hypercapnia augments the acidosis and may cause rapidly irreversible cardiovascular disturbances. If an anesthetized subject breathes poorly, one should resort to respiratory analeptics and especially to artificial respiration. Should the subject remain hypoxic in spite of the artificial respiration, a hyperoxic mixture may be given to breathe, with artificial respiration being continued.

The dangers of hyperoxia are not limited to tissue hypercapnia and the disturbance in the regulation of respiration it can produce. Marked and prolonged increase in pulmonary oxygen may lead to various disturbances, pulmonary congestion and edema, atelectasis, etc. (see Rahn, 1961).

Thus the use of oxygen therapy must be carefully weighed, and is especially indicated in some hypoxias of type I, V, VI, VII, VIII, or IX. One of the major indications of oxygen therapy is to be found in certain hemoglobin hypoxias (type VI), in particular hypoxia due to carbon monoxide poisoning. Finally, it should be noted that, in order to correct hypoxia, it is often unnecessary — and sometimes dangerous, in view of the hypercapnia and pulmonary edema that may follow — to have the subject breathe pure oxygen or even a mixture containing 60% oxygen. For example, hypoxia due to disturbance in pulmonary diffusing capacity can often be corrected by raising alveolar oxygen pressure to about 200 mm Hg, a level that can be achieved by inhalation of a gas mixture containing only one-third oxygen.

II. ARTIFICIAL PULMONARY RESPIRATION

Definition

1) It is quite usual to consider artificial respiration as being synonymous with artificial ventilation, but this definition would be too narrow. As previously discussed, ventilation is only one of the numerous processes involved in body respiration, so that the term artificial respiration should include, in addition to artificial ventilation, also artificial circulation. The following section is devoted to a study of artificial pulmonary respiration; reasons for choosing this name rather than artificial ventilation will be discussed later.

In the past, the aim of artificial respiration was to ensure ventilatory reanimation, that is return to spontaneous ventilation. Artificial respiration was only an emergency procedure, applied for a few hours at most. Nowadays we also have the ability to maintain artificial respiration for several months or several years.

2) A considerable number of methods and techniques of artificial pulmonary respiration have been designed. Only methods and the principle on which their application is based will be reviewed, without going into the exact description of the techniques and their variations, details of which can be found in the specialized texts (Karpovich, 1953).

No classification of artificial pulmonary respiration is entirely satisfactory from the physiological standpoint. In essence, inspiration is always tied to a transthoracic force directed from the alveolar spaces to the outer surface of the thorax, while expiration is related to an opposed force. Some artificial respiration methods are based on forces which maintain the normal relationship between ambient and pulmonary pressures, while others disturb this relationship considerably, in which case the normal hemodynamic conditions are completely changed. In this respect, it should be remembered that during a normal inspiration intrathoracic pressure decreases while abdominal pressure increases, while during expiration the inverse takes place. These variations in abdominal and thoracic pressures play a very important part in normal hemodynamics and are one of the major factors which effect simultaneous adaptation of cardiac and ventilatory flow to the body respiratory needs.

The classification which follows is based on that proposed by Cara (1955). The different methods are divided into two major groups: those which produce artificial pulmonary respiration by acting on the outer surface of the thorax, and those which act by applying pressures at the opening of the airway.

Classification

1) METHODS BASED ON FORCES APPLIED TO THE OUTER SURFACE OF THE THORAX

a) ACTIVE EXPIRATION, PASSIVE INSPIRATION

The relaxed thorax of the subject in ventilatory syncope is compressed and a certain volume of air is expired, which reduces the thorax volume lower than its relaxation volume. When thoracic compression is released, the elastic properties of the thorax restore the relaxation volume. Thus inspiration is passive, and the energy required to perform inspiratory work is derived from the elastic potential energy stored in the thorax during active expiration.

1) *Prone subject.* The best known method is that of Schäfer, in which the

operator places his hands on the lower ribs on each side and compresses rhythmically the lower part of the thorax.

2) *Supine subject.* Compression of the thorax or of the abdomen, either through a breastplate or a bandage around the thorax, or sometimes the abdomen, which is rhythmically tightened and relaxed.

b) ACTIVE INSPIRATION, PASSIVE EXPIRATION

In this case, a force which expands the relaxed thorax of the apneic subject is exerted, and this introduces into the lungs a certain volume of air which is added to the relaxation volume. When the force which produced inspiration is released, the thorax returns to its relaxation volume by expiring some air. The energy required for this expiration is supplied by the potential elastic energy accumulated in the thorax during inspiration. Expiration is said to be passive. In reality, this would occur only if the inspiratory force was released suddenly. For obvious mechanical reasons, this cannot be done, and expiration is braked.

1) *Prone subject.* The arms of the subjects are folded, with the forehead resting on the hands. The operator, placed in front of the head of the subject, raises the forearms and thereby moves the subject's shoulders backwards (this maneuver is the inspiratory phase of the Holger Nielsen method).

2) *Supine subject: Manual method.* The arms of the subject are pulled up and back (first movement of Silvester method) which increases the lateral and antero-posterior diameters of the thorax. Alternatively the spinal column can be hyperextended.

Electrophrenic respiration. Theoretically, this method can produce a pulmonary respiration which maintains the thoraco-abdominal pressure conditions required for normal hemodynamic functions. It consists in stimulating the phrenic nerve through the skin of the neck, on one or both sides. Unfortunately, percutaneous stimulation of phrenic nerves is not easy and the method has not gained wide recognition.

c) ACTIVE INSPIRATION, ACTIVE EXPIRATION

This method combines the preceding two. Expiration is assisted, and generally the expiration is extended beyond relaxation volume, as in the active expiration-passive inspiration method. In other words, the operator is active during both phases of the respiratory cycle, and the end-inspiratory and end-expiratory positions of the thorax are on either side of the relaxation volume.

1) *Prone subject: Holger Nielsen method.* In this case, inspiration is obtained as in the active inspiration-passive expiration method on the prone subject (above). In addition, during expiration, the operator puts his hands on the scapulae and compresses the thorax.

2) *Supine subject: Silvester method.* The inspiration of the supine subject is

active, as in the active inspiration-passive expiration method (p. 214). During expiration, the operator brings the subject's arms against the anterolateral walls of the thorax and compresses.

Iron lung. This improper term is often applied to a closed box in which pressure can be changed by means of a pump. The subject lies supine within the box, with the head protruding through a plastic collar which makes a tight connection as long as the pressure does not exceed a few centimeters of water. When a negative pressure, in relation to atmosphere, is created inside the box using the pump (or a hand-operated bellows in case of emergency) a force directed outwards is applied to the thorax. The thorax expands, the intra-alveolar pressure decreases in relation to ambient pressure, and air enters the lungs. When a sufficient volume of air has been inspired, box pressure is returned to atmospheric level, and passive expiration occurs. Generally, expiration is also made active by creating in the box a pressure higher than atmospheric.

Eve's method, or tilt bed. While all other methods act on the bony structures, this method is based on rhythmic displacement of the abdominal viscera and therefore of the diaphragm. The subject is placed on a bed, or on a board in case of emergency, and secured adequately, generally in the supine position (although the method can be applied, especially following drowning, in the prone position). The bed can tilt around a transversal axis under the center of gravity of the horizontal subject. When the bed is tilted so that the subject's head is low and the feet are high, the abdominal mass presses on the diaphragm which is therefore displaced in the direction of the head and thereby causes expiration. When the bed is brought back to horizontal position, then tilted in the opposite direction (feet low, head high), the abdominal mass pulls down on the diaphragm and inspiration occurs. The maximal angle between the plane of the bed and the horizontal plane is about 45° to 50°.

2) INTERNAL ACTION METHODS

The air pressure at the airway openings is changed rhythmically.

In this method, an increase in air pressure at the airway openings (mask, mouth, intratracheal tube introduced through the mouth, a tracheotomy) will cause expansion of the thorax and active inspiration. Here again, expiration may be passive, due to potential elastic energy, or, as is more often the case, it can be activated by producing at the airway opening a negative pressure in reference to atmosphere. According to the level of inspiratory and expiratory pressures, the tidal volume may be entirely on one side of the relaxation volume, or on both.

a) *Mouth-to-mouth*. This technique has been mainly applied to newborn infants or to babies. At present, it is being extended to all age levels. It is usually very efficient, but care must be taken not to exert too high positive or negative pressures and to remember that the normal tidal volume of the newborn does not exceed 20 to 30 ml. It is possible to replace the mouth-to-mouth technique by a connection, sometimes so designed that it is not actually the operator's own lung gas which is blown into the airways (for example, see Greene, 1957).

b) *Manual or electrical pump*. The pressure supplied by the pump can be applied through a mask but an endotracheal tube is usually used. The technique used by the anesthetists, which consists in squeezing a bag rhythmically, belongs to this category. The artificial respiration pump used in animal physiology cannot be used on man. There are some pumps (for example, the Engström pump) which allow the subject's respiration to be controlled adequately, by varying tidal volume, frequency, and elective duration of inspiration and expiration, and in addition measuring the ventilatory flow. However, operation of these pumps is not simple, which means that they can be used only by trained personnel.

c) *Artificial ventilation without thoracic movements by variations in ambient pressure. Thunberg's barorespirator.* In the preceding methods, the pressure at the airway opening is changed, while the rest of the body remains exposed to ambient pressure. This establishes a force which is directed from the alveolar spaces to the surface of the thorax during inspiration, and which mobilizes the structures that are interposed, namely the chest walls and the lungs.

The principle of Thunberg's method is completely different. The subject's whole body, head included, is placed in a box where the ambient pressure is changed rhythmically from a few centimeters of mercury above atmospheric. For example, when ambient pressure is increased, mouth pressure is higher than alveolar pressure, and air enters the lungs, with no change in thoracic volume. At end-inspiration, *the thorax has exactly the same volume*, but lung gas density has increased, as has the density of ambient air, which has been compressed. When barometric pressure is restored, or it is a few centimeters of mercury lower, air comes out of the lungs.

In reality, during these variations in ambient pressure, the thorax moves slightly, because airway resistance to gas flow delays equilibration of ambient and intra-alveolar pressures. This can be overcome by delaying the pressure changes around the chest in proportion to the variations in pressure around the head (see Barach, 1948).

Physiological effects

1) VENTILATORY EFFECTS

There are several methods for evaluating the ventilatory effects of the various artificial respiration methods. The effects of the different techniques can be studied on the apneic subject.

— during apnea produced by hypocapnia following voluntary hyperventilation. However, the respiratory muscles are not necessarily relaxed and the subject will resist a ventilation for which he feels no need at the time, since he is in hypocapnia and respiratory alkalosis;

— during voluntary apnea with complete relaxation of the ventilatory muscles, which is difficult to achieve;

— during apnea due to pathological or pharmacological (curare) paralysis, without doubt the best method. Effects of artificial ventilation have also been studied on the non-rigid cadaver.

It is also possible to study the effects of artificial respiration maneuvers

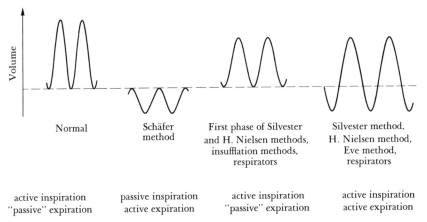

| Normal | Schäfer method | First phase of Silvester and H. Nielsen methods, insufflation methods, respirators | Silvester method, H. Nielsen method, Eve method, respirators |

| active inspiration "passive" expiration | passive inspiration active expiration | active inspiration "passive" expiration | active inspiration active expiration |

FIGURE 54.   Schematic representation of the ventilatory effects of some artificial respiration methods.

On the ordinate, changes in lung volume. Inspiration is upward. Time is on the abscissa.

The horizontal broken line indicates the relaxation volume of the thorax.

Active inspiration and active expiration correspond to cases where thorax volume is increased or decreased by application of the outside force. Expiration and inspiration are passive when the energy required for this ventilatory phase is supplied by the potential elastic energy stored in the thorax because it has been brought to a volume higher or lower than relaxation volume during the preceding phase.

on the subject breathing spontaneously, by measuring the ventilation increase resulting from superimposing on each spontaneous ventilatory movement the maneuver used in artificial respiration (Karpovich, 1953). One can also study what changes in inspiratory or expiratory position are produced by the artificial respiration maneuver, maintained continuously for one minute, and assume that this change is the same as that which occurs transiently when the maneuver is applied intermittently (Asmussen and Nielsen, 1950).

It is generally accepted that, from the standpoint of ventilatory efficiency, all methods are good, except Schäfer's. The relative inefficiency of the latter is due to the fact that the tidal volume which results must be part of the expiratory reserve volume, which is normally rather small, and may be even smaller in subjects in ventilatory syncope, in whom there is often pulmonary edema or liquid in the alveoli (drowning).

At any rate, the artificial respiration maneuver can have the proper ventilatory effect only if the airway is patent. It is necessary to avoid at all costs airway obstruction by secretions, the tongue, or backward movement of the mandibula which displaces the floor of the mouth with it. It is therefore absolutely necessary to position the subject properly, to free the opening of the airway by bending the head back and pushing the mandibula forward, and to aspirate any fluid that may be found in the trachea and the bronchi. The ideal procedure would be to intubate the subject (see Safar, 1959).

When some respiratory movements are present, the artificial respiration maneuver must be timed to obtain perfect synchrony.

It is sometimes useful to have the subject inhale a gas mixture enriched in oxygen, but it is useless, and even dangerous, to give him a hypercapnic mixture, since the subject is already hypercapnic because of the ventilatory syncope.

2) CIRCULATORY EFFECTS (see Whittenberger, 1955)

In case of cardiac arrest, artificial respiration is usually inadequate to reanimate the heart, and pharmacological, electrical, or mechanical cardiac reanimation methods must be used. Artificial respiration *per se* is incapable of maintaining sufficient circulation when the heart is arrested.

Certain artificial respiration methods can enhance circulation, this being the case of methods which do not alter the normal relationship between intrathoracic and intra-abdominal pressures (see p. 62). The Silvester and H. Nielsen methods are those that disturb the least normal hemodynamic conditions.

On the contrary, the respirators and internal action methods create poor hemodynamic conditions. In this respect it should be noted that both decrease in pressure around the thorax, which occurs in an iron lung, and the increase in airway pressure produced by a pump connected to the airways produce inspiration and therefore have the same hemodynamic effects. In either case, the pressure in the alveolar spaces is higher than that acting on the thorax and the abdominal pressure, whereas normally those pressures are essentially the same. The result is that the intrathoracic pressure is abnormally higher than that of the rest of the body and that venous blood return to the thorax is hindered, while under normal conditions this return is enhanced by the increase in thoracic volume and the decrease in intrathoracic pressure in relation to abdominal pressure. In practice, if the pressure variations are not very marked, a new hemodynamic equilibrium will be established. However this new steady state will be achieved only if the respiration pressures are not too great.

3) EFFECTS ON GAS EXCHANGE

Gas exchange depends, among other things, on the cardiac output and ventilation (see p. 119). As previously discussed, this gas exchange takes place under well-defined conditions which bring about certain O_2 and CO_2 alveolar and arterial pressures. Artificial respiration must strive to restore alveolar and arterial O_2 and CO_2 pressures to normal values.

However, when emergency reanimation of a subject in ventilatory syncope is required, the immediate aim is to ventilate the subject, because the chances of survival are nil within a few minutes, and there is neither time nor the technical means of controlling exactly the alveolar ventilation level. The choice of method is often dictated by the prevailing conditions. Only an adequate ventilation (which requires patency of the airways), to which may be added inhalation of pure oxygen, may reanimate the subject.

The methods known as diffusion respiration and apneic oxygenation are not adequate. These methods consist in connecting the subject to a source of pure oxygen — in some cases in producing a continuous flow of oxygen through a tracheal catheter — without producing respiratory movements. In this case it is possible to obtain adequate oxygenation of the arterial blood, because blood binds oxygen and thereby produces a slow oxygen flow into the alveolar spaces (diffusion really plays only a minor role), but the lack of alveolar ventilation causes an alveolar hypercapnia that may reach several hundred millimeters of mercury. Apneic oxygenation is an experimental curiosity but not a valid reanimation method.

At the present time the indications for artificial pulmonary ventilation are much broader than just ventilatory syncope. Artificial respiration is indicated in all cases of prolonged paralysis, such as in poliomyelitis or curarization (which is used, for instance, in treatment of tetanus and in anesthesiology). In these cases the subject must obviously be ventilated, but the artificial alveolar ventilation must produce the proper alveolar gas flow and maintain the normal alveolar oxygen and carbon dioxide pressures. Belief that the best artificial respiration is that which produces the highest alveolar ventilation can stem only from crass ignorance since alveolar hyperventilation means hypocapnia and alkalosis.

Alveolar ventilation must be neither too high nor too low; the proper ventilation level is that which ensures normal oxygen and carbon dioxide partial pressures in the alveolar gas, but this correct ventilation is often difficult to achieve. The proper ventilation level must obviously be based on normal respiratory physiology data. Certain simple calculations, also appearing in the form of nomograms, which are easy to read (Radford, 1955), enable the required ventilation to be approximately determined. However these calculations, which are valid for normal subjects, are not always applicable to patients. It is also possible to try to control alveolar gas composition, but alveolar gas sampling in patients is generally impossible, or may yield inaccurate samples. Thus the artificial ventilation apparatus must be regulated on the basis of the only values which are really important, that is, pH and partial pressures of O_2 and CO_2 in arterial blood, the only valid indices of the respiratory function of the lung. The aim of artificial pulmonary ventilation is therefore not only to ensure exchange of gas in the respiratory spaces, but to provide an adequate alveolar ventilation (a difficult task when thorax and lung mechanical properties, distribution of inspired gas and of blood in the lungs, or oxygen diffusing capacity of the lungs are abnormal), and, in the last resort, to allow gas exchange which results in normal arterial blood P_{O_2}, P_{CO_2}, and pH values. This is why the term "artificial pulmonary respiration" is better than "artificial ventilation" which may lead one to think that the pulmonary respiratory function is only a matter of ventilation. The equipment used in artificial pulmonary respiration is delicate and requires continuous supervision.

III. RESPIRATION AND ABNORMAL GAS PRESSURES

The conditions and desires of modern life create respiratory physiology problems which are unknown in nature. Man has imposed upon himself variations in ambient pressures from 100 mm Hg (one-seventh of an atmosphere, at an altitude of approximately 14,000 meters or 46,000 ft) to several atmospheres (these enormous pressures being obtained during diving). It must be remembered that a column of sea water of 10 meters or 33 ft (10.3 meters or 34 ft for fresh water) exerts a pressure of one atmosphere (or 760 mm Hg, or 1000 millibars, or 14.7 lbs/sq in). Thus a sea diver at a depth of 50 meters (165 ft) is exposed to a total pressure of 6 atmospheres.

Very high partial pressures of oxygen or nitrogen in the inspired gas lead to disturbances which can be fatal. Very low oxygen pressures are also a danger to the body (see p. 187), but, a decrease in nitrogen pressure, however, has no effect on the body. In addition to those effects of prolonged exposure to abnormal pressures, rapid changes from one pressure to another can cause disturbances due to physical causes, the most severe being those that can occur with decompression.

Hyperoxia

1) HYPEROXIA OF LESS THAN ONE ATMOSPHERE
(see Bean, 1945; Comroe, 1950)

The pulmonary disturbances due to prolonged inhalation of mixtures containing more than 60% oxygen are listed on page 211. This phenomenon is sometimes called the "Lorrain Smith effect" (Smith, 1899). Inhalation of pure oxygen at sea level for a few hours causes subjective and pulmonary manifestations (cough, chest pain), while at an altitude of 5600 meters (19,000 feet) no disturbances occur after 24 hours (see Behnke, in *Decompression Sickness;* Becker-Freyseng and Clamann, 1942). Therefore it is not the increase in oxygen fraction which causes these disturbances, but the increase in oxygen pressure to 400 mm Hg or higher. However, in all cases of inhalation of hyperoxic gas mixtures the resulting denitrogenation enhances the occurrence of pulmonary atelectasis (see Rahn, 1961).

In moderate hyperoxia, only the lungs and the walls of the pulmonary veins and of the systemic arteries are subjected to a significantly elevated oxygen pressure. In the tissues and in venous blood the oxygen consumption of the tissues reduces oxygen pressure to a few dozen millimeters of mercury, values nevertheless slightly higher than those observed in normoxia (Lambertsen, 1953). The fact that increased oxygen pressure is maximum in the lungs explains why the disturbances due to inhalation of hyperoxic gas mixtures affect mainly the lungs. In addition, premature children placed in hyperoxygenated incubators run the risk of retrolental fibroplasia, possibly caused by a constriction of retinal vessels under the influence of blood hyperoxygenation.

2) VERY MARKED HYPEROXIA

When the oxygen pressure is well above one atmosphere, disturbances of a different nature take place (Paul Bert, 1878), disturbances sometimes called "oxygen toxicity," "oxygen poisoning," or "Paul Bert effect." In this case, an exposure of several minutes, when the subject is moderately active physically, or of several hours in the subject at rest, leads to nausea, dizziness, subjective feelings of alcoholic intoxication or of anxiety, tremor of the face muscles, pallor, tachycardia, increase in arterial pressure, and sometimes convulsions or syncope. These disturbances and accidents occur earlier if the physical activity is greater or the oxygen pressure is higher. These manifestations of oxygen toxicity are seldom encountered when the oxygen pressure is less than 1.7 atmospheres. The importance of this phenomenon of oxygen toxicity in terms of diving limitations will be discussed subsequently.

The mechanism of oxygen toxicity is related, at least in part, to a change in properties of the enzymatic systems which take part in cellular oxidation reactions (see Lambertsen, 1955). At any rate, the oxygen consumption decreases (a finding duplicated in tissue cultures), and cells exposed to abnormally high oxygen pressures are really in hypoxia, called histotoxic hypoxia, corresponding to type IX on p. 208.

Nitrogen breathing under several atmospheres (hypernitrogenation)

When the partial pressure of nitrogen reaches several atmospheres, consciousness disturbances appear, similar to those observed in hypoxia or in alcoholic intoxication: euphoria, loss of memory, slowing of thought process, lack of motor co-ordination. When nitrogen breathing is maintained or increased under several atmospheres, a state of coma may result. The disturbances appear when the nitrogen pressure exceeds 4 atmospheres, and reach alarming proportions at 6 or 7 atmospheres. The narcotic effect of nitrogen has been attributed to its high solubility in fat (see p. 25), a common property of all anesthetic agents. This interpretation seems to be confirmed by the fact that substitution of hydrogen or helium — both gases poorly soluble in fats — and adjustment of the oxygen fraction so as to avoid oxygen poisoning enables the mixture to go up to pressures of 18 atmospheres (equivalent to a 170-meter or 570-ft dive).

Hypercapnia

The toxic effects of nitrogen and oxygen are enhanced by inhalation of a hypercapnic gas mixture. This means that the disturbances caused by hyperoxygenation or hypernitrogenation occur at lower oxygen or nitrogen pressures when hypercapnia is present. This leads to one important consequence: even the smallest accumulation of CO_2 in the gas inspired by divers must be avoided. For example, if the inspired gas contains 1% CO_2 (a fraction at which no physiological responses can be detected at sea level), the CO_2 partial pressure at a depth of 60 meters (200 ft), where the total pressure is 5320 mm Hg, reaches 53 mm Hg, a value corresponding to 7% CO_2 at sea level. Obviously, in any case, there is also the additional danger caused by the toxic properties of hypercapnia (see p. 155).

Diving

1) DISTURBANCES DUE TO INCREASED GAS PRESSURE

a) INCREASE IN TOTAL PRESSURE. Man has been subjected to a pressure of 17 atmospheres. As long as the pressure of body gas pockets (intestinal gas, lung gases, middle ear gas) is the same as that of ambient water, this increase in total pressure, considerable as it may be, is by itself innocuous because the tissues are not compressible. In the subject wearing a face mask, inspired air pressure, and therefore lung gas pressure, is equal to the pressure of ambient water. The thoracic tissues (lung and chest wall) interposed between alveolar gas and outer surface of the thorax are not subjected to any important difference in pressure, an indispensable condition for normal hemodynamics (see p. 84). (In fact this is true only in the horizontal subject because in the vertical subject the water pressure at the level of the thorax is higher than the pressure at mouth level and therefore within the lungs. This pressure difference, of the order of a few centimeters of water, although not negligible, is well tolerated.)

The only physiological effect of the increase in total pressure is an increase in the work performed by the respiratory muscles, because the increase in inspired air density causes an increase in turbulent resistance (see p. 76).

b) NITROGEN NARCOSIS, OXYGEN TOXICITY. The disturbances due to the narcotic action of nitrogen appear when the nitrogen pressure exceeds 4 atmospheres, as indicated previously. When the subject inspires air (using the Cousteau-Gagnan apparatus) at a depth of 50 meters (165 ft), nitrogen and oxygen pressure are, respectively, 4.75 and 1.25 atmospheres approximately (Fig. 55). This oxygen pressure is theoretically not sufficient to cause toxicity, but nitrogen pressure is capable of producing disturbances after a certain time. This would make it impossible to reside at depths lower than 165 ft for any appreciable length of time. Besides, in this case, the effects of increased oxygen pressure would be added to those of increased nitrogen pressure. Nevertheless, dives of a few minutes duration to depths of more than

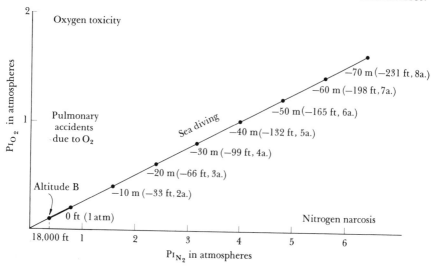

FIGURE 55.   Oxygen and nitrogen pressures in inspired air (P_{IO_2} and P_{IN_2}) expressed in atmospheres, at altitude, at sea level, and during sea diving.

On the diagonal line, point 0 feet corresponds to the oxygen and nitrogen pressures at sea level, that is 0.21 and 0.79 atm. To the left of that point is the area of low pressures, representing altitudes. The thick part of the line shows the region which constitutes man's normal habitat. Point B corresponds to arrow 2 on Figure 46, p. 187.

To the right of point 0 feet is the area where pressure is higher than the pressure at sea level, usually encountered in diving. Each 10 meters (33 ft) of sea water (10.3 meters or 34 ft of fresh water) exert a pressure of one atmosphere, which must be added to the normal atmospheric pressure. At a depth of 10 meters (33 ft), the pressure is therefore 2 atmospheres (2a, as shown in brackets) and so on for each additional 10 meters (33 ft).

The pressure shown on the diagonal line is the sum of the nitrogen pressure on the abscissae and of the oxygen pressure on the ordinates, when the subject breathes air. For instance, at a depth of 40 meters (132 ft), the total pressure is 5 atmospheres, oxygen and nitrogen exerting 1 and 4 atmospheres respectively.

At pressures higher than 4 atmospheres, nitrogen has a narcotic effect in a few minutes or a few hours.

At pressures higher than 0.7 atmospheres of oxygen, maintained for at least 20 hours, lung disturbances (Lorrain Smith effect) may occur. When the pressure reaches or exceeds 2 atmospheres, signs of oxygen toxicity (Paul Bert effect) may appear.

Note that the point labeled 1 atmosphere on the ordinate corresponds to oxygen breathing at sea level and is in the area of pulmonary disturbances caused by oxygen.

100 meters (330 ft), breathing air, have been made for demonstration purposes.

If inspired air nitrogen is replaced by helium or hydrogen (oxygen-hydrogen mixtures may however be explosive), it is possible to dive to greater depths without danger of narcosis, provided however that the oxygen fraction be lowered enough for the oxygen pressure to remain below 1.7 atmospheres. For instance, if a sea dive to a depth of 100 meters (330 ft) is planned, the helium-oxygen mixture must contain less than 15% oxygen.

2) DISTURBANCES DUE TO RAPID CHANGES IN AMBIENT PRESSURE

a) MECHANICAL EFFECTS OF VOLUME CHANGE OF BODY GAS POCKETS. As discussed above (p. 223), changes in total pressure have no effect on the body as long as the pressure in gas-filled cavities (middle ear, sinuses, lungs, gastrointestinal tract) is the same as the ambient pressure. This is why in diving, during descent and ascent to the surface, it is necessary to allow the pressure in the middle ear to equilibrate with ambient pressure. In other words, pressure on both sides of the tympanic membrane must be equal. Pressure inequality would cause severe pain and may rupture the membrane.

Compression of intestinal gases during diving and subsequent decompression during ascent, or decompression during flight in non-pressurized planes, may cause abdominal pain.

During free dives, that is dives with no breathing apparatus, such as those executed by pearl divers, lung volume decreases during descent and increases during ascent. For example, the 5 liters of gas contained in the lungs at the surface are reduced to 1 liter at 40 meters (130 ft). These changes in volume are necessary to allow the intrapulmonary pressure to equilibrate with ambient pressure. Under no circumstances should the subject try to resist those changes by contraction of the thoracic muscles, since very severe complications may arise. Assuming a subject to be at a depth of 30 meters (99 ft) with 3 liters of gas inside the lungs (this could occur in assisted dives), if this subject ascended rapidly to 10 meters (33 ft) below the surface, the gas volume in the lungs would double, and at the surface the volume would theoretically reach 12 liters. This makes it obvious that air must be expired during ascent. Otherwise the lung volume would increase and after reaching the maximum lung volume, a marked increase in intrathoracic pressure would appear. This may rupture the lungs and cause hemorrhage or gas embolism. The cardinal rule that the subject must observe during ascent is not to oppose gas movement across the airways (if the subject is using a breathing system, it is sufficient to continue to breathe freely in order to allow the lung volume to readjust).

This rule is also paramount in aviation in the case of rapid or explosive decompression of a pressurized cabin.

b) DENITROGENATION DISTURBANCES (see *Decompression Sickness*, 1951)

1) When an air-breathing subject dives, the volume of nitrogen dissolved in his body increases. Nitrogen diffuses only slowly through the body tissues because of its low solubility in water. However, the ability of the body to store nitrogen is considerable because of the high solubility of nitrogen in fat. In addition, blood flow through fatty tissues is extremely small. As a result of all this, when the nitrogen pressure in the inspired air is raised, the nitrogen stores of the body increase slowly, over a period of 5 to 6 hours, the uptake by the stores ceasing only when the partial pressure of nitrogen in all body tissues is equal to that prevailing in alveolar gas and arterial blood. Similarly, when the subject surfaces, complete elimination of the nitrogen accumulated during the dive is extremely long. The volume taken up during compression, as well as the volume given up during decompression, can be considered as the sum of several exponential functions of time. Each of these functions has a certain "half time," defined as the time required to store or release half of the total quantity that can be stored according to this exponential curve. According to Haldane, the body can be visualized as being made of five tissues, having half-time values of 5, 10, 20, 40, and 75 minutes, respectively. The last value shows why body nitrogen saturation or desaturation requires several hours. It is also possible to explain the curve which describes nitrogen uptake or elimination on the basis of only two or three exponentials.

At sea level, the volume of nitrogen present in the body tissues is about one liter, and at a few atmospheres reaches a few liters. The increase in oxygen stores is relatively much lower than that of the nitrogen stores because cellular oxygen uptake decreases O_2 pressure considerably in tissues and venous blood.

When a gas in equilibrium within a liquid is decompressed, bubbles may form in the liquid. In reality these bubbles form only if the decrease in pressure is marked. Otherwise the gas may remain in solution, without evolving bubbles, a condition known as *supersaturation*. Bubble formation is enhanced by shocks or movement, as can be demonstrated by the additional gas loss that is produced by shaking an open champagne bottle. Therefore, when the subject has remained at depth a certain time without any disturbances, rapid ascent is dangerous since it may cause decompression accidents, which are enhanced by movement, especially if they are sudden.

2) *Description of the disturbances.* The accidents which constitute "caisson disease" usually do not occur during decompression, but a few minutes

later, 85% of these occurring during the first hour following decompression. In exceptional cases, accidents have been observed more than fifteen hours after decompression.

The most common form consists of dull or sharp pain, usually localized near the joints ("bends"), especially around the knees in divers and around the shoulders in swimmers. Less often seen are a burning or itching sensation under the skin, sometimes accompanied by papular formations or skin swelling, as well as retrosternal pain ("chokes") which is especially felt during deep inspiration and may be accompanied by cough. These painful sensations appear late and are related to accumulation of bubbles in thoracic blood vessels. There can also be neurological disturbances (deafness, visual disturbances, dizziness), motor disturbances, and even paraplegia, or more rarely hemiplegia. These can be ascribed to bubble formations in the central nervous system.

The cause of these accidents had already been clearly recognized by Paul Bert who stated: "These accidents must be attributed to the release of nitrogen, an excessive amount of which had been stored in the body, in accordance with Dalton's law.

"This gas passes in the blood vessels, the various body fluids, and even tissues themselves. It can therefore, according to the conditions, arrest pulmonary circulation, decrease perfusion, and produce softening of certain parts of the central nervous system, especially the lumbar enlargement of the spinal cord, disrupt tissues, and produce tumors or various degrees of emphysema. The seriousness of these accidents depends on both location and the extent of these multiple disturbances."

3) "Faced with these awful accidents a double question comes naturally to mind: How can they be prevented? How should they be treated?"

"*Immediate recompression* . . . is the only means of combating efficiently decompression accidents." (Paul Bert, 1878) This is why, in places where people are engaged in diving or where caisson work is done, there are always compression chambers in which subjects who have become victims of accidents can be recompressed. These chambers are large enough for a physician to accompany a subject. This therapy is extremely efficient because recompression decreases the volume of the bubbles. However, a very long time may be required to drive back into solution the nitrogen they contain.

As to prevention of these terrible accidents, Paul Bert has written "They can be prevented, as common sense shows and experience proves, by an adequately slow decompression." Paul Bert recommended slow and progressive decompression, but at present *step decompresssion*, introduced by Haldane, is used. Because of the phenomenon of supersaturation without bubble formation during decompression, bubbles form only when the pressure becomes less than one-half the initial pressure. It is therefore safe to bring a subject rapidly from a pressure of 4 atmospheres to 2 atmospheres of *nitrogen* (from 40 meters to 15 meters, breathing air), just as it is safe to bring him from 1.6 atmospheres to 0.8 atmospheres of nitrogen (10 meters to sea level). On the other hand, to bring a subject rapidly from 20 meters to the surface (from 2.4 to 0.8 atmospheres of nitrogen, a pressure change in the ratio of 3 to 1) would create the risk of decompression accidents. In order to avoid these accidents, step decompression tables have been established. These tables are based on the dive depth and duration, and are calculated so that at no time and in no part of the body is the nitrogen pressure double that corresponding to saturation. For example, it is safe, after a dive of one hour at 70 meters, to ascend rapidly to 24 meters, remain there a few minutes, then ascend to 21 meters, remain there for the indicated time, and so on. In this example the total decompression time is approximately 6 hours. Since diving operations are of utmost interest to some forms of naval warfare, it is not surprising that most of the decompression tables have been developed by the naval authorities, and in the English-speaking countries, the U.S. Navy Diving Tables and the Royal Navy Diving Tables are standard operational guides.

4) At present we have at our disposal three *means of shortening decompression time*.

1. During ascent above 10 meters (33 ft) it is possible to have the subject breathe oxygen (at this depth, oxygen is not rapidly toxic), a procedure which speeds denitrogenation.

2. It would be possible to be safe from decompression accidents if the subject breathed oxygen during the dive. This possibility is however limited by the dangers of oxygen poisoning, which must be feared at depths of 7 to 8 meters (20–25 ft). For this reason, oxygen breathing is used only in prolonged shallow dives, usually of military nature, during which it is imperative to avoid the bubbles which would enable the divers to be detected immediately. For this type of dive the apparatus used is a closed circuit oxygen system in which carbon dioxide is absorbed by chemical means, a modification of Benedict's apparatus.

At depths greater than 7 to 8 meters (20–25 ft), provided the pressure is only a few atmospheres, it is possible to have the subject inhale a hyperoxic mixture, always keeping the partial pressure of oxygen below 1.7 atmospheres. The decrease in nitrogen fraction and pressure reduces the amount of dissolved nitrogen, and thereby permits a decrease in the time required for the decompression steps.

3. The high solubility of helium in body fluids and its low atomic weight make helium a very diffusible gas (see p. 17), and therefore it is eliminated

rapidly during ascent from diving. This makes it preferable to give the subject an O_2–He mixture instead of an O_2–N_2 mixture.

This substitution is indicated, however, only in *deep and prolonged dives*. It has the additional advantage of safeguarding the subject from the narcotic effects of nitrogen. For short shallow dives, there is no advantage in using an O_2–He mixture instead of air, because during a short dive on the O_2–He mixture, helium, being very soluble in water and very diffusible, dissolves rapidly and in large amounts in the body fluids, while breathing air would lead to a solution of only a small volume of nitrogen, since this is not very diffusible. This makes it easy to understand why the decompression time saved by breathing an O_2–He mixture (because of the high diffusibility of helium) is lost because of the large volume of dissolved helium.

When a subject has followed exactly the appropriate decompression table schedule and has surfaced, the amount of nitrogen dissolved in the body remains high. Several additional hours are required for complete nitrogen elimination. Therefore, if a new dive is undertaken less than 6 hours after the preceding ascent, the step decompression which must follow the second dive must take into account the fact that the subject dived with more nitrogen than a subject not exposed recently. Special tables for repetitive dives are based on this assumption and extend the duration of the different decompression steps.

5) *Decompression accidents in flying personnel.* Decompression accidents are not exclusive to caisson workers and various divers. Since airplane pilots can rapidly reach high altitudes in nonpressurized planes, they are also subjected to pressure decreases which are sufficient to lead to nitrogen supersaturation of such a degree that gas bubbles may be formed (at 5400 meters or 18,000 ft, barometric pressure is half of that found at sea level). Decompression accidents can occur and are sometimes labeled "Aeroembolism." Although similar to those due to diving, they are usually less dangerous because the stay at altitude is usually very brief. Descent alone produces recompression, which has been shown above to be specific treatment of decompression accidents.

Bibliography

GENERAL

Since *Physiologie* was written, several texts, monographs, and articles dealing with respiratory physiology have appeared. Although part of the contents of the following are not at the beginner's level, they can be consulted not only for their intrinsic value, but also as sources of additional references.

BATES, D. V. and CHRISTIE, R. V. *Respiratory Function in Disease* (Philadelphia, 1964, Saunders).

CARO, C. G. (ed.) *Advances in Respiratory Physiology* (London, 1966, Arnold).

COMROE, J. H. JR. *The Physiology of Respiration* (Chicago, 1965, Year Book).

DE REUCK, A. V. S. and O'CONNOR, M. (ed.) Ciba Foundation Symposium on Pulmonary Structure and Function (London, 1962, J. A. Churchill).

FENN, W. O. and RAHN, H. (ed.) *Handbook of Physiology*, Section 3: Respiration (Washington, D.C., Vol. I, 1964; Vol. II, 1965, American Physiological Society).

BASIC CONCEPTS IN RESPIRATORY PHYSIOLOGY

BERT, P. (ed.) *Leçons sur la physiologie comparée de la respiration* (1 vol., 588 p., Paris, 1870, Baillière).

CANGUILHEM, G. *Histoire de la Physiologie Animale au XVIIIe siècle dans Histoire Générale des Sciences* (Vol. II, Paris, 1958, Presses univ. France, 593–619).

DOUGLAS, C. G. *Pulmonary function. Historical* (in *Handbook of Respiratory Physiology*, USAF School of Aviation Medicine, 1954, Randolph Field, Texas, 1–18).

GAVARRET, J. (ed.) *De la chaleur produite par les êtres vivants* (1 vol., Paris, 1855, Masson et Cie).

HALDANE, J. S. and PRIESTLEY, J. G. (ed.) *Respiration* (1 vol., 493 p., London, 1935, Oxford Univ. Press).

LEFÈVRE, J. (ed.) *Chaleur animale et bioénergétique* (1 vol., 1107 p., Paris, 1911, Masson et Cie).

LUSK, G. (ed.) *Science of Nutrition* (1 vol., Philadelphia, 1917, Saunders).

ROTHSCHUH, K. E. (ed.) *Entwicklungsgeschichte physiologischer Probleme in Tabellenform* (1 vol., 122 p., Munich, 1952, Urban).

ZUNTZ, N. *Physiologie der Blutgase und des respiratorischen Gaswechsels* (in *Handbuch der Physiologie*, by L. HERMANN, IV, Leipzig, 1882, Vogel, 1–8).

GAS LAWS

ALBERS, C. *Zwei Nomogramme zur Umrechnung von Gasvolumina auf Normalbedingungen* (*STPD*) *bzw. Lungenverhältnisse* (*BTPS*) (Klin. Wchnschr., 1959, **37**, 402).

CARPENTER, T. M. *Tables, factors and formulas for computing respiratory exchange and biological transformations of energy* (Carnegie Institution of Washington, Publication 303C, Washington, 1948).

ROUGHTON, F. J. W. *Respiratory Functions of Blood* (in *Handbook of Respiratory Physiology*, USAF School of Aviation Medicine, 1954, Randolph Field, Texas, 51–102).

BASIC CONCEPTS OF THE BODY AS A GAS EXCHANGE SYSTEM

FARHI, L. E. and RAHN, H. *Gas stores of the body and the unsteady state* (J. Appl. Physiol., 1955, 7, 472–484).

FARHI, L. E. and RAHN, H. *Dynamics of changes in carbon dioxide stores* (Anesthesiology, 1960, **21**, 604–614).

GAS TRANSPORT IN BLOOD

AGOSTONI, E., TAGLIETTI, A. and SETNIKAR, I. *Absorption force of the capillaries of the visceral pleura in determination of the intrapleural pressure* (Am. J. Physiol., 1957, **191**, 277–282).

Blood and Other Body Fluids (Federation Amer. Soc. for Exp. Biology, Washington, 1961).

BOHR, C., HASSELBALCH, K. and KROGH, A. *Über einen in biologischer Beziehung wichtigen Einfluss, den die Kohlensäurespannung des Blutes auf dessen Sauerstoffbindung übt* (Skandinav. Arch. Physiol., 1904, **16**, 402–412).

BRADLEY, A. F., STUPFEL, M. and SEVERINGHAUS, J. W. *Effect of temperature on* P_{CO_2} *and* P_{O_2} *of blood in vitro* (J. Appl. Physiol., 1956, **9**, 201–204).

CHRISTIANSEN, J., DOUGLAS, C. G. and HALDANE, J. S. *The absorption and dissociation of carbon dioxide by human blood* (J. Physiol., 1914, **48**, 244–271).

DAVENPORT, H. B. (ed.) *A.B.C. of Acid-Base Chemistry* (4th edition, Chicago, 1958, Univ. Chicago Press).

DILL, D. B., EDWARDS, H. T. and CONSOLAZIO, W. V. *Blood as a physicochemical system.* XI. *Man at rest* (J. Biol. Chem., 1937, **118**, 635–648).

FENN, W. O., RAHN, H. and OTIS, A. B. *A theoretical study of the composition of the alveolar air at altitude* (Am. J. Physiol., 1946, **146**, 637–653).

HENDERSON, L. J. *Blood* (1 vol., 397 p., 1928, Yale Univ. Press).

RAHN, H. (ed.) *The role of* N_2 *gas in various biological processes with particular reference to the lung* (The Harvey Lectures, 1961, **55**, 173–199, New York, Acad. Press).

RAHN, H. and FENN, W. O. *A graphical analysis of the respiratory gas exchange. The* O_2–CO_2 *diagram* (American Physiological Society, Washington, 1955).

ROUGHTON, F. J. W. *Respiratory functions of blood* (in *Handbook of Respiratory Physiology*, USAF School of Aviation Medicine, 1954, Randolph Field, Texas, 55–102).

SCHMIDT-NIELSEN, K. and LARIMER, J. L. *Oxygen dissociation curves of mammalian blood in relation to body size* (Am. J. Physiol., 1958, **195**, 424–428).

SEVERINGHAUS, J. W. *Oxyhemoglobin dissociation curve correction for temperature and* pH *variation in human blood* (J. Appl. Physiol., 1958, **12**, 485–486).

SEVERINGHAUS, J. W., STUPFEL, M. and BRADLEY, A. F. *Accuracy of blood* pH *and* P_{CO_2} *determinations* (J. Appl. Physiol., 1956, **9**, 189–196).

MECHANICS OF VENTILATION

AGOSTONI, E., SANT'AMBROGIO, G. and DEL PORTILLO CARRASCO, H. *Electromyography of the diaphragm in man and transdiaphragmatic pressure* (J. Appl. Physiol., 1960, **15**, 1093–1097).

BALDWIN, E. F., COURNAND, A. and RICHARDS, D. W. *Pulmonary insufficiency*. I. *Physiological classification, clinical methods of analysis, standard values in normal subjects* (Medicine, 1948, **27**, 243–278).

BOUHUYS, A. and LUNDIN, G. *Distribution of inspired gas in lungs* (Physiol. Rev., 1959, **39**, 731–750).

BRISCOE, W. A. and DuBois, A. B. *The relationship between airway resistance, airway conductance and lung volume in subjects of different age and body size* (J. Clin. Invest., 1958, **37**, 1279–1285).

CAMPBELL, E. J. M. (ed.) *The respiratory muscles and the mechanics of breathing* (1 vol., 131 p., London, 1958, Lloyd-Luke).

CARA, M. *Bases physiques pour un essai de mécanique ventilatoire avec application à la cinésithérapie* (Le Poumon, 1953, **9**, 371–428).

CARA, M. *Mécanique ventilatoire intérieure* (Le Poumon, 1955, **9**, 969–995).

CHRISTIE, R. V. *Lung volume and its subdivisions*. I. *Methods of measurement* (J. Clin. Invest., 1932, **11**, 1099–1118).

COMROE, J. H., FORSTER, R. E., DuBois, A. B., BRISCOE, W. A. and CARLSEN, E. (ed.) *The Lung. Clinical physiology and pulmonary function tests* (1 vol., 310 p., Chicago, 1962, Year Book Pub.).

DALY, M. DE BURGH and SCHWEITZER, A. *Reflex bronchomotor responses to stimulation of receptors in the regions of the carotid sinus and arch of the aorta in the dog and cat* (J. Physiol., 1951, **113**, 442–462).

DARLING, R. C., COURNAND, A. and RICHARDS, D. W. *Studies on the intrapulmonary mixture of gases*. III. *An open circuit method for measuring residual air* (J. Clin. Invest., 1940, **19**, 609–618).

FLEISCH, A. *Der Pneumotachograph : ein Apparat zur Geschwindigkeitsregistrierung der Atemluft* (Pflügers Arch. ges. Physiol., 1925, **209**, 713–722).

FOWLER, W. S. *Intrapulmonary distribution of inspired gas* (Physiol. Rev., 1952, **32**, 1–20).

HAYEK, H. VON (ed.). *Die menschliche Lunge* (1 vol., 289 p., Berlin, 1953, Springer).

MARSHALL, R., LANPHIER, E. H. and DuBois, A. B. *Resistance to breathing in normal subjects during simulated dives* (J. Appl. Physiol., 1956, **9**, 5–10).

MEAD, J. *Measurement of inertia of the lungs at increased ambient pressure* (J. Appl. Physiol., 1956, **9**, 208–212).

MEAD, J. *Mechanical properties of lungs* (Physiol. Rev., 1961, **41**, 281–330).

MEAD, J. and WHITTENBERGER, J. L. *Physical properties of human lungs measured during spontaneous respiration* (J. Appl. Physiol., 1953, **5**, 779–796).

MILLER, W. S. (ed.) *The Lung* (1 vol., 222 p., Springfield, Ill., 1950, Thomas).

OTIS, A. B. *The work of breathing* (Physiol. Rev., 1954, **34**, 449–458).

OTIS, A. B. and BEMBOWER, W. C. *Effect of gas density on resistance to respiratory gas flow in man* (J. Appl. Physiol., 1949, **2**, 300–306).

OTIS, A. B., FENN, W. O. and RAHN, H. *Mechanics of breathing in man* (J. Appl. Physiol., 1950, **2**, 592–607).

PETIT, J. M., MILIC-EMILI, G. and DELHEZ, L. *Role of the diaphragm in breathing in conscious normal man : an electromyographic study* (J. Appl. Physiol., 1960, **15**, 1101–1106).

POLICARD, A. (ed.) *Le Poumon* (1 vol., 263 p., Paris, 1955, Masson et Cie).

RAHN, H., OTIS, A. B., CHADWICK, L. E. and FENN, W. O. *The pressure-volume diagram of the thorax and lung* (Am. J. Physiol., 1946, **146**, 161–178).

ROHRER, F. *Physiologie der Atembewegung* (Handb. Norm. Pathol. Physiol., 1925, **2**, 70–127).

STAUB, N. C. and STOREY, W. F. *Relation between morphological and physiological events in lung studied by rapid freezing* (J. Appl. Physiol., 1962, **17**, 381–390).

TAYLOR, A. *The contribution of the intercostal muscles to the effort of respiration in man* (J. Physiol., 1960, **151**, 390–402).

WEIBEL, E. R. and GOMEZ, D. M. *Architecture of the human lung* (Science, 1962, **137**, No. 3530, 577–585).

WIDDICOMBE, J. G. *Reflex control of airway calibre* (Proc. 22nd Internat. Congr. Physiol. Sc., Leiden, 1962, Vol. 1, 115–120 : Lectures and Symposia).

WYSS, O. A. M. *La motilité de la paroi bronchique* (Les Bronches, 1952, **2**, 101–151).

PULMONARY GAS EXCHANGE

ASMUSSEN, E. and NIELSEN, M. *Physiological dead space and alveolar gas pressures at rest and during muscular exercise* (Acta physiol. scandinav., 1956, **38**, 1–21).

BANNISTER, R. G., CUNNINGHAM, D. J. C. and DOUGLAS, C. G. *The carbon dioxide stimulus to breathing in severe exercise* (J. Physiol., 1954, **125**, 90–117).

BARTELS, H. *Neuere Anschauungen über den Vorgang des Gasaustausches in der Lunge* (Verhandl. deutsch. Gesellsch. inn. Med., 1956, **62**, 25–34).

BJURSTEDT, H., HESSER, C. M., LILJESTRAND, G. and MATELL, G. *Effects of posture on alveolar-arterial CO_2 and O_2 differences and on alveolar dead space in man* (Acta physiol. scandinav., 1962, **54**, 65–82).

BOHR, C. *Über die Lungenathmung* (Skandinav. Arch. Physiol., 1890, **2**, 236–268).

BOHR, C. *Über die spezifische Tätigkeit der Lungen bei der respiratorischen Gasaufnahme und ihr Verhalten zu der durch die Alveolarwand stattfindenden Gasdiffusion* (Skandinav. Arch. Physiol., 1909, **22**, 221–280).

COMROE, J. H., FORSTER, R. E., DuBois, A. B., BRISCOE, W. A. and CARLSEN, E. (ed.) *The Lung. Clinical physiology and pulmonary function tests* (1 vol., 390 p., Chicago, 1962, Year Book Pub.).

CONSOLAZIO, C. F., JOHNSON, R. E. and MAREK, E. (ed.) *Metabolic Methods* (1 vol., 471 p., St. Louis, 1951, Mosby).

DuBois, A. B. *New concepts in cardio-pulmonary physiology developed by the use of body plethysmograph* (Physiologist, 1959, **2**, 8–23).

DuBois, A. B., BRITT, A. G. and FENN, W. O. *Alveolar CO_2 during the respiratory cycle* (J. Appl. Physiol., 1952, **4**, 535–548).

DuBois, A. B., FOWLER, R. C., SOFFER, A., FENN, W. O. *Alveolar CO_2 measured by expiration into the rapid infrared gas analyzer* (J. Appl. Physiol., 1952, **4**, 526–534).

DuBois, A. B. and MARSHALL, R. *Measurements of pulmonary capillary blood flow and gas exchange throughout the respiratory cycle in man* (J. Clin. Invest., 1957, **36**, 1566–1571).

FARHI, L. E. and RAHN, H. *A theoretical analysis of the alveolar-arterial O_2 difference with special reference to the distribution effects* (J. Appl. Physiol., 1955, **7**, 699–703).

FOLKOW, B. and PAPPENHEIMER, J. R. *Components of the respiratory dead space and their variation with pressure breathing and with bronchoactive drugs* (J. Appl. Physiol., 1955, **8**, 102–110).

FORSTER, R. E. *Exchange of gases between alveolar air and pulmonary capillary blood : pulmonary diffusing capacity* (Physiol. Rev., 1957, **37**, 391–452).

FORSTER, R. E. *The determination and significance of the diffusing capacity of the lungs and its clinical applications* (Progr. Cardiovasc. Dis., 1959, **1**, 268–283).

FOWLER, W. S. *Intrapulmonary distribution of inspired gas* (Physiol. Rev., 1952, **32**, 1–20).

Gas exchange in the lung (Proc. Internat. Cong. Physiol. Sc., Leiden, 1962, vol. 1, Part 1. Symposium No. 5).

HALDANE, J. S. and PRIESTLEY, J. G. *The regulation of the lung-ventilation* (J. Physiol., 1905, **32**, 225–266).

HASSELBALCH, K. A. *Neutralitätsregulation und Reizbarkeit des Atemzentrums in ihren Wirkungen auf die Kohlensäurespannung des Blutes* (Biochem. Ztschr., 1912, **46**, 403–439).

KROGH, A. *On the mechanisms of the gas exchange in the lungs* (Skandinav. Arch. Physiol., 1910, **23**, 248–278).

KROGH, M. *The diffusion of gases through the lungs of man* (J. Physiol., 1914, **49**, 271–300).

LOESCHCKE, H. H. *Über die Wirkung von Steroidhormonen auf die Lungenbelüftung* (Klin. Wchnschr., 1954, **32**, 441–445).

RAHN, H. *A concept of mean alveolar air and the ventilation blood flow relationships during pulmonary gas exchange* (Am. J. Physiol., 1949, **158**, 21–30).

RAHN, H. *The sampling of alveolar gas* (in *Handbook of Respiratory Physiology*, USAF School Aviation Medicine, 1954, Randolph Air Force Base, Texas, 29–37).

RAHN, H. and FENN, W. O. *A graphical analysis of the respiratory gas exchange. The O_2–CO_2 diagram* (The American Physiological Society, Washington, 1955).

RAHN, H. and OTIS, A. B. *Continuous analysis of alveolar gas composition during work, hyperpnea, hypercapnia and anoxia* (J. Appl. Physiol., 1949, **1**, 717–724).

REED, D. J. and KELLOGG, R. H. *Changes in respiratory response to CO_2 during natural sleep at sea level and at altitude* (J. Appl. Physiol., 1958, **13**, 325–330).

RILEY, R. L. and COURNAND, A. *Ideal alveolar air and the analysis of ventilation-perfusion relationships in the lungs* (J. Appl. Physiol., 1949, **1**, 825–847).

RILEY, R. L., COURNAND, A. and DONALD, K. W. *Analysis of factors affecting partial pressures of oxygen and carbon dioxide in gas and blood of lungs : Methods* (J. Appl. Physiol., 1951, **4**, 102–120).

SEVERINGHAUS, J. W. and STUPFEL, M. *Alveolar dead space as an index of distribution of blood flow in pulmonary capillaries* (J. Appl. Physiol., 1957, **10**, 335–348).

WEST, J. B. and DOLLERY, C. T. *Distribution of blood flow and ventilation-perfusion ratio in the lung, measured with radioactive CO_2* (J. Appl. Physiol., 1960, **15**, 405–410).

WINTERSTEIN, H. *Die chemische Steuerung der Atmung* (Ergebn. Physiol., 1955,. **48**, 328–528).

NEUROGENESIS — THE VENTILATORY SYSTEM

ADOLPH, E. F. *Quantitative relations in the physiological constitution of mammals* (Science, 1949, **109**, 579–585).

ADRIAN, E. D., *Afferent impulses in the vagus and their effect on respiration* (J. Physiol., 1933, **79**, 332–358).

ANREP, G. V. and SAMAAN, A. *Double vagotomy in relation to respiration* (J. Physiol., 1933, **77**, 1–15).

BOYD, T. E. *The mechanism of vagal effects on pulmonary ventilation* (Am. J. Physiol., 1941, **132**, 571–577).

BREUER, J. and HERING, E. *Die Selbststeuerung der Atmung durch den Nervus vagus* (S. B. Akad. Wiss., Wien, 1868, **57**, 672–677).

BRODY, S. (ed.) *Bioenergetics and Growth* (1 vol., 1023 p., New York, 1945, Reinhold Pub.).

CHRISTIANSEN, J. and HALDANE, J. S. *The influence of distention of the lungs on human respiration* (J. Physiol., 1914, **48**, 272–277).

CROSFILL, M. L. and WIDDICOMBE, J. G. *Physical characteristics of the chest and lungs and the work of breathing in different mammalian species* (J. Physiol., 1961, **158**, 1–14).

DAVIS, H. L., FOWLER, W. S. and LAMBERT, E. H. *Effect of volume and rate of inflation and deflation on transpulmonary pressure and response of pulmonary stretch receptors* (Am. J. Physiol., 1956, **187**, 558–666).

GUYTON, A. C. *Measurement of the respiratory volumes of laboratory animals* (Am. J. Physiol., 1947, **150**, 70–77).

GUYTON, A. C. *Analysis of respiratory patterns in laboratory animals* (Am. J. Physiol., 1947, **150**, 78–83).

HAMMOUDA, M. *The central and the reflex mechanism of panting* (J. Physiol., 1933, **77**, 319–336).

HAMMOUDA, M., SAMAAN, A. and WILSON, W. H. *The origin of the inflation and the deflation pulmonary reflexes* (J. Physiol., 1943, **101**, 446–459).

Handbook of Respiration (edited by D. S. DITTMER and R. M. GREBE, 1 vol., 403 p., Philadelphia and London, 1958, Saunders).

HEAD, H. *On the regulation of respiration* (J. Physiol., 1889, **10,** Part I, Experimental, 1–70; Part II, Theoretical, 279–290).

HERMANN, H. (Ann. physiol., 1935, **11,** 758–761).

HOFF, H. E. and BRECKENRIDGE, C. G. *The neurogenesis of respiration* (in J. F. Fulton (ed.), *Textbook of Physiology*, 17th ed., Philadelphia, 1955, Saunders, 843–866).

KAYSER, C., LEBRETON, E. and SCHAEFFER, G. *Grandeur de la respiration des tissus et masse active au cours du développement des organismes* (C. R. Acad. sc., 1925, **181,** 255–257).

KAYSER, C. *La loi des surfaces* (Rev. scient., 1951, **89,** 267–278).

KNOWLTON, G. C. and LARRABEE, M. G. *A unitary analysis of pulmonary volume receptors* (Am. J. Physiol., 1946, **147,** 100–114).

KREBS, H. A. *Body size and tissue respiration* (Biochim. et biophys. acta, 1950, **4,** 249–269).

KRUTA, V. *Comparaison entre les variations thermiques de la fréquence cardiaque de quelques mammifères, reptiles et batraciens* (Acta physiol. et pharmacol. neerl., 1957, **6,** 143–152).

LAMBERT, R. and TEISSIER, G. *Théorie de la similitude biologique* (Ann. physiol., 1927, **3,** 212–246).

LARRABEE, M. G. and KNOWLTON, G. C. *Excitation and inhibition of phrenic motoneurones by inflation of the lungs* (Am. J. Physiol., 1946, **147,** 90–99).

LE GALLOIS, C. (ed.) *Expériences sur le principe de la vie* (Paris, 1812, d'Hautel, 218–219).

LUMSDEN, T. *Observations of the respiratory centers in the cat* (J. Physiol., 1923, **57,** 153–160).

LUMSDEN, T. *Observations on the respiratory centers* (J. Physiol., 1923, **57,** 354–367).

MARTIN, A. W. and FUHRMAN, F. A. *The relationship between summated tissue respiration and metabolic rate in the mouse and dog* (Physiol. Zool., 1955, **28,** 18–34).

MEAD, J. *Control of respiratory frequency* (J. Appl. Physiol., 1960, **15,** 325–336).

OTIS, A. B., FENN, W. O. and RAHN, H. *Mechanics of breathing in man* (J. Appl. Physiol., 1950, **2,** 592–607).

PITTS, R. F. *Organization on the respiratory center* (Physiol. Rev., 1946, **26,** 609–630).

SCOTT, F. H. *On the relative parts played by nervous and chemical factors in the regulation of respiration* (J. Physiol., 1908, **37,** 301–326).

SMITH, R. E. *Quantitative relations between liver mitochondria metabolism and total body weight in mammals* (Ann. New York Acad. Sc., 1956, **62,** art. 17, 403–422).

STELLA, G. *On the mechanism of production, and the physiological significance of "apneusis"* (J. Physiol., 1938, **93,** 10–23).

WANG, S. C., NGAI, S. H. and FRUMIN, M. J. *Organization of central respiratory mechanisms in the brain stem of the cat : Genesis of normal respiratory rhythmicity* (Am. J. Physiol., 1957, **190,** 333–342).

WIDDICOMBE, J. G. *Respiratory reflexes in man and other mammalian species* (Clinical Science, 1961, **21,** 163–170).

WYSS, O. A. M. *The mode of functioning of the respiratory center* (Helvet. physiol. et pharmacol. acta, 1954, **12,** suppl. 10, 5–25).

WYSS, O. A. M. *The part played by the lungs in the reflex control of breathing* (Helvet. physiol. et pharmacol. acta, 1954, **12,** suppl. 10, 26–35).

REGULATION OF VENTILATION

ALBERS, C. *Der Mechanismus des Wärmehechelns beim Hund. I. Die Ventilation und die arteriellen Blutgase während des Wärmehechelns* (Pflügers Arch. ges. Physiol., 1961, **274,** 125–147).

ASMUSSEN, E. and CHIODI, H. *The effect of hypoxemia on ventilation and circulation in man* (Am. J. Physiol., 1941, **132,** 426–436).

BANUS, M. G., CORMAN, H. H., PERLO, V. P. and POPKIN, G. L. *The sensitivity of the respiratory center to hydrogen ion concentration* (Am. J. Physiol., 1944, **142,** 121–130).

BARCROFT, H., BASNAYAKE, V., CELANDER, O., COBBOLD, A. F., CUNNINGHAM, D. J. C., JUKES, M. G. M. and YOUNG, I. M. *The effect of carbon dioxide on the respiratory response to noradrenaline in man* (J. Physiol., 1957, **137,** 365–373).

BARTELS, H. and WITZLEB, E. *Der Einfluss des arteriellen CO_2-Druckes auf die chemorezeptorischen Aktionspotentiale im carotissinus-nerven* (Pflügers Arch. ges. Physiol., 1956, **262,** 466–472).

BESSOU, P., DEJOURS, P. and LAPORTE, Y. *Effets ventilatoires réflexes de la stimulation de fibres afférentes de grand diamètre, d'origine musculaire, chez le chat* (C. R. Soc. Biol., 1959, **153,** 477–481).

BJURSTEDT, H. A. G. *Interaction of centrogenic and chemoreflex control of breathing during oxygen deficiency at rest* (Acta physiol. scandinav., 1946, **12,** suppl. 38, 1–88).

COLLE, J. and MASSION, J. *Effet de la stimulation du cortex moteur sur l'activité électrique des nerfs phréniques et médians* (Arch. internat. physiol., 1958, **66,** 496–514).

COMROE, J. H. *The hyperpnea of muscular exercise* (Physiol. Rev., 1944, **24,** 319–339).

COMROE, J. H. and SCHMIDT, C. F. *The part played by reflexes from the carotid body in the chemical regulation of respiration in the dog* (Am. J. Physiol., 1938, **121,** 75–97).

CUNNINGHAM, D. J. C. and LLOYD, B. B. (ed.) *The Regulation of Human Respiration* (1 vol., 591 p., Oxford, 1963, Blackwell).

DALY, M. DE BURGH, LAMBERTSEN, C. J. and SCHWEITZER, A. *Observations on the volume of blood flow and oxygen utilization of the carotid body in the cat* (J. Physiol., 1954, **125,** 67–89).

DAVIES, H. W., HALDANE, J. B. S. and KENNAWAY, E. L. *Experiments on the regulation of the blood's alkalinity* (J. Physiol., 1920, **54,** 32–45).

DEJOURS, P. *Chemoreflexes in breathing* (Physiol. Rev., 1962, **42,** 335–358).

DEJOURS, P. *La régulation de la ventilation au cours de l'exercice musculaire chez l'homme* (J. physiol., Paris, 1959, **51,** 163–261).

DEJOURS, P., LABROUSSE, Y., RAYNAUD, J. and FLANDROIS, R. *Étude du stimulus gaz carbonique de la ventilation chez l'homme* (J. physiol., Paris, 1958, **50,** 239–243).

DEJOURS, P., LABROUSSE, Y., RAYNAUD, J., GIRARD, F., TEILLAC, A. *Stimulus oxygène de la ventilation au repos et au cours de l'exercice musculaire à basse altitude (50 m) chez l'homme* (Rev. franç. études clin. et biol., 1958, **3,** 105–123).

DOMIZI, D. B., PERKINS, J. F. Jr. and BYRNE, J. S. *Ventilatory response to fixed acid evaluated by "iso-P_{CO_2}" technique* (J. Appl. Physiol., 1959, **14,** 557–561).

DOUGLAS, C. G. and HALDANE, J. S. *The regulation of normal breathing* (J. Physiol., 1909, **38,** 420–440).

DUKE, H. E., GREEN, J. H. and NEIL, E. *Carotid chemoceptor impulse activity during inhalation of carbon monoxide mixtures* (J. Physiol., 1952, **118,** 520–527).

EULER, U. S. VON, LILJESTRAND, G. and ZOTTERMAN, Y. *The excitation mechanism of the chemoreceptors of the carotid body* (Skandinav. Arch. Physiol., 1939, **83,** 132–152).

EYZAGUIRRE, C. and LEWIN, J. *Chemoreceptor activity of the carotid body of the cat* (J. Physiol., 1961, **159,** 222–237).

FITZGERALD, M. P. VIII. *The changes in the breathing and the blood at various high altitudes* (Philos. Trans. Roy. Soc. B., 1913, **203,** 351–371).

GEMMILL, C. L. and REEVES, D. L. *The effect of anoxemia in normal dogs before and after denervation of the carotid sinuses* (Am. J. Physiol., 1933, **105,** 487–495).

GESELL, R. *On the chemical regulation of respiration. I* (Am. J. Physiol., 1923, **66,** 5–49).

GESELL, R., LAPIDES, J. and LEVIN, M. *The interaction of central and peripheral chemical control of breathing* (Am. J. Physiol., 1940, **130,** 155–170).

GRAY, J. S. (ed.) *Pulmonary ventilation and its physiological regulation* (1 vol., 82 p., Springfield, Ill., 1950, Thomas).

GUYTON, A., CROWELL, J. W. and MOORE, J. W. *Basic oscillating mechanism of Cheyne-Stokes breathing* (Am. J. Physiol., 1956, **187**, 395–398).

HAAB, P., RAMEL, F. and FLEISCH, A. *La respiration périodique lors de l'assoupissement* (J. physiol., Paris, 1957, **49**, 190–194).

HALDANE, J. S. and PRIESTLEY, J. G. *The regulation of the lung-ventilation* (J. Physiol., 1905, **32**, 225–266).

HARRISON, T. R., HARRISON, W. G., CALHOUN, J. A. and MARSH, J. P. *Congestive heart failure. XVII. The mechanism of dyspnea on exertion* (Arch. Int. Med., 1932, **50**, 690–720).

HESSER, C. M. *Central and chemoreflex components in the respiratory activity during acid-base displacements in the blood* (Acta physiol. scandinav., 1949, **18**, suppl. 64, 1–70).

HEYMANS, C., BOUCKAERT, J. J. and REGNIERS, P. (ed.) *Le sinus carotidien et la zone homologue cardio-aortique* (1 vol., 334 p., Paris, 1933, Doin).

HEYMANS, C. and NEIL, E. (ed.) *Reflexogenic areas of the cardiovascular system* (1 vol., 271 p., London, 1958, Churchill).

HORNBEIN, T. F., GRIFFO, Z. J. and ROOS, A. *Quantitation of the chemoreceptor activity: Interrelation of the hypoxia and hypercapnia* (J. Neurophysiol., 1961, **24**, 561–568).

HOUGARDY, A. *Apnée par injection intraveineuse de soude chez le chien et le lapin* (Arch. internat. physiol., 1904, **1**, 17–25).

KATSAROS, B., LOESCHCKE, H. H., LERCHE, D., SCHÖNTHAL, H. and HAHN, N. *Wirkung der Bicarbonat-Alkalose auf die Lungenbelüftung beim Menschen. Bestimmung der Teilwirkungen von pH und CO_2-Druck auf die Ventilation und Vergleich mit den Ergebnissen bei Acidose* (Pflügers Arch. ges. physiol., 1960, **271**, 732–747).

LAMBERTSEN, C. J., KOUGH, R. H., COOPER, D. Y., EMMEL, G. L., LOESCHCKE, H. H. and SCHMIDT, C. F. *Comparison of relationship of respiratory minute volume to P_{CO_2} and pH of arterial and internal jugular blood in normal man during hyperventilation produced by low concentration of CO_2 at 1 atmosphere and by O_2 at 3.0 atmospheres* (J. Appl. Physiol., 1953, **5**, 803–813).

LAMBERTSEN, C. J., SEMPLE, S. J. G., SMYTH, M. G. and GELFAND, R. *H^+ and P_{CO_2} as chemical factors in respiratory and cerebral circulatory control* (J. Appl. Physiol., 1961, **16**, 473–484).

LAMBERTSEN, C. J., SMYTH, M. G., SEMPLE, S. J. G. and GELFAND, R. *Respiratory effects in normal men of blood pH change at "constant" arterial and internal jugular venous P_{CO_2}* (Fed. Proc., 1958, **17**, No. 361, 92).

LEUSEN, I. R. (ed.) *Aspects of the central chemosensitivity of the respiratory centres* (J. S. Haldane Centenary Symposium, Oxford, 1961, Blackwell).

LOESCHCKE, H. H., KATSAROS, B. and LERCHE, D. *Differenzierung der Wirkungen von CO_2-Druck und Wasserstoffionenkonzentration im Blut auf die Atmung beim Menschen* (Pflügers Arch. ges. Physiol., 1960, **270**, 461–466).

LOESCHCKE, H. H., KOEPCHEN, H. P. and GERTZ, K. H. *Über den Einfluss von Wasserstoffionenkonzentration und CO_2-Druck im liquor cerebrospinalis auf die Atmung* (Pflügers Arch. ges. Physiol., 1958, **266**, 569–585).

NIELSEN, M. and SMITH, H. *Studies on the regulation of respiration in acute hypoxia* (Acta physiol. scandinav., 1951, **24**, 293–313).

REED, D. J. and KELLOGG, R. H. *Changes in respiratory response to CO_2 during natural sleep at sea level and at altitude* (J. Appl. Physiol., 1958, **13**, 325–330).

REED, D. J. and KELLOGG, R. H. *Effect of sleep on CO_2 stimulation of breathing in acute and chronic hypoxia* (J. Appl. Physiol., 1960, **15**, 1135–1138).

ROBIN, E. D., WHALEY, R. D., CRUMP, C. H., BICKELMANN, A. G. and TRAVIS, D. M. *Acid-base relations between spinal fluid and arterial blood with special reference to control of ventilation* (J. Appl. Physiol., 1958, **13**, 385–392).

ROBIN, E. D., WHALEY, R. D., CRUMP, C. H. and TRAVIS, D. M. *Alveolar gas tension, pulmonary ventilation and blood pH during physiologic sleep in normal subjects* (J. Clin. Invest., 1958, **37**, 981–989).

Ross, B. B., Gramiak, R. and Rahn, H. *Physical dynamics of the cough mechanism* (J. Appl. Physiol., 1955, **8**, 264–268).

Rossi, G. F. and Zanchetti, A. *The brain stem reticular formation. Anatomy and Physiology* (Arch. ital. biol., 1957, **95**, 199–435).

Schmidt, C. F. *Respiration* (in P. Bard (ed.), *Medical Physiology*, St. Louis, 1956, Mosby).

Walter, F. *Untersuchungen über die Wirkung der Säuren auf den thierischen Organismus* (Arch. exper. Path. u. Pharmakol., 1877, **7**, 148–178).

Watt, J. G., Dumke, P. R. and Comroe, J. H. *Effects of inhalation of 100 per cent and 14 per cent oxygen upon respiration of unanesthetized dogs before and after chemoreceptor denervation* (Am. J. Physiol., 1943, **138**, 610–617).

Winterstein, H. *Die Regulierung der Atmung durch das Blut* (Pflügers Arch. ges. Physiol., 1911, **138**, 167–184).

Winterstein, H. *Die Reaktionstheorie der Atmungsregulation* (Pflügers Arch. ges. Physiol., 1921, **187**, 293–298).

Winterstein, H. *Die chemische Steuerung der Atmung* (Ergebn. Physiol., 1955, **48**, 328–528).

Witzleb, E., Bartels, H., Budde, H. and Mochizucki, M. *Der Einfluss des arteriellen O₂-Drucks auf die chemoreceptorischen Aktionspotentiale im Carotissinusnerven* (Pflügers Arch. ges. Physiol., 1955, **261**, 211–218).

RESPIRATION AT HIGH ALTITUDE

Asmussen, E. and Consolazio, F. *The circulation in rest and work on Mount Evans* (Am. J. Physiol., 1941, **132**, 555–563).

Barcroft, J. (ed.) *The respiratory function of the blood. Part I. Lesson from high altitudes* (1 vol., 207 p., London, 1925, Cambridge Univ. Press).

Bert, P. (ed.) *La pression barométrique* (1 vol., 1168 p., Paris, 1878, Masson et Cⁱᵉ).

Boycott, A. E. and Haldane, J. S. *The effects of low atmospheric pressures on respiration* (J. Physiol., 1908, **37**, 355–377).

Christensen, E. H. and Forbes, W. H. *Der Kreislauf in grossen Höhen* (Skandinav. Arch. Physiol., 1937, **76**, 75–87).

Dejours, P., Girard, F., Labrousse, Y. and Teillac, A. *Stimulus oxygène de la ventilation chez l'homme acclimaté à l'altitude* (3613 m) (J. physiol., Paris, 1958, **50**, 237–238).

Dill, D. B., Edwards, H. T. and Consolazio, W. V. *Blood as a physicochemical system. XI. Man at rest* (J. Biol. Chem., 1937, **118**, 635–648).

Dill, D. B., Talbott, J. H. and Consolazio, W. V. *Blood as a physicochemical system. XII. Man at high altitudes* (J. Biol. Chem., 1937, **118**, 649–666).

Fenn, W. O., Rahn, H. and Otis, A. B. *A theoretical study of the composition of the alveolar air at altitude* (Am. J. Physiol., 1946, **146**, 637–653).

Fitzgerald, M. P. *Further observations on the changes in the breathing and the blood at various high altitudes* (Proc. Roy. Soc., London, s. B., 1914, **88**, 248–258).

Grandjean, E. *Physiologie du climat de la montagne* (J. physiol., Paris, 1948, **40**, 51–96 A).

Haggard, H. W. and Henderson, Y. *Hemato-respiratory functions. III. The fallacy of asphyxial acidosis* (J. Biol. Chem., 1920, **43**, 3–13).

Haggard, H. W. and Henderson, Y. *Hemato-respiratory functions. IV. How oxygen deficiency lowers the blood alkali* (J. Biol. Chem., 1920, **43**, 15–27).

Haldane, J. S., Kellas, A. M. and Kennaway, E. L. *Experiments on acclimatization to reduced atmospheric pressure* (J. Physiol., 1919, **53**, 181–206).

Handbook of Respiration (edited by D. S. Dittmer and R. M. Grebe, 1 vol., 403 p., Philadelphia, 1958, Saunders).

Hurtado, A. and Aste-Salazar, H. *Arterial blood gases and acid-base balance at sea level and at high altitudes* (J. Appl. Physiol., 1948, **1**, 304–325).

HURTADO, A., MERINO, C. and DELGADO, E. *Influence of anoxemia on the hemopoietic activity* (Arch. Int. Med., 1945, **75**, 284–323).

KAYSER, C. (ed.), *Physiologie du travail et du sport* (1 vol., 264 p., Paris, 1947, Hermann, see p. 162 : Modifications physiologiques qu'entraîne la dépression barométrique).

MALMÉJAC, J. (ed.) *Médecine de l'aviation* (1 vol., 333 p., Paris, 1948, Masson et Cie).

MARGARIA, R. and CERRETELLI, P. *Physiological aspects of life at extreme altitude* (2nd Internat. Congr. of Bioclimatology and Biometeorology, London, 1960).

PACE, N. *Adaptations of sejourners at high altitude* (XXIe Congrès Internat. Physiol. Symposium, Buenos-Aires, 1959, 16–21).

RAHN, H. and OTIS, A. B. *Man's respiratory responses during and after acclimatization to high altitude* (Am. J. Physiol., 1949, **157**, 445–462).

REYNAFARJE, B. *Estudios de quimica tisular en la hipoxia* (XXIe Congrès Internat. Physiol. Symposium, Buenos-Aires, 1959, 21–22).

STICKNEY, J. C. and VAN LIERE, E. J. *Acclimatization to low oxygen tension* (Physiol. Rev., 1953, **33**, 13–34).

VAN LIERE, E. J. (ed.) *Anoxia, its effects on the body* (1 vol., 269 p., Chicago, 1942, Univ. Chicago Press).

APPLIED PHYSIOLOGY

HYPOXIA. CYANOSIS. HYPERCAPNIA AND ASPHYXIA

BARCROFT, J. *Anoxemia* (Lancet, 1920, **199**, 485–489).

COMROE, J. H., DRIPPS, R. D. (ed.) *The Physiological Basis for Oxygen Therapy* (1 vol., 85 p., Springfield, Ill., 1950, Thomas).

GESELL, R. *On the chemical regulation of respiration.* I. *The regulation of respiration with special reference to the metabolism of the respiratory center and the coordination of the dual function of hemoglobin* (Am. J. Physiol., 1923, **66**, 5–49).

HUSSON, G. and OTIS, A. B. *Adaptive value of respiratory adjustments to shunt hypoxia and to altitude hypoxia* (J. Clin. Invest., 1957, **36**, 270–278).

LUNDSGAARD, C. and VAN SLYKE, D. D. *Cyanosis* (Medicine, 1923, **2**, 1–76).

MARSHALL, E. K. and ROSENFELD, M. *Depression of respiration by oxygen* (J. Pharmacol. and Exper. Therap., 1936, **57**, 437–457).

OTIS, A. B. *Physiological adaptation to the chronic hypoxia associated with right to left shunts of the circulation. A comparison with the hypoxia of high altitudes* (XXIe Congrès Internat. Physiol., Buenos-Aires, 1959, 14–16).

PETERS, J. P. and VAN SLYKE, D. D. *Quantitative Clinical Chemistry* (London, 1931, Baillière, Tindall and Cox, vol. I, 577–607).

RAHN, H. (ed.) *The role of N$_2$ gas in various biological processes with particular reference to the lung* (The Harvey Lectures, 1961, **55**, 173–199, New York, Acad. Press).

ARTIFICIAL RESPIRATION

ASMUSSEN, E. and NIELSEN, M. *Efficacy of artificial respiration* (J. Appl. Physiol., 1950, **3**, 95–102).

BARACH, A. L. (ed.) *Physiologic Therapy in Respiratory Diseases* (1 vol., 408 p., Philadelphia, 1948, Lippincott).

CARA, M. *Technique de la respiration artificielle* (Anesth. and Analg., 1955, **12**, 974–1021).

GREENE, D. G., BAUER, R. O., JANNEY, C. D. and ELAM, J. O. *Expired air resuscitation in paralyzed human subjects* (J. Appl. Physiol., 1957, **11**, 313–318).

Journal of Applied Physiology (1951, **4**, 403–495 : there are several articles on artificial respiration).

KARPOVICH, P. V. (ed.) *Adventures in Artificial Respiration* (1 vol., 303 p., New York, 1953, Assoc. Press).

RADFORD, E. P. JR. *Ventilation standards for use in artificial respiration* (J. Appl. Physiol., 1955, **7**, 451–460).
SAFAR, P. *Failure of manual respiration* (J. Appl. Physiol., 1959, **14**, 84–88).
WHITTENBERGER, J. L. *Artificial respiration* (Physiol. Rev., 1955, **35**, 611–628).

RESPIRATION AND ABNORMAL GAS PRESSURES

BEAN, J. W. *Effects of oxygen at increased pressure* (Physiol. Rev., 1945, **25**, 1–147).
BECKER-FREYSENG, H. and CLAMANN, H. G. *Die Wirkung langdauernder Sauerstoffatmung in verschiedenen Höhen auf den Menschen* (Luftfahrtmedizin, 1942, **7**, 272–291).
BERT, P. (ed.) *La pression barométrique* (1 vol., 1168 p., Paris, 1878, Masson et Cie).
COMROE, J. H. and DRIPPS, R. D. (ed.) *The physiological basis for oxygen therapy* (1 vol., 85 p., Springfield, Ill., 1950, Thomas).
Decompression Sickness (1 vol., 437 p., Philadelphia, 1951, Saunders).
FENN, W. O. *Physiology of exposures to abnormal concentration of the respiratory gases* (Proc. Am. Philosop. Soc., 1948, **92**, 144).
Groupe d'Études et de Recherches sous-marines (ed.) *La Plongée* (1 vol., 190 p., Paris, 1961, Arthaud).
GUILLERME, J. and RIVOIRE, J. (ed.) *Traité de Plongée* (1 vol., 213 p., Paris, 1955, Dunod).
HALDANE, J. S. and PRIESTLEY, J. G. (ed.) *Respiration* (1 vol., 493 p., London, 1935, Oxford Univ. Press).
LAMBERTSEN, C. J., KOUGH, R. H., COOPER, D. Y., EMMEL, G. L., LOESCHCKE, H. H., and SCHMIDT, C. F. *Oxygen toxicity. Effects in man of oxygen inhalation at 1 and 3.5 atmospheres upon blood gas transport, cerebral circulation and cerebral metabolism* (J. Appl. Physiol., 1953, **5**, 471–486).
LAMBERTSEN, C. J., EWING, J. H., KOUGH, R. H., GOULD, R. and STROUD, M. W. *Oxygen toxicity. Arterial and internal jugular blood gas composition in man during inhalation of air, 100 p. 100 O_2 and 2 p. 100 CO_2 in O_2 at 3.5 atmospheres ambient pressures* (J. Appl. Physiol., 1955, **8**, 255–263).
MALMÉJAC, J. (ed.) *Médecine de l'aviation* (1 vol., 333 p., Paris, 1948, Masson et Cie).
RAHN, H. (ed.) *The role of N_2 gas in various biological processes with particular reference to the lung* (The Harvey Lectures, 1961, **55**, 173–199, New York, Acad. Press).
SMITH, J. LORRAIN. *The pathological effects due to increase of oxygen tension in the air breathed* (J. Physiol., 1899, **24**, 19–35).
Underwater Physiology Symposium (153 p., Washington, 1955, National Acad. Sciences).

Index